A. P. Colbert

Mechanics of Materials

Mechanics of Materials

PHILIP GUSTAVE LAURSON, M.S.

Associate Professor Emeritus of Civil Engineering
School of Engineering of Yale University
M. Am. Soc. C. E.

WILLIAM JUNKIN COX, C.E.

Formerly Commissioner of Highways, State of Connecticut
Formerly Assistant Professor of Engineering Mechanics
School of Engineering of Yale University
M. Am. Soc C. E.

THIRD EDITION

JOHN WILEY & SONS, INC., NEW YORK
CHAPMAN & HALL, LIMITED, LONDON

Library of Congress Catalog Card Number: 53-12199

Preface

This textbook is designed for use in the standard courses in mechanics of materials (strength of materials) of one term, one semester, or one year.

The first fourteen chapters deal with principles and methods used in the design of ordinary structural and machine parts. We believe that after the student has studied these principles and methods he is better prepared for the somewhat specialized material in the later chapters.

Every effort has been made to present material in such form that students will have no unreasonable difficulty in grasping the principles involved. Extreme conciseness, although admirable in a reference handbook, is not desirable in a first textbook for undergraduates in any subject. Clear statements with ample explanations and a free use of solved illustrative problems are needed.

The physical behavior of stressed bodies has been emphasized, as well as the mathematical expression of this behavior. The ultimate purpose of a course in mechanics of materials is to prepare the student for an eventual clear understanding of machine and structural design. From the beginning, therefore, the student is encouraged to think of the realities of the situations with which he is called on to deal. Unusual attention has been given to outlining the principles that govern the determination of allowable stresses.

In addition to developing as clearly as possible the simplified expressions on which most engineering design rests, the limitations of these expressions have also been carefully noted and discussed throughout.

Both the double integration of the elastic curve and the area-moment method of deflection have been presented, so arranged that either method may be used in whole or in part.

A feature of the text is the large number of carefully designed problems. To stimulate the student's interest many of these problems have been based on actual well-known engineering structures and machines. The problems culminate in a group of "comprehensive problems," which form the final chapter. The solution of each of these problems requires the application of a number of principles drawn from different parts of the text.

It is not believed that all chapters can be assigned in any course. A minimum course in mechanics of materials (strength of materials) should cover the major parts of the first thirteen chapters. From the remaining chapters, as time permits, the teacher will select such topics as seem most useful. There is some latitude in the order in which chapters may be assigned.

It is not possible to list the many changes made in preparing this edition. Some of the most notable are:

1. Increased emphasis is given to the determination of stresses by the methods of statics and the use of free-body diagrams.

2. Cases in which unit stresses are determined by deformations are postponed to Chapter 5 and later chapters. This rearrangement simplifies the early assignments.

3. Chapter 2, "Mechanical Properties of Materials," has been largely rewritten.

4. The chapter on combined stress has been rearranged and partly rewritten to give increased emphasis to Mohr's circle.

5. Tables of structural shapes have been revised to conform to present standards, and allowable stresses are based on widely used specifications.

6. Many new problems and worked examples have been added.

This edition retains many features of the earlier editions that were suggested by Professor Dana Young of Yale, Professor J. P. Colbert of the University of Nebraska, and Professor S. T. Carpenter of Swarthmore College.

In preparing the third edition much valuable help in all aspects of the undertaking has been given by Professor Henry A. Lepper, Jr., of the Yale School of Engineering. Professor Robert P. Vreeland read much of the manuscript and made many suggestions. Professor John N. Eckle assisted in the preparation of figures used in the text.

P. G. L.
W. J. C.

New Haven, Connecticut
January, 1954

Contents

1

Stress and Deformation

1-1. Introduction. The forces that hold a body in equilibrium have two additional effects on the body: they deform it, and they cause other forces to act *within* it. Mechanics of materials is the science which establishes the relationships between the forces applied to a body, the resulting deformation of the body, and the intensity of the *internal* forces produced by the applied external forces.

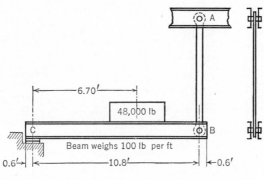

F IG. 1-1

To a very large extent all engineering design rests on mechanics of materials. A structure such as the beam and supporting eyebar (Fig. 1-1) is to support some known load—the weight of a machine, perhaps. This load causes forces to act on the beam, on the hanger, and on the pin connecting them. The amounts of these forces can be determined by applying the principles of statics, which the student is assumed to know. The principles of mechanics of materials may then be used to determine the size which each of the members must have in order to perform its function satisfactorily, and other principles of mechanics of materials may be used to ascertain how much the tie rod will be stretched by the forces on it, and how much the beam will be deflected or bent. Other illustrations of the application of the principles of mechanics of materials are the determination of the diameter of a shaft to transmit a given amount of power and the required thickness of the shell of a boiler or tank to withstand a given steam or water pressure. By means of mechanics of materials the maximum loads which may be applied to existing structures without causing excessive deformations or internal stresses also may be determined.

1-2. Stress. Since mechanics of materials is concerned with the *stresses* and *deformations* of bodies, it is desirable to understand clearly what is meant by these terms.

Consider the eyebar AB shown in Fig. 1-1. For the loads shown on beam CB, the force which the eyebar AB has to exert on the beam at B to hold the beam in equilibrium is found by the principles of statics to

be $\dfrac{1{,}200 \times 5.40 + 48{,}000 \times 6.70}{10.8} = 30{,}400$ lb.

A free-body diagram of AB is shown in Fig. 1-2a with the axial forces of 30,400 lb at A and B. Now suppose that a transverse plane be

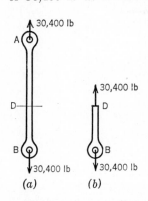

FIG. 1-2

imagined to cut AB into two parts at any point D, and consider the portion BD as shown in Fig. 1-2b. Equilibrium requires a force of 30,400 lb on BD at D. This force is exerted on BD by the rest of the member; and, since D may be taken at any point between A and B, it follows that any segment of AB is exerting a force of 30,400 lb on the other segment. The *stress* in AB is said to be 30,400 lb.

What has been spoken of as the stress in AB is often called the *total* stress in the member, to distinguish it from the *intensity of stress* or the stress per unit of cross-sectional area, or, more simply, the *unit stress*. To illustrate this distinction, if AB is a steel bar 1 in. by 4 in. in cross-section, the total stress of 30,400 lb in it is distributed over 4 sq in. of metal. Then the intensity of stress or the *unit stress* in the bar is 30,400/4 or 7,600 lb per sq in. If the bar were round, with a diameter of 2 in., the total stress in it would be 30,400 lb as before, but the unit stress would be 30,400/3.1416 = 9,680 lb per sq in. Whenever a total stress P is uniformly distributed over a cross-section A, the unit stress S on the cross-section is given by the equation

$$S = \frac{P}{A}$$

It should be noted that total stress is a *force*, expressed in the units of force, usually pounds in the United States. Intensity of stress, however, is expressed in units of force divided by units of area, almost always pounds per square inch in this country. It is a somewhat loose, but convenient and very general, practice to refer to both total stress and unit stress simply as "stress" if the context makes clear whether total stress or intensity of stress is meant.

The unit of stress *pounds per square inch* and the abbreviation *lb per sq in.* are both somewhat cumbersome to write and print. The abbreviation psi is being used increasingly and will generally be used hereafter in this book.

1-3. Kinds of Stress. The stresses that occur in bodies are of three kinds or are combinations of these kinds. These three fundamental stresses are tension, compression, and shear. Tension and compression will be considered in this article.

Tensile stress or tension is the kind of stress that exists on cross-sections of a prismatical bar subject to a pair of axial (and consequently collinear) forces which are directed away from one another. The stress in the bar AB of Art. 1-2 was a tensile stress.[1] Forces that cause tensile stress in a body also *lengthen* the body.

Compressive stress or compression is the kind of stress that exists on cross-sections of a prism subject to a pair of axial forces directed *toward* one another, and consequently *shortening* the member. Tensile and compressive stresses act perpendicularly or normally to the surfaces on which they act. If the lines of action of the collinear forces that cause stress pass through the centroid of the cross-section of the body, the stress is generally uniformly distributed over the cross-section. There are many important examples of this sort of stress distribution. There are also many important instances in which loads do not pass through the centroid of a cross-section, and then a non-uniform stress distribution results. Such cases will not be considered until later, however.

PROBLEMS

1-1. Kent's *Mechanical Engineers' Handbook* gives the breaking load for a steel piano wire 0.039 in. in diameter as 400 lb. What tensile unit stress does this load cause?   *Ans.* $S_t = 335,000$ psi.

1-2. A piece of $3\frac{1}{2}$-in. standard steel pipe (see Appendix C for dimensions) 6 in. long stands on end on a flat steel surface. What is the unit stress in the pipe when an axial load of 9,000 lb is placed on its upper end?

---

[1] Other combinations of forces often cause tensile stresses in *parts* of a member. For example, there is tension at some points in a bent beam. Tension is most simply produced as stated above, however, and consideration of a loaded bar like AB gives the clearest idea of what tension is.

1-3. What load can be carried on the upper end of a $9\frac{1}{2} \times 9\frac{1}{2}$ in. wood post if the average compressive unit stress is not to exceed 1,200 psi?

1-4. A $7\frac{1}{2} \times 7\frac{1}{2}$ in. timber post rests upon a 12×12 in. steel bearing plate on top of a concrete pier as shown in Fig. 1-3. The base of the concrete pier is 3 ft 0 in. square. If the total load P carried by the post is 94,000 lb, find (a) unit stress in the timber post, (b) bearing stress on concrete at top of pier, and (c) unit pressure on foundation. Neglect the weight of the concrete pier. *Ans.* (b) $S = 652$ psi.

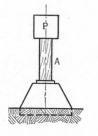

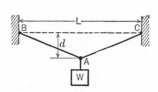

FIG. 1-3   FIG. 1-4

1-5. In Fig. 1-4 a weight W is suspended by two wires, AB and AC, of equal length. $L = 8d$ and $W = 300$ lb. Calculate the required diameter of wire if the unit stress is not to exceed 15,000 psi. (Neglect weight of the wire.)

1-6. In Fig. 1-4 the weight W is suspended by two wires AB and AC. The diameter of the wires is 0.36 in., and $L = 10d$. Calculate the allowable value of W if the unit stress in the wires is not to exceed 20,000 psi.

1-7. A bin which weighs 96,000 lb when filled is carried on a framework that has four legs, each made of a $4 \times 4 \times \frac{1}{2}$ in. steel angle. This frame is supported on a concrete floor, the unit compressive stress in which is not to exceed 500 psi. In order to distribute the pressure from the legs of the frame, a steel bearing plate is placed under each leg. Find the necessary area, and suitable dimensions for these plates, assuming that the force exerted by them on the floor is uniformly distributed.

Ans. $A = 48$ sq in.

1-8. Each cable of the Golden Gate bridge at San Francisco consists of 27,572 steel wires, each having a diameter of 0.192 in. What is the total load in the cable when the unit stress in each wire has the value used in design, 82,000 psi?

1-4. Shearing Stress. Shearing stress acts along a plane and resists the tendency of the part of the body on one side of the plane to slide relative to the part of the body on the other side of the same plane. As an example consider the block shown in Fig. 1-5a which supports the load of 6,000 lb, the resultant of which is shown. The middle third of this block is a body in equilibrium, and it is evident that there must be an upward force of 3,000 lb on the plane AB and an upward force of 3,000 lb on the plane CD as shown in Fig. 1-5b. These upward forces are the resultants of shearing stresses on the planes AB and CD. If these stresses are uniformly distributed, the shearing unit stress on the plane CD is $S_s = 3,000/(1 \times 1.5) = 2,000$ psi.

The bolt shown in Fig. 1-6a is another example of shearing stress. It supports the steel plate, to which a load of 10,000 lb is applied. The total shear on each of two planes equals 5,000 lb as shown in Fig. 1-6b. If the bolt were made of a material with low shearing strength, such as lead, it would be "sheared off" on two planes.

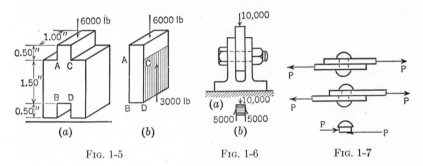

FIG. 1-5   FIG. 1-6   FIG. 1-7

As another example of shear, consider two plates held together by a rivet as in Fig. 1-7. When tensile forces are applied to the plates, as shown, the plates tend to slide past one another and to shear the rivet at the plane of their adjoining surfaces.

Like tensile and compressive stress, *shearing stress* may refer either to the total internal shearing force or stress acting on a section through a body, or it may refer to the intensity of the stress. The force causing shearing stress is frequently called *shear*. The expression "shearing stress" generally refers to shearing unit stress, but the context will make clear which is meant. The symbol that will be used in this work for shearing unit stress is S_s.

Shear may frequently be considered to be uniformly distributed over a cross-section; under such circumstances

$$S_s = \frac{P}{A}$$

Uniformly distributed shearing stress is less common than uniformly distributed tension or compression. If the stress is not uniform, the value of shearing stress given by $S_s = P/A$ is the *average* value, which will often be useful in judging whether the stress is too high.

Example. In punching a round hole in a metal plate, the plate rests on an "anvil" having a hole of the size to be punched. The cylindrical punch moving downward forces a round disc from the plate into the hole of the anvil. Calculate the shearing unit stress that results in a $\frac{1}{4}$-in. plate when a $\frac{3}{4}$-in.-diameter punch exerts a force of 12,000 lb as shown in Fig. 1-8a. Assume that the shearing stress is uniformly distributed.

Solution: Consider the $\frac{3}{4}$-in.-diameter disc of the plate directly below the cylindrical punch as shown in Fig. 1-8b. Because of the hole in the anvil there is no force acting

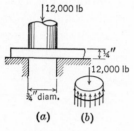

on the under face of the disc, and since $\Sigma V = 0$ there must be shearing stresses on the cylindrical surface of the disc which cause an upward resultant force of 12,000 lb. Hence

$$S_s = \frac{P}{A} = \frac{12,000}{0.25 \times 0.75\pi} = 20,350 \text{ psi}$$

(a) **(b)**

Fig. 1-8

Shearing stress differs from tensile stress or compressive stress in that it acts along the plane or parallel to the plane, whereas tensile and compressive stresses exert forces perpendicular to the planes on which they act. Because of the way they act, tensile stresses and compressive stresses are sometimes called "normal stresses" and shearing stress is called "tangential stress."

PROBLEMS

(In solving these problems assume all stresses to be uniformly distributed.)

1-9. *A* and *C* of Fig. 1-9 are two flat bars of steel attached to an overhead structure. The bar *B* is pinned to *A* and *C* by a $1\frac{1}{4}$-in.-

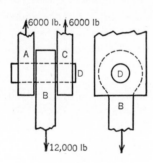

Fig. 1-9

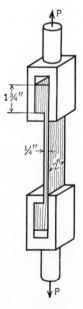

Fig. 1-10

diameter steel pin *D*. If *B* is midway between *A* and *C*, what is the shearing unit stress in *D*? *Ans.* $S_s = 4,890$ psi.

1-10. A white oak specimen held in holders, as shown in Fig. 1-10, failed under a total pull *P* of 4,250 lb by shearing off the upper ear of the specimen. (*a*) What was the shearing unit stress at failure? (*b*) What was the tensile unit stress in the shank?

1-11. A punch whose diameter is 1 in. punches a hole in a $\frac{3}{8}$-in. steel plate with a force of 58,000 lb. (*a*) What is the shearing unit stress in the plate? (*b*) What is the compressive unit stress in the punch?

1-12. A thrust P of 25,000 lb on a shaft is supported by a collar bearing, as shown in Fig. 1-11. What is the shearing unit stress on the cylindrical surface where the collar joins the shaft?   *Ans.* $S_s = 7{,}260$ psi.

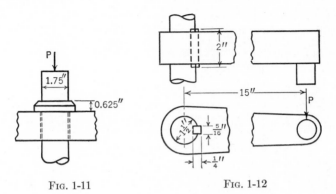

FIG. 1-11   FIG. 1-12

1-13. A hand crank 15 in. long is keyed to a $1\frac{1}{2}$-in. shaft by a key 2 in. long, $\frac{5}{16}$ in. wide, and $\frac{1}{4}$ in. thick, as shown in Fig. 1-12. When the pull P on the handle of the crank is 80 lb, what is the shearing stress in the key?

1-5. Deformation or Strain. A body made of any material will be deformed if forces act on it and stress it. In bodies made of some materials, such as rubber, small loads produce relatively large deformations. But bodies made of even the most nearly rigid materials, such as steel, are deformed by any forces producing stress.

Deformation as used in engineering is the change in any linear dimension of a body. It is often spoken of as "total deformation" to distinguish it from unit deformation.

Unit deformation is the total deformation in a given length divided by the original length, or it is the deformation per unit of length. The word "strain" in engineering has the same meaning as deformation. Unit deformation is sometimes thought of as a ratio, but the units are $\dfrac{\text{Length}}{\text{Length}}$. In engineering work, unit deformation (or unit strain) is expressed in inches per inch. Whenever the deformation of a body is stated, it should also be indicated whether the unit deformation is an increase or decrease in length. The symbol δ, the Greek small d (pronounced "delta"), is generally used to represent unit deformation. Total deformation is represented by Δ, the Greek capital D. Then

$$\Delta = L \times \delta$$

in which L is the length of the body.

Example. A bar 100 in. long is subject to tensile forces at the ends which cause it to change in length $\frac{1}{10}$ in. What is the unit deformation?

Solution: Unit deformation $= \dfrac{\text{Change in length}}{\text{Length}} = \dfrac{\frac{1}{10}}{100} = 0.001$ in. per in. of

length. Since the forces are tensile forces, the rod increases in length.

A prism with compressive loads on the ends not only shortens but also becomes a little wider, and a prism stressed in tension becomes a little narrower. These changes in dimensions are called *transverse deformations.*

The transverse unit deformations are very small, being between 0.1 and 0.4 of the longitudinal unit deformations for common engineering materials. They will be discussed in Chapter 15.

Shearing stresses cause a shearing deformation, just as tensile stresses cause elongation. In Fig. 1-13 the distance Δ_s is the shearing deformation in the originally rectangular body A. The unit shearing deformation is the total deformation Δ_s divided by the length L. It is the deformation per unit length.

FIG. 1-13

Shearing deformation is often regarded as an angle. Note that, in Fig. 1-13, $\delta_s = \Delta_s/L = \tan \phi$. If ϕ is small, as it is for most materials, $\Delta_s/L = \phi$, where ϕ is expressed in radians. Shearing deformation is often accompanied by deformation due to bending. The twisting of a shaft is the only common example of shearing deformation without bending. This deformation will be discussed in Chapter 6.

PROBLEMS

1-14. How much will a steel wire 50 ft long lengthen if the unit deformation is 0.00067 in. per in.?   *Ans.* $\Delta = 0.402$ in.

1-15. A steel rail 33 ft long is shortened 0.450 in. by forces acting on the ends. What is the unit deformation of the rail, assuming that it is held straight by transverse supports?

1-16. What is the unit deformation of the rail if expressed in feet per foot?

1-17. What is the angular distortion in degrees and minutes when the shearing deformation is 0.001 in. per in.?   *Ans.* $\phi = 3.44$ min.

1-6. The Relation between Unit Stress and Unit Deformation. For many important engineering materials there is a constant ratio of unit stress to unit deformation, so long as the unit stress is not too great. If a bar of steel, for example, is subjected to axial tensile loads, it is found that the elongation produced by 10,000 lb of load is just twice that produced by 5,000 lb. This fact, that strain is proportional to stress, was first stated by Robert Hooke (1678) and is known as *Hooke's law.* Most wrought metals obey this law very closely; many other materials follow it so closely that its application to them does not involve important error.

It follows from Hooke's law that if loads P_1 and P_2 act on a member made of some material that obeys Hooke's law, and produce unit stresses of S_1 and S_2, accompanied by unit deformation of δ_1 and δ_2, respectively, then

$$S_1/\delta_1 = S_2/\delta_2 = S/\delta = \text{a constant}$$

This constant is known as the *modulus of elasticity* of the material in question, or sometimes as Young's modulus, after Thomas Young, who is credited with having first defined it in 1802. The symbol E is commonly used for modulus of elasticity.[1] The modulus of elasticity for all grades of steel is about 30,000,000 psi. For some species of timber, however, it is only 1,000,000 psi, or less. For most other materials of engineering importance it lies between these extremes. The experimental determination of values of the moduli of elasticity for different materials will be discussed in Chapter 2. That chapter will also consider the stress limits within which the constant ratio holds. Here it is desired merely to bring out the fact that, for many important materials and at the stresses ordinarily used in design, there is such a constant ratio. Values of the moduli of elasticity of a number of the more important materials are given in Appendix C.

If this constant ratio of unit stress to unit strain did not exist, either exactly or at least closely enough to be assumed, a great deal of engineering design would be much more difficult and less exact. This very important relationship is expressed by the equation

$$E = \frac{S}{\delta}$$

Since the modulus of elasticity of steel is about 30,000,000 psi, if a bar of steel 100 in. long is stressed in tension to 20,000 psi, the unit deformation is

$$\delta = S/E = 20,000/30,000,000 = 0.00067 \text{ in. per in.}$$

The length of the 100-in. bar, therefore, is increased 0.067 in., or a little more than $\frac{1}{16}$ in.

For almost all materials the modulus of elasticity is nearly the same in tension as in compression. For any material, however, the ratio of *shearing* stress to shearing deformation is different from the corresponding

---

[1] Since S is pounds per square inch, and δ is inches per inch, it follows that E, like S, is pounds per square inch.

ratio for normal stresses. The unqualified term "modulus of elasticity" always implies normal stresses. The shearing modulus of elasticity is sometimes called the *modulus of rigidity*. The symbol for it is E_s. For all materials the modulus of rigidity is less than the modulus of elasticity, as is demonstrated in Chapter 16.

The shearing modulus of elasticity of steel is commonly assumed to be 12,000,000 psi.

PROBLEMS

1-18. A cylinder of structural steel is 2.50 in. in diameter and 20.00 in. long. (*a*) What force applied axially to the end will stress it up to 24,000 psi? (*b*) If the stress is compressive, what will be the change in length of the cylinder? (*c*) How long will the cylinder be when the load is 50,000 lb? *Ans.* (*a*) $P = 118,000$ lb.

1-19. Heat-treated steel bolts 2 in. in diameter and 20.6 in. long are used for clamping the cable bands onto the $28\frac{3}{4}$-in.-diameter cables of the San Francisco-

Courtesy, American Bridge Co.

FIG. 1-14.   An application of Hooke's law (Problem 1-19).

Oakland Bay bridge. Each bolt was designed to have 68,000 lb of stress in it when fully tightened. To determine the amount of tightening necessary, the stretch of a bolt due to a 68,000-lb load was calculated. The bolt was then tightened until its stretch (measured with calipers as shown in Fig. 1-14) reached the calculated value. What was this value?

1-20. A homogeneous prismatical bar hangs vertically. Its cross-sectional area is A sq in., its length L ft, its weight w lb per ft, and its modulus of elasticity E psi. What is the total elongation of the bar due to its own weight? (*Hint:* Set up an expression for the elongation of an elementary length dx at a distance x from the lower end of the bar, and integrate.)

1-21. Cement for making concrete for the Shasta dam was stored in steel bins, each of which was supported by four steel "legs" or columns. To determine quickly the approximate amount of cement in a bin, the shortening of a 16-ft length of each leg was observed.   The upper end of a steel rod about 16 ft long was attached to each column, and the lower end of the rod rested against the stem of a dial attached to the column.   The dial indicated the change in length in 16 ft of the column, each division of the dial representing a change in length of 0.0001 in.   If it is assumed that each leg carries one-quarter of the total load, how many dial divisions will indicate a change in the contents of the bin from 200,000 lb to 2,000,000 lb?   Assume the area of the cross-section of each column to be 56 sq in.   (See *Engineering News Record*, July 17, 1941, p. 62.)   *Ans.*   515 divisions.

1-22. The height of the Empire State Building is approximately 1,250 ft from the top of the concrete foundations on which the steel columns rest to the top of the building.   Assuming a compressive unit stress of 14,000 psi throughout the length of each column in the occupied building, calculate the difference in length of a column and the sum of the finished lengths of the column sections as fabricated in the shop.

1-7. The Method of Mechanics of Materials.   Some of the problems arising in the applications of mechanics of materials were mentioned at the beginning of this chapter.   Such problems are of three types: problems of analysis, problems of investigation, and problems of design. The problem of analysis is the determination of the location and magnitude of the unit stresses, usually the greatest, in a given member subject to known forces.   Investigation consists in finding the greatest load that may be applied to a given body without exceeding limiting values of unit stress.   Design involves determining the required size and shape of a member to support given loads without exceeding limiting unit stress values.   The solution of each of these problems depends upon the determination of unit stress at a given point in a given plane within the body.

This determination of unit stress generally requires the following steps:

1. Calculate, by the use of statics, the loads and reactions on the individual member taken as a free body.   Omit this step if loads and reactions are known.

2. Cut the member into two segments by a plane passing completely through the member at the point where the stress is to be found.   The external forces on each segment thus formed must be held in equilibrium by resisting forces exerted by the stresses on the cut section.

3. Choose one of the two segments and apply one or more of the equations of equilibrium to find the resisting forces.   These equations are $\Sigma F_x = 0$, $\Sigma F_y = 0$, and $\Sigma M = 0$.

4. Compute the unit stresses from the resisting forces on the section. These unit stresses depend upon the size and shape of the area of the section and the manner in which they are distributed over the section. The examples previously worked in this chapter illustrated uniformly distributed stress.   In other cases to be taken up later the stress distribution is determined by consideration of the deformations of the body.

GENERAL PROBLEMS

1-23. A weight of unknown magnitude is suspended from a steel wire (E = 30,000,000 psi) which when unstressed is 10 ft long and 0.08 in. in diameter. The total deformation that results is 0.06 in. The same weight is then suspended from a copper wire 8 ft long and 0.14 in. in diameter. The total deformation is 0.0274 in. What is the modulus of elasticity of the copper?

1-24. A block of steel (Fig. 1-15) is supported by a steel rod $2\frac{1}{4}$ in. in diameter. If two loads of 22,000 lb each are applied to the block as shown, calculate the tensile stress and the maximum shearing unit stress in the rod.

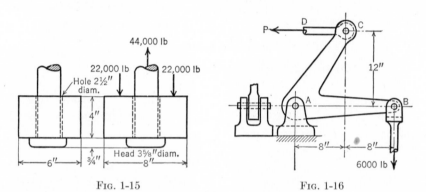

Fig. 1-15   Fig. 1-16

1-25. In the bell-crank mechanism shown in Fig. 1-16, determine the necessary cross-sectional area of CD if the tensile unit stress in it is to be 1.25 the shearing unit stress in the pin at A. The pin at A is 1.20 in. in diameter.

Ans. $A = 1.45$ sq in.

1-26. (*a*) What force will be required to punch a round hole 1 in. in diameter in a $\frac{5}{8}$-in. plate of steel for which the ultimate strengths are: tension = 64,000 psi, shearing = 48,000 psi? (*b*) What is the compressive unit stress in the punch? (*c*) A punch is made of steel with an ultimate strength of 150,000 psi in compression. What is the greatest thickness of plate (with strengths as above) in which it can punch a round hole 1 in. in diameter? (*d*) What is the smallest round hole that a punch of this material can punch in the $\frac{5}{8}$-in. plate?   *Ans.* (*a*) $F = 94,200$ lb.

1-27. In a laboratory test of its properties a cypress block $2\frac{1}{4} \times 2\frac{1}{4}$ in. in cross-section and 10.00 in. long was loaded on the ends with 9,900 lb. The shortening in a length of 8 in. was measured and found to be 0.0160 in. What was the modulus of elasticity of this piece of cypress?   *Ans.* $E = 978,000$ psi.

1-28. In Fig. 1-17, A and B are steel blocks $1\frac{1}{2} \times 3\frac{1}{2} \times 9$ in. which rest upon two supports E and F. D is a steel bar $1\frac{1}{4} \times 1\frac{1}{2} \times 6$ in. which passes through a $1\frac{1}{4} \times 1\frac{1}{2}$ in. slot in C and which rests upon A and B. The steel bar C is $3\frac{1}{2} \times 1\frac{1}{4}$ in. and carries a load P of 13,800 lb. D is midway between E and F. A and B are in contact with C. Calculate (*a*) the shearing unit stress and maximum compressive unit stress in A and B; (*b*) the shearing, compressive, and maximum tensile unit stress in C; and (*c*) the shearing stress and maximum compressive stress in D.

1-29. In the structure shown in Fig. 1-18, find the tensile unit stress in the eyebars and the shearing unit stresses in pins A, B, and C. W = 32,000 lb; diameters are: A = 1.75 in., B = 2.00 in., C = 2.50 in. BD consists of two eyebars each 3.50 in. wide and 0.50 in. thick.

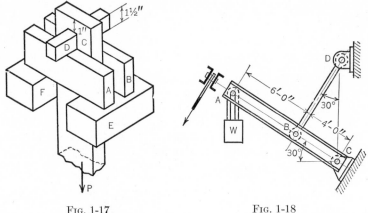

FIG. 1-17   FIG. 1-18

1-30. A weight of unknown magnitude is suspended from a brass wire (E = 14,000,000 psi), and the amount that the wire stretches is carefully measured. The weight is then suspended from an aluminum wire the length of which is 0.75 times the length of the brass wire and the diameter of which is 1.5 times the diameter of the brass wire. The stretch of the aluminum wire is found to be 0.45 times the stretch of the brass wire. Calculate E for the aluminum wire.

1-31. A weight of 1,500 lb is to be suspended by a steel wire 24 ft long. The unit stress in the wire must not exceed 20,000 psi, and the total deformation must not exceed 0.18 in. What is the required diameter of the wire? *Ans.* $D = 0.32$ in.

1-32. A straight steel bar is 12 ft long and has a rectangular cross-section which varies uniformly from 1×1 in. to 1×5 in. What change occurs in its length when it is subjected to an axial load of 24,000 lb?

1-33. A steel tape for measuring distances is 0.30 in. wide and 0.020 in. thick. It is exactly 100 ft long when supported throughout its length and pulled with a force of 15 lb. What will be its length if the chainmen pull with a force of 50 lb?

1-34. A frame made of wooden timbers carrying a load P of 8,400 lb is shown in Fig. 1-19. Calculate the maximum unit stresses of the following types caused in

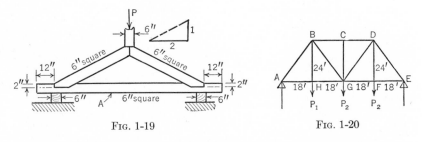

FIG. 1-19   FIG. 1-20

member A by the load: (a) tension, (b) compression parallel to the grain, (c) shear parallel to the grain. Neglect friction between the sloping member and member A. Diagonals slope $1:2$.

1-35. The tensile unit stress in the members of the truss shown in Fig. 1-20 is not to exceed 20,000 psi. Calculate the required cross-section of the member BG. If the member GH is composed of two eyebars, side by side, each 4 in. wide, calculate the required thickness. $P_1 = 70,000$ lb, $P_2 = 90,000$ lb.   *Ans.   BG* = 3.13 sq in.

1-36. Solve Problem 1-35, substituting DG for BG and FG for GH.

1-37. A chain used for hoisting movable gates in a dam is made of steel links 3 in. wide (Fig. 1-21).   Link (*a*) is $\frac{3}{8}$ in. thick, links b and c are $\frac{3}{4}$ in. thick, and the diameter of the pins is 1.20 in.   The load P is 32,000 lb.   (*a*) Calculate the maximum

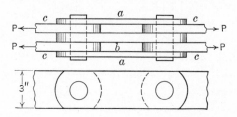

FIG. 1-21

tensile stress in the links and the maximum shearing stress in the pins.   (*b*) If links a and b were both $\frac{1}{2}$ in. thick, what would be the maximum shearing stress in the pin?   *Ans.* (*a*) $S_s = 14,140$ psi.

1-38. A balcony in a factory is 16 ft square.   One side is supported by a horizontal sill attached to a brick wall.   The opposite side is hung from two steel rods, one at each corner.   The balcony is designed to carry a "live load" of 130 lb per sq ft.   The "dead-load" weight of the balcony is an additional 25 lb per sq ft.   The ends of the rods are threaded, and the tensile unit stress in the rods at the root of the thread (see Appendix C) is not to exceed 18,000 psi.   (*a*) What is the necessary area of a rod at the root of the thread?   (*b*) What size of rods should be used?   (*c*) How much will each rod elongate under full load if the rods are 28 ft long?

1-39. Determine the required diameter of the pin at A in Fig. 1-1 if the shearing unit stress is not to exceed 12,000 psi.   Also determine the diameter of the pin at B.

1-40. Solve Problem 1-34 but let the load be 7,000 lb and let the timbers all be 5.5 in. square.   All other dimensions to be the same.

2

Mechanical Properties
of Materials

2-1. Engineering Materials. Engineering materials include metals and metallic alloys, timber, concrete, brick and clay products, and natural stones; and many special materials like plastics, rubber compounds, ceramics, and glass. Each material is characterized by its physical, chemical, and mechanical properties. Experience with materials in use, together with laboratory measurement of the various properties, provides the engineering knowledge necessary for the selection and effective application of a material to a certain purpose.

2-2. Mechanical Properties. The characteristics of the behavior of a material when subjected to applied forces are its mechanical properties. Elasticity, stiffness, strength, resilience, ductility, malleability, brittleness, and toughness are qualities, possessed in different degrees, that describe the resistance of materials to load. The suitability of a material for use in a structural member or a machine part, a boiler shell or an airplane frame depends to a large extent on its *mechanical* properties. For this reason, the mechanical properties are the most important ones from the standpoint of the *mechanics of materials*.

2-3. Elasticity, Stiffness, and Strength. Elasticity is that property which enables a body deformed by stress to regain its original dimensions when the stress is removed. This technical definition is somewhat different from the meaning of the word as frequently used in everyday speech in referring to a material like rubber, which is capable of deforming *greatly* under stress, and of regaining its approximate original dimensions when the stress is removed. In a mechanical sense the criterion of elasticity is not the amount of deformation, but the completeness with which the original dimensions are regained when the stress is removed. From this standpoint both steel and glass are highly elastic, since they have the ability to go back to their original dimensions when relieved of stress.

The opposite quality to elasticity is plasticity. A perfectly plastic body is one which does not make any recovery of its original dimensions upon the removal of a stress. No material is perfectly plastic. Simi-

15

larly, no body is wholly elastic *at all ranges of stress.* Even steel can be stressed so greatly that some deformation remains after the stress has been removed. It is only up to a certain unit stress that steel is an elastic material. Above that stress it is partially elastic and partially plastic. This limiting unit stress beyond which a material cannot be stressed without causing a permanent deformation is called its *elastic limit.* The deformation which remains when a body is stressed above the elastic limit and the stress is then removed is called *permanent set.* Fortunately, most of the important engineering materials are elastic, or very nearly elastic, over considerable ranges of stress.

Many materials possess the property of *proportionality of stress and deformation.* This property, as expressed by Hooke's law, "Stress varies as strain," was discussed in Art. 1-6. In no material, however, does a constant ratio between unit stress and unit deformation hold throughout the entire range of stress which the material can resist. As the unit stress is increased, eventually a value is reached at which the same increment of stress causes a different (usually larger) increment of strain from those previously observed. The stress value at which unit strain ceases to be proportional to unit stress is called the *proportional limit* of the material. For most materials the proportional limit appears to be the same as the elastic limit; that is, when the material ceases to be elastic, it also ceases to follow Hooke's law.[1]

Stiffness is the property that enables a material to withstand high unit stress without great unit deformation. Steel is said to be very stiff because a load which causes a large unit stress produces only a small unit deformation. Wood is much less stiff because a greater deformation accompanies a much lower stress. In everyday speech stiffness is associated with resistance to *bending.* There is no such restriction, however, in the technical use of the term. Stiffness is resistance to any sort of deformation. The definition of stiffness shows that this property is measured by the modulus of elasticity of a material. Values of the moduli of elasticity of several common materials are given in Table XII (Appendix C).

The strength of a material is the property that determines the greatest unit stress that the material can withstand without fracture or excessive distortion. Since the behavior under load differs with the kind of stress and the nature of the loading, no single property is adequate to define strength. Ultimate strength is the greatest unit stress a material can withstand. In brittle materials the tensile and compressive ultimate

---

[1] Cast iron is a common exception. The curve in Fig. 2-4 shows a very low proportional limit. If the elastic limit were not higher, permanent deformations would occur at very low stresses and the material would not be very useful.

strengths occur just before fracture; ductile materials in tension attain their ultimate strength and then, after considerable stretching, break at a lower stress. Ductile materials distort so greatly before fracture (some, in fact, do not fracture in compression) that their usefulness is limited by the elastic strength. Under loads repeated a great many times, under suddenly applied loads, and, in some circumstances, under steady loads of long duration, the behavior of a material differs from its behavior under static loads. The behavior under such loading is defined or measured by *fatigue* strength, *impact* strength, and *creep* strength respectively.

2-4. Ductility, Brittleness, Toughness. Ductility is the property that enables a material to undergo plastic deformation under tensile stress. Ductile materials are commonly defined as those which can be readily drawn into wires.

Malleability is the property which enables a material to undergo plastic deformation under compressive stress. Malleable materials are those readily beaten into thin sheets. Most materials which are very ductile are also quite malleable.

Brittleness is the absence of plasticity. A brittle material is neither ductile nor malleable.

Ductility and malleability are important properties in any member to which severe loads may be applied suddenly, particularly if the consequences of sudden failure would be serious. For example, a crane hook should be made of a ductile, rather than a brittle, material.

Even in uses where impact is not to be anticipated, it is often important that materials be not too brittle, because there is always a degree of approximation in saying that a stress is uniformly distributed over a cross-section. Even in a tension member of the same nominal cross-section throughout and of material as nearly homogeneous as can be obtained, although the stress under an axial load will have very nearly the average value over almost the entire cross-section, there will be minute areas where the stress will be decidedly above the average. These will be points where there are slight flaws in the material, or where there are sudden small changes in cross-section, such as may be due to an accidental tool mark or scratch in the surface of the member. In a ductile material under a steady load this condition of minute areas with relatively high stresses is of small consequence.[2] Further increase in load simply causes the minute area of overstressed metal to yield plastically, instead of fracturing. If the material is brittle rather than ductile, however, it may crack instead of flowing. The end of the crack

[2] However, in situations where "fatigue" must be considered, it may be very important. See Art. 2-10.

will be a point of high stress concentration, a fact which may cause the crack to spread until failure of the entire member results.   Therefore it is advantageous to use materials possessing a fair degree of ductility.   If brittle materials must be used, precautions should be taken to reduce points of high stress concentration to the minimum.

Toughness is the property of a material that enables it to endure shock or blows.   When a blow is struck on a body, some of the energy of the blow is transmitted to the body and absorbed by it.   In absorbing this energy, work is done on the body.   This work is the product of the deformation and the average stress while the deformation is being produced.   Consequently, a body which can be both highly stressed and greatly deformed will withstand a heavy blow and is said to be tough.

The energy that can be absorbed without causing a stress greater than the elastic limit is the elastic toughness or resilience.   The term resilience implies the fact that this energy is stored as potential energy of strain in the deformed material and is recovered when the material is unloaded.   The modulus of elastic resilience measures the amount of energy absorbed by a unit volume of material when stressed to the elastic limit.

2-5. The Determination of Mechanical Properties; Testing.   The mechanical properties of materials are most readily ascertained by subjecting the materials to appropriate tests in laboratories equipped for the purpose and called materials-testing laboratories.   Such tests are made from two standpoints.   They may have as their aim research on a material to discover additional facts concerning one or more of its properties, or they may be made in order to determine whether the properties of a given *lot* of material meet the standard specified for the use for which that particular material is intended.

Tests are made to determine mechanical properties under static, repeated, sustained, and impact loads, since the behavior of a material cannot be predicted for one kind of load from its properties under another.   Simple tension, compression, or shear tests are made to determine basic properties for each kind of stress.   Members may be tested in bending, torsion, or combined stress to shed further light on the behavior of the material.   Special conditions, such as high or low temperatures or corrosive surroundings, may be imposed when data are needed for materials to be used under these conditions.

Most of the important basic tests, including all the routine tests for determining the quality of a given lot of material, have been evolved over a period of years, and the procedure for each has been carefully worked out and standardized so that the results of different laboratories will be comparable. The American Society for Testing Materials (abbreviated A.S.T.M.) is an organization which is engaged in determining the best procedure for each test. It publishes directions for making such tests and specifies the limits within which certain results should lie if the material for any particular use is to be regarded as acceptable.[3]

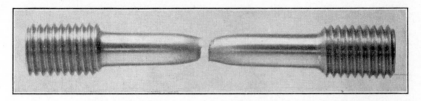

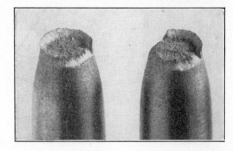

Fig. 2-1. Above: test specimen of ductile steel broken in tension (about $\frac{3}{4}$ full size).

Right: fracture of same specimen (enlarged).

2-6. Static Tensile Test. The static tensile test is one of the simplest tests which can be made, and for a large number of engineering materials, including most of the metals, it is the most informing. It may be used to determine the elasticity, stiffness, strength, ductility, resilience, and toughness of the materials.

In this test a specimen, usually a round or rectangular bar, is placed in a testing machine, which stretches it, thus subjecting it to tensile forces. The stretching, done at a slow and uniform rate, sets up stresses in the specimen which eventually result in its failure. Figure 2-1 shows a common form of specimen for this test. The grips for holding a tensile test specimen are shown in Fig. 2-2b.

A record of the static tensile test is kept by observing at frequent intervals the total stress in the specimen as measured by the weighing device of the machine and simultaneously observing the elongation as measured by a strain gage or "extensometer." These simultaneous readings are recorded opposite one another. The observed values are completed by taking the specimen from the machine after it has been

[3] A collection of some important specifications of the A.S.T.M. is published under the title *Selected A.S.T.M. Standards for Students in Engineering*.

broken, fitting the ends closely together, and measuring the final length
between gage points.   The diameter at the cross-section of failure is also
measured.   A record of all these observations and measurements
constitutes the "log" of the test.

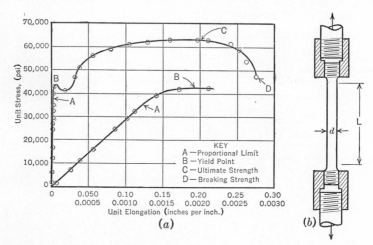

FIG. 2-2.   (a) Stress-strain diagram for ductile steel.   (b) Tension test specimen
with "grips."

2-7. Stress-Strain Diagram.   The data of a static tensile test are
often shown graphically by means of a curve, of which the ordinates are
the unit stresses and the abscissas the corresponding unit elongations.   Such a curve is called a *stress-strain diagram.*

The upper curve of Fig. 2-2a is a stress-strain diagram representing a
test of "mild" or ductile steel of (approximately) 0.1 per cent carbon
content.   The test specimen was cylindrical, the original diameter d
being 0.619 in.   The final diameter of the fracture was 0.38 in.   Deformations were measured in a *gage length L* of 8 in.   When the specimen
broke, this length had increased to 10.16 in.   Points on the curve represent simultaneous values of unit stress and unit deformation computed
from the observed loads and the *original* dimensions.   A *smooth* curve
is drawn, rather than one that passes through every plotted point.   It is
probable that the true behavior of the specimen is represented by a
smooth curve and that the slight deviations of the plotted points from
the smooth curve are mostly due to small errors of the instruments and
of observation.   The origin is a point on the curve, since for zero unit
stress there is zero unit deformation.

Until the unit stress exceeds the proportional limit, the "curve" is a straight line OA, since the unit stress and unit deformations are proportional. For the upper curve in Fig. 2-2*a* a scale was chosen which would permit the entire diagram to be shown. Plotted to this scale, the part of the curve below the proportional limit is nearly vertical. The lower curve shows this part of the diagram drawn to a scale of unit deformation which is 100 times as large as the scale of the upper curve.

Somewhere near the point A on the diagram, the deviation of the curve from a straight line indicates that the material is no longer conforming to Hooke's law.[4] The unit stress corresponding to the upper end of the straight line is the *proportional limit*. It could be shown that this stress is also the *elastic limit*, at least for all practical purposes. The elastic limit also measures the *elastic strength* of the material.

A short distance above the proportional limit the curve is seen to be horizontal. This fact indicates that the specimen is stretching without any increase in the load. This unit stress is the *yield point.* The unit elongation which occurs at the yield point may be 2 per cent or more of the gage length — 20 or 30 times as great as the elongation produced in stressing the specimen up to the proportional limit.[5] When the yield point has been reached, the curve dips downward for a short distance, representing a period of the test during which the specimen transmits less load as it stretches. Then there follows a long length of the curve rising continuously but becoming flatter until the maximum ordinate is reached at C, at which point the curve is again horizontal. The unit stress represented by the maximum ordinate is the *ultimate strength*.

Further stretching is produced by a *decreasing* force. During this

Yield Point

[4] The statement that the proportional limit is "somewhere near the point A" is intentionally indefinite. The more accurate the measurements of stress and strain are, the lower the proportional limit is found to be. Lack of proportionality of unit stress and unit strain commences *very gradually* and has probably existed through a stress range of several thousand pounds per square inch before it can be detected even by the most sensitive measuring devices that have been invented. This indefiniteness of the proportional limit is not of great practical importance, however, because, so long as lack of proportionality of unit stress and unit strain is too small to be detected, its consequences are ordinarily too small to be serious.

[5] The existence and significance of the yield point are strikingly brought out by a simple experiment. Let a length of ten or a dozen feet of soft "iron" wire of about 1/30-in. diameter be unwound from a small coil, and let one end be firmly attached to a hook or nail. If the other end is held in the hand and pulled slowly and steadily, the sudden increase in length that occurs without increase in load can be very clearly felt. Before the wire is pulled, moreover, it will not be straight but will be crooked or wavy, as a result of its having been unrolled from the coil. A light pull on the wire will keep it straight, so long as the pull is applied; but the wire will return to its crooked condition when the pull is released. However, after the pull has been increased until the yielding of the wire is felt, the wire remains straight when the pull is released. Why?

stage of the test the observer notices that somewhere, throughout a short length, the specimen begins visibly to decrease in diameter and to increase in length. This is called *necking*. It progresses rapidly until at this reduced section the specimen suddenly pulls apart with a loud report. While this necking is in progress, the load which the specimen transmits decreases because the cross-sectional area is rapidly decreasing. The unit stress at which the specimen actually breaks is called the *breaking strength*.

In addition to the proportional limit, yield point, ultimate strength, and breaking strength, the stress-strain curve indicates the modulus of elasticity. This is the *slope* of the straight part of the curve from the origin to the proportional limit. The lower curve shows that a unit deformation of 0.001 in. per in. corresponds to a unit stress of 30,000 psi. The slope of the line is the ordinate divided by the abscissa, or

$$\text{Slope} = \frac{30,000 \text{ psi}}{0.001 \text{ in. per in.}} = 30,000,000 \text{ psi}$$

Since these are simultaneous values of S and δ below the proportional limit, it is apparent that this slope is S/δ, which equals E. This is the measure of stiffness of the material.

The *percentage of elongation* is 100 times the total change in length divided by the original length. This value is a measure of ductility. It is usually calculated even when the curve is not drawn. For this specimen the calculation is

$$\text{Percentage of elongation} = \frac{10.16 - 8.00}{8.00} \times 100 = 27 \text{ per cent}$$

Another index of ductility is usually calculated. This is the *percentage of reduction of area*. For the specimen described, the diameter of the fracture was found to be approximately 0.38 in. This figure is approximate because the fracture is not a perfect circle. The reduction of area in square inches equals the area of a circle 0.619 in. in diameter minus the area of a circle 0.38 in. in diameter. This is $0.301 - 0.113 =$ 0.188 sq in. The percentage of reduction of area is equal to $\frac{0.188}{0.301} \times$ 100 = 62 per cent. For a given grade of steel this percentage of reduction of area is less dependent on the gage length than is the percentage of elongation.

The work done in stretching the specimen is the product of the deformation Δ by the average force, P_{av}, required to produce this deformation. Dividing by the volume of the specimen, $A \times L$, the work per unit of volume is

$$U = \frac{P_{av} \times \Delta}{A \times L} = S_{av} \times \delta$$

Note that a given strain multiplied by the average stress producing the strain is also represented by the area below the stress-strain diagram. Thus the area under the entire stress-strain diagram represents the work per unit volume that must be done in breaking the material and is therefore the toughness.   For this specimen, the toughness is approximately[6]

$$59{,}000 \times 0.27 = 15{,}900 \text{ in.-lb per cu in.}$$

Elastic resilience is measured by the area below the elastic portion of the curve.   Thus the work that is done in loading this steel to the proportional limit and which is recoverable upon unloading is

$$\frac{36{,}000}{2} \times 0.0012 = 21.6 \text{ in.-lb per cu in.}$$

2-8. Stress-Strain Diagrams for Other Materials.   Figures 2-3 and 2-4 show stress-strain diagrams in tension and in compression for a variety of common engineering materials.   For the ductile metals, the full stress-strain diagram to fracture is shown in Fig. 2-3, and the initial portion to somewhat beyond the elastic limit is shown in Fig. 2-4 for three ductile metals, low-carbon (0.1 per cent) steel, Duralumin, and brass.

Many ductile metals have gradually curving stress-strain diagrams beyond the proportional limit, rather than a definite yield point.   In such cases, an arbitrary, practical measure of elastic strength, the *yield strength*, for a specified offset is used.   For instance, for most aluminum alloys the yield strength is commonly taken as the stress corresponding to an offset of 0.2 per cent of the original gage length.   In Fig. 2-4, the yield strength of Duralumin is found by constructing a line parallel to the straight part of the stress-strain diagram through a point 0.002 in. per in. from the origin on the horizontal axis.   The ordinate of the intersection of this line and the stress-strain curve (at 32,500 psi) is the yield strength.

Yield Strength

Brittle materials exhibit relatively little strain before fracture in either tension or compression, as shown in Fig. 2-4.   The stress-strain

---

[6] This measure of toughness is not always significant for different conditions of impact or for members of greatly different proportions from those of the test specimen.   For example, a slender member struck at one end will undergo local plastic distortion near the end rather than deform uniformly over the entire length as the test specimen does.   The familiar bulging or flattening of the struck end of a cold chisel illustrates this behavior.

Example of toughness

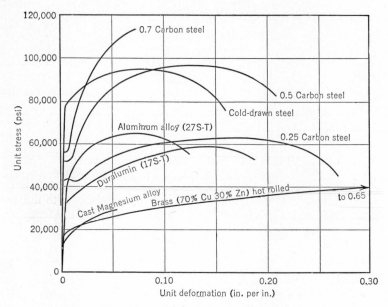

FIG. 2-3.   Stress-strain diagrams for ductile metals in tension.

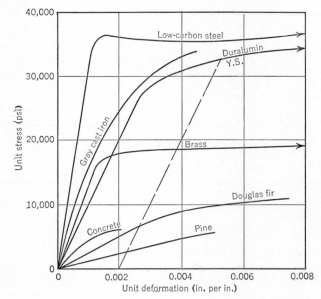

FIG. 2-4.   Tensile stress-strain diagrams for gray cast iron and the initial portions of curves for steel, Duralumin, and brass.   Compression stress-strain diagrams for concrete, fir, and pine.

diagram merely deviates gradually from the tangent when the proportional limit is reached.   Since brittle materials are those that are incapable of much plastic deformation, they do not draw down or neck before tensile failure, but snap without warning (Fig. 2-5).   A stress-strain diagram for such a material ends before it becomes horizontal; consequently the ultimate strength and the breaking strength are the same.   Tensile strength of brittle material, such as cast iron, is but a small fraction of the compressive strength.

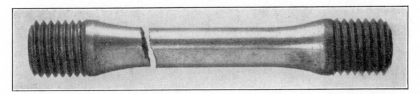

FIG. 2-5.   Tensile fracture of cast iron.

A compressive stress-strain diagram of a short specimen of ductile material would show no ultimate or breaking strengths.   The unit stress would simply increase indefinitely until the capacity of the testing machine was reached.

Comparison of these various stress-strain diagrams reveals the different degrees of strength, elasticity, stiffness, ductility, resilience, and toughness possessed by these common materials.   For example, the strength of the 0.70 per cent carbon steel is seen to be much greater than that of the low-carbon steel (Fig. 2-2a), but comparison of the areas under the curves indicates much greater toughness for the low-carbon steel.   This lack of toughness of brittle materials is confirmed by impact experiments.   On the other hand, since both the steels whose properties are pictured have the same value of E, the "strong" steel is seen to be much more *resilient* than the more ductile steel.   Springs, axles, and other parts which are ruined if permanently deformed by shock loads are therefore made of strong steels.   On the other hand, for such objects as crane hooks, the rupture of which would be much more serious than the permanent distortion only, weaker but more ductile and therefore tougher steels are used.

These diagrams represent static properties at normal temperatures. When materials are to be used at temperatures greatly above or below the atmospheric range, it is necessary to obtain stress-strain curves for the temperature range of anticipated use.   Similarly, when other conditions of use or environment cause changes in properties, these changes must be studied by appropriate tests.

PROBLEMS

2-1. The log of a tensile test of hot-rolled steel is given below. Calculate unit stresses and corresponding deformations and draw the stress-strain curve, using scales of 1 in. = 16,000 psi and 1 in. = 0.08 in. per in. Also replot the curve up to the yield point, using a scale of 1 in. = 0.0008 in. per in. Start this curve at the same origin. Determine and state values for (a) proportional limit, (b) modulus of elasticity, (c) yield point, (d) ultimate strength, (e) breaking strength, (f) per cent elongation, (g) per cent reduction of area. Arrange data in four columns headed: Load, Unit Stress, Elongation, Unit Elongation.

Tensile Test of Hot-Rolled Steel

Gage Length, 2 in.   Diameter of Specimen, 0.503 in.

Load (lb)	Elongation (in.)	Load (lb)	Elongation (in.)
0	0.00000	7,500	0.038
1,600	0.00054	8,700	0.08
2,400	0.00079	9,400	0.11
3,600	0.00118	10,000	0.15
4,600	0.00159	10,500	0.18
6,400	0.00215	11,200	0.45
7,200	0.00247	10,800†	0.64
8,000	0.00311	10,200	0.73
7,500*	0.00466	8,700‡	0.76
7,300	0.017		

* Strain-gage removed. Subsequent elongations measured with dividers and steel scale.

† Necking begins to show.

‡ Specimen broke. Final diameter at fracture = 0.28 in.

2-2. The log of a tensile test of gray cast iron is given below. Calculate unit stresses and corresponding unit deformations and draw the stress-strain curve, using scales of 1 in. = 8,000 psi and 1 in. = 0.002 in. per in. Determine the value of E when the stress is 4,000 psi; when the stress is 8,000 psi. Specimen broke when load was 11,800 lb. Arrange data in four columns headed: Load, Unit Stress, Elongation, Unit Elongation.

Tensile Test of Gray Cast Iron

Gage Length, 2 in.   Diameter of Specimen, 0.720 in.

Load (lb)	Elongation (in.)	Load (lb)	Elongation (in.)
0	0.00000	7,000	0.00340
1,000	0.00024	8,000	0.00450
2,000	0.00064	9,000	0.00600
3,000	0.00103	10,000	0.00800
4,000	0.00146	11,000	0.01100
5,000	0.00200	11,500	0.014
6,000	0.00260	11,800	

2-3. A bar of the cast iron shown in Fig. 2-4 is 24 in. long and $\frac{7}{8}$ in. square. How much will it lengthen when the load on it is increased from 2,000 lb to 12,000 lb? When the load is increased from 13,000 lb to 23,000 lb?

2-4. Determine the modulus of elasticity, modulus of elastic resilience, and yield strength for 0.002 offset for the low-carbon steel, Duralumin, and brass shown in Fig. 2-4.

2-9. The Effect of Overstress; Cold Working. The properties of a material are largely, but not entirely, fixed by its chemical composition. Even after the material has been incorporated into the machine or

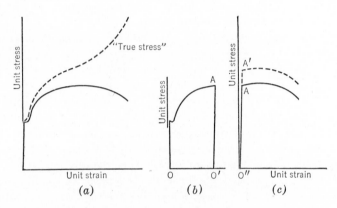

Fig. 2-6. Effect on ductile steel of stress above the elastic limit.

structure of which it is to form a part, many of its mechanical characteristics may be greatly changed. This fact can be illustrated as follows.

If two specimens of mild hot-rolled[7] steel are cut from the same bar, their chemical composition and the manufacturing processes to which they have been subjected are identical, and therefore the mechanical properties of the two specimens should be very nearly the same. Figure 2-6a represents the stress-strain diagram for one such specimen tested to failure in the usual manner.   In Fig. 2-6b, OAO' represents the stress-strain diagram of a similar specimen, loaded to a unit stress A well above the elastic limit and then unloaded. As the unit stress is decreased, the unit elongation decreases and A–O' is a straight line with a slope equal to the modulus of elasticity of the material. The distance O–O' represents the permanent set which has been given to the specimen. If this specimen, after having been stressed above the elastic limit and then unloaded, is again tested, this time to failure, the stress-strain curve

[7] Hot-rolled steel is rolled into bars or other shapes between grooved rolls, the final "passes" being completed before the steel has cooled below a red heat.   Cold-rolled steel is subjected to additional rolling after it has cooled.

is found to be as represented in Fig. 2-6c. The modulus of elasticity is unchanged. The proportional limit, however, has been raised to practically the value of the maximum unit stress to which the specimen was subjected in its first test.[8] The ultimate strength (computed on the basis of the *original* cross-section) is found to be slightly greater than the strength of the specimen which was tested to failure without unloading. The ultimate elongation is found to have been decreased by approximately the amount of the permanent set which was given the specimen the first time it was tested.

During the loading cycle OAO', the cross-section area of the specimen decreases. If the stresses for the curve of second loading (from O'') are calculated on the basis of this new, smaller area, then the dotted line curve of Fig. 2-6c is obtained. An apparent great increase in both elastic (to A') and ultimate strengths is observed to be the result of the cold working. Such effects, whether obtained by simple stretching or by fabricating processes like rolling or drawing, are studied more readily by using stresses calculated on the basis of the actual area. These so-called "true stresses" are calculated from the load divided by the actual area of cross-section. The dotted line curve of Fig. 2-6a shows such true stresses for the tension test and reveals that these stresses increase continuously to fracture although the load decreases when necking occurs.

Comparison of the stress-strain curve for cold-drawn steel in Fig. 2-3 with the curve of Fig. 2-2a reveals the effect of more severe cold working obtained by drawing such a metal through dies.

2-10. Repeated Stress; Fatigue Failures. Many machine and structural parts are acted on by loads that are applied and removed a great many times, or the parts are loaded so that the stress at a point in the material varies as the part moves relative to the load. Connecting rods and crankshafts in engines, blades of water wheels or steam or gas turbines, railroad rails, members in the floor system of bridges, percussion drills, and plungers of pneumatic hammers are examples of parts subject to repetition of load. Live axles, wheels, and cables passing around sheaves are parts in which reversed or repeated stress occurs. In both situations, the strength of the material is not as great as it is under static load. Fracture may occur when stresses less than the elastic limit are repeated a sufficiently large number of times.

The failure resulting from a very great number of repetitions of stress is called a "fatigue" failure. The exact nature of this failure is imper-

---

[8] This increase in the tensile proportional limit is accompanied, however, by a roughly corresponding decrease in the compressive proportional limit. Conversely, overstress in compression raises the compressive proportional limit but lowers the tensile proportional limit.

fectly understood. However, the failure apparently results from the fact that, even though the calculated stress in the member is within the elastic limit, there are minute regions where the localized stress is far above the average stress. Repetition of a sufficiently high stress (probably above the elastic limit) in these regions leads to the formation of an invisible crack after enough cycles are applied. At the boundaries of this minute crack are regions of still higher stress, causing progressive extension of the crack with further repetitions of stress until eventually the cross-section of the member is so reduced that the part suddenly snaps. Throughout the failure, however, the region of high stress has

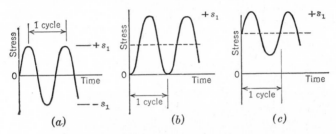

Fig. 2-7.   Stress-time diagrams for repeated stress.

always been so small that the deformation does not extend through a sufficiently large volume of the material for it to become visible.

The strength of a material under repeated stress cannot be found from any static properties but must be determined by "fatigue tests" that subject the material to repetitions of stress. Testing machines for this purpose subject the specimen to cyclic loading of an appropriate range of stress, as shown on the stress-time diagrams of Fig. 2-7. Completely reversed stress varies from a maximum tensile stress s_1 to an equal compressive stress $-s_1$ during each cycle, whereas fluctuating or pulsating repeated stresses range between peak stresses of different magnitudes. "Fatigue" tests are conducted by adjusting the testing machine for the desired range of stress and peak value, s_1, for the particular specimen, then allowing the machine to run until the specimen breaks. The number of cycles to failure is read from a counter. Several identical specimens are tested to failure for the same stress range but different peak stresses.

The results of a series of such tests on a given material under certain conditions of environment may be shown by an S–N (stress-number of cycles to failure) diagram (Fig. 2-8), on which each point represents the test of a single specimen. The ordinate of a point on the S–N curve is the peak stress s_1 in the cycle, and the abscissa is the number of repetitions causing failure. The lower the value of the stress, the larger the number of repetitions before failure. For some metals such a curve eventually becomes horizontal as S decreases. The ordinate to the horizontal part of the curve is the value of the computed stress which can be repeated an indefinitely great number of times without causing failure. This stress value is called the *endurance limit* of the material. Other metals do not have a well-defined endurance limit but will eventually fail at relatively low stresses. The stress that can be repeated

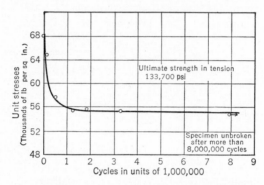

FIG. 2-8. *S-N* curve for a chrome-nickel steel.

without failure for a large number of cycles, say 100 million or 500 million, is taken as a practical endurance limit for such metals.

The basic measure of strength under repeated stress is the endurance limit for reversed tensile and compressive stress as determined from tests of carefully polished specimens. Endurance limits so determined for wrought steels are about one-half the static ultimate tensile strength, but for other metals this "endurance ratio" (endurance limit/tensile strength) is less than one-half. Stress ranges other than fully reversed show higher endurance limits. Under completely reversed shearing stress, the endurance limit is about 55 per cent of the endurance limit for reversed normal stresses in wrought steels. Much research has revealed these general trends, but it is necessary to establish exact values by test for a particular material.[9]

2-11. Sustained Load: Creep of Metals. Under steady stress of long duration there may occur a continuing strain if either the temperature or

[9] For values of the endurance limits of various materials, and a fuller discussion of this topic, see reports of the Research Committee on Fatigue of Metals, *Proc. A.S.T.M.*, Vol. 30, Part 1 (1930), and Vol. 32, Part 1 (1932). See also H. F. Moore, "The Fatigue of Metals—Its Nature and Significance," *Trans. A.S.M.E., Applied Mechanics Journal*, March, 1933; and *Prevention of the Failure of Metals under Repeated Stress*, Staff of the Battelle Memorial Institute, John Wiley & Sons, 1941.

the stress is sufficiently high for the material. Such deformations are termed "creep" strains and may become great enough after a time to impair the functioning of a member.

The nature of this phenomenon is illustrated by the tension strain-time curve of Fig. 2-9, which is typical of the observed behavior. Immediately upon application of load, a large strain occurs, partly elastic and partly in-elastic, for a short time after the load is fully applied. The strain rate decreases gradually and in many cases becomes practically constant for a long time (from A to B). After this stage, the strain rate may increase, leading to fracture.

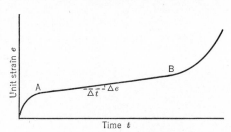

FIG. 2-9.   Typical strain-time curve for creep conditions (not to scale).

These strains occur at stresses that are small compared to the ultimate tensile strength of the metal ascertained by a short-time static test at the same temperature. Thus, as for repeated stress, special tests are needed to establish the strength of the metal under temperature conditions at which creep can occur.

Creep tests are made by loading specimens by dead weights acting through levers and observing the strain at appropriate time intervals. Several specimens are tested, each at a different stress, for a given temperature. Tests are continued until a steady strain rate is observed, or for as long as practicable to obtain reliable data from which to estimate the strains that will occur in longer times. Strain-time curves are plotted for each test, and the slope of the straight-line portion $(A-B)$ is calculated. This slope $\Delta e/\Delta t$ is the *creep rate*.

If several creep test series are made at different temperatures, then stress-temperature curves for a specific creep rate may be plotted as shown in Fig. 2-10.[10] The creep rate of 1 per cent in 100,000 hours of load application (11.4 years) is one standard often used to compare the creep strengths of metals. The stress corresponding to this creep rate is the *creep limit*. It is an arbitrary measure of strength, corresponding to an amount of strain that can take place in many members without producing damage. The creep limit for steel A, Fig. 2-10, is 26,000 psi at 900°F, for example.

[10] Data for curves of Fig. 2-10 are from *Symposium on Effect of Temperature on Metals*, pp. 370, 371, joint publication of American Society for Testing Materials and American Society of Mechanical Engineers, 1931. See also H. F. Moore and M. B. Moore, *Materials of Engineering*, McGraw-Hill Book Co., 1953.

For some materials, such as asphalt, and very soft metals like lead, creep is present at ordinary temperatures. For most metals, however, creep is either not present at ordinary temperatures, or the rate of creep is so extremely slow that it has not been detected with the measuring equipment available. It is not yet known definitely which situation

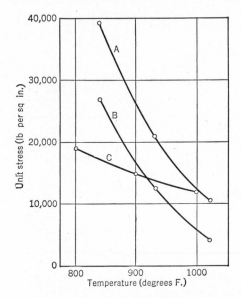

Fig. 2-10.   Creep curves for three low-alloy steels.

exists. It is also unknown whether, at a temperature at which creep is known to exist under high stress, there is any limiting stress below which no creep occurs. It is known that, at temperatures high enough for creep to occur, the higher the temperature, the greater is the rate of creep produced by any given stress intensity. Conversely, at any given temperature, increasing the stress increases the rate of creep. A given rate of creep may therefore be produced in any material by an infinite number of combinations of temperature and stress.

PROBLEM

2-5. Tabulate the creep limits of steels A, B, and C, Fig. 2-10, at the given rate of creep and at each of the following temperatures: 850°, 920°, 1,000°F.

3

Allowable Stresses

3-1. The Nature and Causes of "Failure" of a Member. When a specimen is "tested to failure," as described in Chapter 2, "failure" ordinarily means the breakage of the specimen. On the other hand, a member of a structure or machine is said to have "failed" when it ceases to be able to perform its intended function satisfactorily.

If a member made of a ductile material is overloaded, it ceases to function satisfactorily because of excessive distortion. A water tank, for example, as the pressure is increased excessively, generally begins to leak because of distortion in the neighborhood of the rivet holes long before there is any marked fracture. This type of failure through distortion at ordinary temperature has been termed "failure through *elastic breakdown*." It is the principal source of failure in overloaded structures and in some machine frames where any pronounced deformation of the frame leads to a lack of precision of movement too large to be tolerated. In brittle materials, on the other hand, the breakdown of elastic properties usually results in *fracture* before the amount of distortion has become important.

Where loads fluctuate and are repeated a great many times, as in many machines, failure of ductile as well as of brittle materials generally results from fracture unaccompanied by visible distortion. As was stated in Art. 2-10, this type of failure by gradual fracture is called *fatigue failure.*

At high temperatures, as stated in Art. 2-11, the *very gradual* continuous flow of material, resulting from too high a stress, may after a long time render a member useless for further service. Failures of this type are called *creep failures.*

Parts of structures or machines may fail in any one of these four ways, depending on the conditions of their use and the characteristics of the material.

3-2. The "Usable Strength" of a Material. From what has been said it should be apparent that the fraction of the *ultimate strength* of a material which can be utilized practically is not entirely determined by the material itself. A stress perfectly satisfactory under a static load

33

at ordinary temperature may result in a fatigue failure under repetitions of load, or in a creep failure under high-temperature loading. Under steady loads at ordinary temperatures, the *yield-point stress* is ordinarily the stress limiting the usefulness of wrought iron and the milder grades of steel. So long as the stress remains below the yield point, distortion will generally not be excessive; as soon as the stress reaches the yield point, however, the deformation may become ten or twenty times what it was at a slightly smaller stress and be too great. Only wrought iron and the milder grades of steel, however, have a definite yield point. For steady loading at ordinary temperatures the usable strength of a ductile material may therefore generally be considered to equal its *yield point* (if it has one) or its *yield strength* (Art. 2-8). The usable strength of a brittle material equals its ultimate strength, since fracture occurs before distortion has become pronounced.

In the discussion of high-temperature loading it was brought out that the maximum stress which can be considered satisfactory is affected by the temperature to be resisted and by the allowable rate of creep, and that this stress is called the *creep limit*. The creep limit therefore fixes the usable strength of a material used at high temperature. If the temperature is sufficiently high, or if the rate of creep must be very small, the usable strength may be a very small fraction of the ultimate strength of the cold material.

Under repetitions of stress, the *endurance limit* may be taken as the usable strength of the material, since stresses less than this may be repeated an indefinitely great number of times without causing failure. The ratio of the ultimate strength to the endurance limit is called the "fatigue ratio" of the material.

Depending on conditions of use, therefore, the yield point or yield strength, the creep limit, or the endurance limit may be said to determine the usable strength of a material.

3-3. Allowable Stress and Working Stress. The *allowable unit stress* or simply the *allowable stress* is the unit stress value specified or selected as proper for use in calculating the dimensions of a member which is to carry any stated load, or in calculating the maximum load which should be applied to any given member. Since members may be designed to resist tension or compression or shear, there are allowable tensile, compressive, and shearing unit stresses. Allowable stresses are either specified by some authority, such as a bridge engineer of a railroad or the building department of a city, or selected by a designer of competent judgment after careful consideration of the materials to be used and the conditions of service of the machine or structure.

The *working unit stress* is the unit stress (as calculated) which results in a given member from the loads actually carried or assumed to be carried.   When the loads on a structure are variable, the working stress is a variable stress.   In this respect it differs from allowable stress, which, once selected for a given member, has a fixed value.   The working stress may be at times only a small fraction of the allowable stress.   The working stress should not exceed the allowable stress, although it does in structures that carry loads greater than the "design loads."

The allowable stress used in design is sometimes called the "allowable working stress," a term which is sometimes shortened to "working stress."   In such usage the term "working stress" has the same meaning as "allowable stress" as used in this book.   It is preferable, however, to reserve the term "working stress" for the actual unit stress in the member under whatever load it may be carrying, and to speak of the design stress as the "allowable stress."

3-4. Determination of Allowable Stresses.   It should be evident that the unit stress in a member should not exceed the usable strength of the material of which the member is made.   To insure this, the allowable stress used in the design of the member must be considerably less than the usable strength of the material.   This difference between the allowable stress and the usable stress constitutes a margin of safety which is necessary to provide for the following possibilities:

1. Actual loads may exceed design loads.   This may be a consequence of a deliberate increase in loading in the future or of careless or accidental overloading.

2. Actual maximum stresses may be more than the stresses calculated by ordinary, accepted procedures.   This may be due to simplifying assumptions made in stress calculations[1] or to the effects of shocks, vibrations, and other stresses which are indeterminate.

3. The actual usable strength of the material may not be as great as that assumed.   This situation may exist because of uncertainties inherent in the material or because of defects in the member which escape inspection.

4. Through corrosion, weathering, or decay the effective cross-section of a member may be appreciably lessened with the passage of time.   For example, unless kept well painted, steel members may lose appreciable strength by rusting away; wooden members may rot.

For a simple case of loading where the stress could be computed with perfect accuracy, and with a type of load that could never be greater than that assumed, and such that no shocks or vibrations could ever be

---

[1] For example, the assumption is made that members of riveted trusses are subjected to axial loads only, although it is known that they are subjected to relatively small bending forces as well.

caused by the loading, and with a perfect material known to be free from defects and used under such circumstances that deterioration would be absolutely prevented, it might be permissible to use an allowable stress *almost* equal to the usable strength, but this is an ideal combination that never occurs.

The necessity for a margin of safety having been considered, some of the conditions that together influence its size may be discussed. These include:

1. Exactness with which loads are known.
2. Nature of loads—whether steady or variable.
3. Accuracy with which stresses due to known loads can be calculated.
4. Reliability of material.
5. Resistance of material to corrosion and deterioration.
6. Nature of material from standpoint of whether it gives warning of failure.
7. Seriousness of failure if it occurs.
8. Other practical considerations which sometimes limit the margin of safety.   In the design of an airplane frame all conditions indicate the desirability of a large margin of safety.   Practical requirements of lightness result in a design in which, for certain parts, the difference between the design stress and the usable strength is probably less than in other important structures.

It is not customary to specify the margin of safety, but rather to specify the allowable stresses for the materials to be used in a structure. Such specifications must, of course, take into consideration the variables just enumerated.   A given material such as structural steel, for example, may have allowable stresses for some certain use very different from its allowable stresses for some other use.   Hence there are allowable stresses "for structural steel for buildings" which are, in general, considerably higher than the allowable stresses for the same steel in machines where shock and vibration may be caused by the loads, and where high localized stresses (which would be unimportant in a building frame) would probably result in fatigue failure.

3-5. Allowable Stress Values.   In designing machines—locomotives, automobile engines, power shovels, lathes—many different materials, with widely different mechanical properties, are used.   Furthermore, the conditions under which these various machines are employed differ greatly in severity.   For these reasons it is not feasible to attempt to give here any general tables of allowable stresses for materials as used in machines.   The design department of each manufacturing organization generally decides on the stresses which will be used in its own designing, basing them on the materials to be utilized and on the purpose of the product.

TABLE I

ALLOWABLE STRESSES

(All stresses are given in pounds per square inch.)

Structural Steel for Bridges and Buildings

	A	B
Tension on net section of rolled steel............	20,000	18,000
Compression on short lengths (not columns)......	20,000	18,000
Shear on pins and power-driven rivets...........	15,000	13,500

Values specified in column A are in the 1946 American Institute of Steel Construction Specifications for the Design, Fabrication, and Erection of Structural Steel for Buildings, and are permitted by a number of cities in their building codes. Values in column B are in the 1952 American Railway Engineering Association Specifications for Steel Railway Bridges. Both these values are based on an ultimate tensile strength of 72,000 psi for structural steel, which is now the standard.

Cast Iron

(New York City Building Code, 1952)

Tension......... 3,000   Compression..... 16,000   Shear........... 3,000

Bearing on Brick Masonry

(New York City Building Code, 1952)

Kind of mortar:

Portland cement... 325   Cement-lime...... 250   Lime............. 100

(For brick having an ultimate strength greater than 4,500 psi, higher stresses are allowed.)

Bearing on Concrete and Stone Masonry

(American Railway Engineering Association, 1952 Specifications for Steel Railway Bridges)

Granite masonry (Portland cement mortar) 800
Sandstone and limestone masonry (Portland cement mortar) ... 400
Concrete masonry.. 600

Lumber

(Based on stresses recommended by the National Lumber Manufacturers' Association 1951.)

NOTE: Appendix C gives nominal and actual sizes of commercial lumber.

Kind of Wood and Grade	Compression		Shear
	On Short Lengths Parallel to Grain (Load on end)	Perpendicular to Grain (Load on side)	Parallel to Grain (Along grain)
Southern pine (longleaf)			
Prime structural	1,450	455	120
Structural	1,325	455	120
Spruce, Eastern			
Select	975	300	95
Common	900	300	95
Oak, white or red			
Select	1,375	600	145
Common	1,200	600	145

Stresses given above are for dry locations. In damp or wet locations lower stresses should be used (see Table XI, Appendix C).

In structural work, however, the variety of conditions encountered is much narrower and the range of materials ordinarily used is much less, so that allowable stresses in structural work can be more nearly standardized. Various bodies of engineers from time to time prepare specifications which include allowable stresses for material that meets certain strength standards. For example, the American Railway Engineering Association, the American Society of Civil Engineers, and the American Institute of Steel Construction are typical organizations which at one time or another have prepared specifications that include allowable stresses for structural carbon steel for bridges or for buildings. In addition to stating the allowable stresses, such specifications also include the physical characteristics of the material to be used and cover the more important aspects of design, fabrication, and erection, so as to insure that the stresses used shall be consistent with the conditions of material and of use that were presupposed in the preparation of the specification. Table I of allowable stresses consists of extracts from such specifications but is limited to the simple stresses that have so far been considered in this book. In Appendix C will be found a more comprehensive set of tables which include allowable values for bending and other stresses.

PROBLEMS

3-1. (a) A short common grade spruce post $9\frac{1}{2}$ in. by $9\frac{1}{2}$ in. bears against an oak sill of the same size as shown in Fig. 3-1. What is the allowable load on the post? (b) If a cast-iron bearing plate $9\frac{1}{2}$ in. wide and 15 in. long is placed between the sill and the end of the post in (a), what is the allowable load? *Ans.* (b) 81,200 lb.

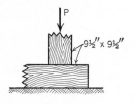

FIG. 3-1

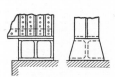

FIG. 3-2

3-2. A cast-iron bridge "pedestal" (Fig. 3-2) carries a load of 330,000 lb. It rests on a concrete pier. The dimensions in contact with the concrete are 22×22 in. Does this comply with the specifications of the American Railway Engineering Association?

3-3. A tension member in a roof truss is composed of two angles which together have a net section of 8.62 sq in. (a) What total load is permitted by the A.I.S.C. Specifications on this member? (b) If the total tension in the member is 150,000 lb, what is the working stress? *Ans.* (a) P = 172,400 lb.

3-4. A pump rod, a, is $1\frac{3}{4}$ in. in diameter. It is attached to another section of the rod by a cottered joint (Fig. 3-3). A slot is cut through the enlarged end of the rod for a cotter $\frac{1}{2}$ in. thick and $2\frac{3}{4}$ in. deep.   If allowable tensile stress is 10,000 psi and allowable shearing stress is 8,000 psi, what is the allowable load on the rod? With this load, what is the minimum value of the dimension l as limited by shearing stress?

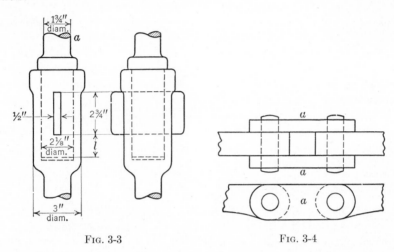

FIG. 3-3   FIG. 3-4

3-5. A small sprocket chain is made of links of steel as shown in Fig. 3-4.   The links marked a are $\frac{5}{8}$ in. wide and $\frac{1}{4}$ in. thick.   The pins are $\frac{5}{16}$ in. in diameter.   If allowable stresses are tension, 9,000 psi and shear, 5,000 psi, what is the greatest allowable load on the chain?

3-6. Factor of Safety.   "Factor of safety" is a term denoting the ratio of the greatest load a member or structure could carry, to the design load.   For instance, if the tensile load which would cause failure of a tensile member is known (on the basis of the specified minimum strength of the material composing the member) to be at least 80,000 lb, and if the member is designed to carry a tensile load of only 20,000 lb, its factor of safety is said to be at least 4.   This is a *design* factor of safety.   The *working* factor of safety is the ratio of the load causing failure to the load actually being carried.   The working factor of safety can be greater or less than the design factor of safety, depending on whether the load being carried is less or greater than the design load.

In most structural and machine parts the maximum stress is proportional to the load.[2]   In such cases the design factor of safety may be obtained by dividing the *ultimate strength* of the material by the allowable stress; the working factor of safety is found by dividing the ultimate strength by the working stress.

[2] Columns are an exception to this rule, the maximum stress increasing more rapidly than the load.

The concept of a factor of safety is of special value in examining a structure that has its different parts subjected to different kinds of stress (tension, compression, or shear) in order to ascertain which part is likely to give way first, in the event of an excessive load. The term "factor of *safety*" is misleading, however. There are few structures that could have the loads increased in the ratio of the design factor of safety without *failing* long before the loading was completed. This is the situation because, as has been pointed out, failure under steady loads results more frequently from excessive distortion than from actual fracture or collapse; and under repeated loads failure results from fatigue. Nevertheless, the concept has its uses, particularly in comparing the strengths of different parts of a structure. The abbreviation F.S. will be used sometimes for factor of safety.

Example. A steel eyebar carries a load of 100,000 lb and is $1\frac{1}{2} \times 4$ in. in cross-section. The end of the bar is held by a pin, arranged as shown in Fig. 3-5. If it is assumed that the shearing stress is uniformly distributed over the cross-sections of the pin, what is the proper diameter of the pin to make its factor of safety in shear equal to the factor of safety of the eyebar in tension? Ultimate strengths of the material composing bar and pin are: tension, 60,000 psi, shear, 45,000 psi.

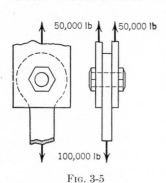

50,000 lb   50,000 lb

100,000 lb

Fig. 3-5

Solution: S_T in eyebar $= 100,000/6 = 16,700$ psi.

Therefore for the eyebar in tension, F.S. $= 60,000/16,700 = 3.59$.

Hence for same factor of safety in pin, $S_S = 45,000/3.59 = 12,500$ psi.

Therefore the necessary area to support shear in pin $= 100,000/12,500 = 8.00$ sq in.

The shearing stress is distributed over two cross-sections of the pin. Therefore the required cross-section of pin $= 4.00$ sq in.

Whence, required pin diameter $= 2.26$ in.

PROBLEMS

3-6. Find the allowable weight W that may be supported by the bracket shown in Fig. 3-6 with a factor of safety of 6 as limited by the stresses in the member BC and in the pins B and C. Pins are $\frac{1}{2}$ in. in diameter, bars BC are $1\frac{1}{4} \times \frac{1}{4}$ in. Ultimate strengths are: tension 72,000 psi; shearing 48,000 psi.   *Ans.* $W = 1,570$ lb.

3-7. The weight W in Fig. 3-6 is 2,000 lb. Calculate the tensile factor of safety of BC and the shearing factor of safety of the pin at C. Ultimate strengths are: tension 72,000 psi; shearing 48,000 psi. Determine the necessary diameter of the pin at A if its factor of safety is to be 5. Bars BC are $1 \times \frac{3}{8}$ in. Pin C is $\frac{1}{2}$ in.

3-8. In Fig. 3-7, a is a steel rod ($t = 1$ in., $h = 1.75$ in.) which carries a load P. The rod is supported by a steel pin b, 0.75 in. square, passing through a hole of the same size as shown. The ultimate tensile strength of the steel is 64,000 psi, and the

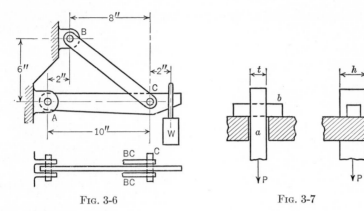

FIG. 3-6   FIG. 3-7

ultimate shearing strength is 48,000 psi. If the factor of safety is not to be less than 4, what is the greatest allowable load P?

3-9. If, in Problem 3-8, $h = 1.80$ in., (a) what is the factor of safety when the load P is 12,000 lb; (b) if the factor of safety is to be not less than 5 what is the maximum allowable value of P?   *Ans.* (a) F.S. = 4.5.

3-10. If the pin in Problem 3-8 is 0.85 in. square and the load P equals 12,500 lb, what is the factor of safety? If the factor of safety is not to be less than 4, what is the maximum allowable value of P?

3-11. What should be the size of a square pin b to pass through the rod a if the factor of safety of the pin in shear is to be equal to the factor of safety of the rod in tension? Strengths and size of bar a as in Problem 3-8.

3-12. Solve Problem 3-8 if $t = 0.8$ in. and $h = 2.0$ in.

3-13. In Fig. 3-7, a is a steel bar ($t = 1.0$ in. and $h = 2.0$ in.) carrying a load P. It is supported by the steel pin b, which is 0.80 in. wide and 1.10 in. vertically, passing through a hole of the same size. Ultimate strengths in the steel are tension 72,000 psi and shearing 54,000 psi. Calculate the factor of safety when $P = 15,000$ lb.

3-14. What must be the width of the pin b in Problem 3-13 if the factors of safety in tension and shear are to be equal? Other dimensions and strengths are as stated in Problem 3-13. *Ans.* $W = 0.754$ in.

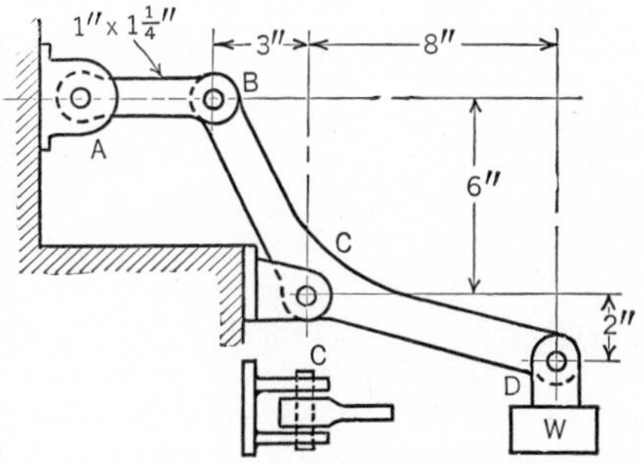

3-15. The link AB (Fig. 3-8) is made of steel having a tensile ultimate strength of 72,000 psi. The pins are of steel having a shearing ultimate strength of 54,000 psi. Calculate the required cross-sectional area of the pin at C if the factor of safety of the pin is to be 6. Also find the factor of safety of the link AB. $W = 12,000$ lb.

3-16. The link AB (Fig. 3-8) is made of steel having a tensile ultimate strength of 65,000 psi. Pins are made of steel having a shearing ultimate strength of 50,000 psi. $W = 15,000$ lb.

FIG. 3-8

Calculate the required diameter of the pin at C if its factor of safety is to be the same as the factor of safety of the link AB.   *Ans.* $D = 1.137$ in.

GENERAL PROBLEMS

3-17. An I-beam (Fig. 3-9) rests on a brick wall laid with portland cement mortar. The maximum end reaction of the beam is 23,000 lb, and the beam projects 8 in. over the wall.　Find the width of bearing plate required.　　　*Ans.*　$b = 8.86$ in.

3-18. A steel beam in a bridge rests on a cast-iron pedestal of the dimensions shown (Fig. 3-10).　The pedestal rests on a pier of sandstone masonry.　It is proposed to move over the bridge an exceptionally heavy load which would cause a

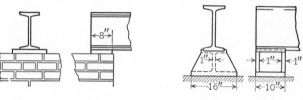

Fɪɢ. 3-9　　　　　　　　　　　　Fɪɢ. 3-10

reaction of 79,000 lb at the end of the beam.　(*a*) Calculate the unit compressive stress which this load would cause in the masonry.　(*b*) Does this comply with the American Railway Engineering Association specifications?　(*c*) Would you allow this load to be moved over the bridge?

3-19. A southern pine beam (prime structural grade) is shown in Fig. 3-11.　The ends rest on steel bearing plates supported by brick walls laid up with cement-lime mortar.　$P = 25,000$ lb, $m = 2$ ft, and $n = 3$ ft.　(*a*) Calculate the required length a of the center steel bearing plate.　(*b*) Calculate the minimum dimension b for the left-end bearing plate.　(*c*) Find the width c of the end bearing plate.　Assume location to be continuously dry.

3-20. Solve Problem 3-19 if both m and n are 2.5 ft.

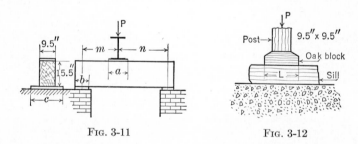

Fɪɢ. 3-11　　　　　　　　　　　　Fɪɢ. 3-12

3-21. The post and sill shown in Fig. 3-12 are both of spruce, and each is 9.5 in. square.　(*a*) If the post rested directly on the sill (no oak block), what would be the allowable load P?　(*b*) What is the allowable load as determined by bearing of the post on the oak block?　(*c*) For this allowable load what length L is required?
　　　　　　　　　　　　　　　　Ans.　(*c*)　$L = 19.0$ in.

3-22. Figure 3-13 shows a bell-crank lever such as those used in various mechanisms to change the direction and magnitude of a force.　Determine the sizes of pins B and C so that the factor of safety of each pin in shear will equal the factor of safety of rod

D in tension. Tensile ultimate strength of the steel is **70,000 psi**. Shearing ultimate strength of the pin steel is **50,000 psi**. Diameter of D is 1.40 in., $P = 9,000$ lb.

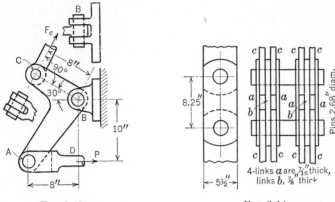

FIG. 3-13   FIG. 3-14

3-23. Chain used in operation of the spillway gates at the Fort Peck dam has links and pins with the dimensions shown in Fig. 3-14. These links and pins are of chrome-nickel steels, heat treated. Ultimate tensile strength is 180,000 psi, and ultimate shearing strength of steel in pins is 65,000 psi. Calculate the factors of safety in tension and in shear when the load on the chain is 540,000 lb. Why are links a and b of different thicknesses?

3-24. The forging shown in Fig. 3-15 fits over the shaft A and is prevented from rotating by the bolt D which is 0.75 in. in diameter. Diameter of shaft is 2.20 in. Calculate the allowable value of W if the allowable shearing stress in D is 10,000 psi. With this value of W determine the required diameter of the pin C using the same allowable shearing stress

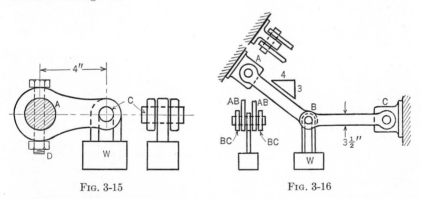

FIG. 3-15   FIG. 3-16

3-25. The pins at A, B, and C in Fig. 3-16 are made of steel having a shearing strength of 40,000 psi. The bars AB and BC are of steel having a tensile strength of 65,000 psi. AB consists of two bars $3\frac{1}{2}$ in. wide and $\frac{3}{4}$ in. thick. BC consists of two bars $3\frac{1}{2} \times \frac{5}{8}$ in. Calculate the size of the pin at A if it is to have a factor of safety in shear equal to the factor of safety in tension of the more highly stressed bars. $W = 50,000$ lb. *Ans.* $D = 2.33$ in.

3-26. Same as Problem 3-25 except calculate the size of the pin at B.

3-27. In Fig. 3-7 the bar a is 2 in. square. The bar b is square and passes through a closely fitting square hole in the center of a 2-in. face. What should be the size of bar b if the factor of safety of the bar b in shear is to be the same as the factor of safety of a in tension? Ultimate strength in tension is 70,000 psi and in shearing is 50,000 psi.

4

Pressure Containers;
Riveted and Welded Joints

4-1. Introduction. Two topics are discussed in this chapter. First, a method is demonstrated for finding the forces caused by fluid pressure in a closed container or vessel. After the force is found the unit stress in the wall of the vessel is found by using $S = P/A$.

Second, the riveted, bolted, and welded joints used in making tanks, boilers, pipe, and many types of structures are described, and the stresses in these joints are considered.

The two topics are closely associated because it is necessary to determine the rupturing forces in a boiler, for instance, in order to determine the kind of riveted joints or welded joints needed to join the plates without exceeding allowable stresses.

STRESSES CAUSED BY INTERNAL PRESSURE

4-2. Rupturing Forces in Pressure Containers. The pressure of a liquid or of any confined gas acts normally to the surface of the container in which the pressure exists. This normal pressure sets up stresses in the walls of the container and tends to rupture them. The design of such a container, or the investigation of the stresses set up in one by a given unit pressure, includes two distinct steps: first, the determination of the force which tends to rupture the container along the surface or surfaces where rupture is most likely to occur; second, the determination of the stresses which result from the action of this force.

As an example consider the pressure container shown in Fig. 4-1a. Suppose that the unit stress on the section AB is wanted. This unit stress may be found by considering the part of the container above the plane AB as a body in equilibrium, shown in Fig. 4-1b. The upward force F is the resultant in a direction *perpendicular* to the plane AB of all the force exerted on the interior surface by the fluid pressure. The downward forces shown represent forces due to the tensile stress in the wall of the container and the sum of these downward forces equals SA, where S is the unit tensile stress and A is the area of the cross-section of the wall cut by the plane. Evidently $S = F/A$.

45

A method of determining the force F perpendicular to the plane will now be given. In Fig. 4-2 is shown the part of a pressure container above a horizontal plane through the walls of the container. In this figure one-half of the part above the plane has been removed in order to make some of the interior surface visible

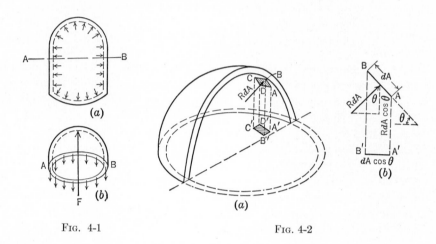

FIG. 4-1   FIG. 4-2

A small rectangular area $ABCD$ on the interior surface is shown. Let the angle between the surface at this point and the horizontal plane be θ, let the area of $ABCD$ be dA sq in., and let the unit pressure of the fluid in the container be R psi. The force P exerted by the fluid on this area equals RdA and is normal to the surface, and therefore makes an angle θ with the vertical (Fig. 4-2b). Hence the vertical component of this force is $RdA \cos \theta$.

Now, if perpendiculars to the horizontal plane are dropped from A, B, C, and D, it will be seen that the area $A'B'C'D'$ equals $dA \cos \theta$. Hence the vertical component of P, which is $RdA \cos \theta$, is seen to be equal to R times the projection of the area dA on the horizontal plane. The total vertical force F is the sum of the vertical components of the forces on all the elementary areas comprising the interior surface above the plane. The foregoing reasoning shows that F equals the area of the part of the horizontal plane within the inner surface of the wall multiplied by R. This method of finding F may be stated as a general proposition thus:

The force F tending to rupture a pressure container along any intersecting plane is equal to the area of the part of the plane included within the interior surface multiplied by the unit pressure of the fluid.

The above reasoning applies to a vessel of any shape.   Consequently for any vessel, such as those in Fig. 4-3, the resultant force exerted by the pressure on the part on one side of a plane a–a equals the unit pressure times the area of the part of the plane included within the inner surface of the vessel.

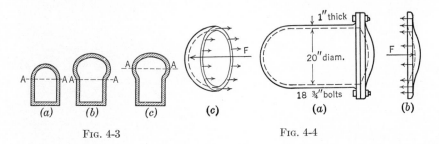

(a)   (b)   (c)   (c)   (a)   (b)

FIG. 4-3   FIG. 4-4

4-3. Unit Stresses in Pressure Vessels.   Examples showing applications of the principles of Art. 4-2 will now be given:

Example 1.   A cast-iron cylinder with a bolted cover is shown in Fig. 4-4a.   The cover is attached with 18 bolts, $\frac{3}{4}$ in. in diameter and equally spaced.   Calculate the maximum unit tensile stress in the bolts when the pressure of the gas in the cylinder is 80 psi.

Solution: The cover is shown as a body in equilibrium in Fig. 4-4b.   The force $F = 100\pi \times 80 = 25{,}200$ lb.   The area of one $\frac{3}{4}$-in. bolt at the root of the thread is found in Appendix C to be 0.302 sq in.   Hence $S = F/A = 25{,}200/18 \times 0.302 = 4{,}630$ psi.

Example 2.   Calculate the unit stress that occurs on any cross-section of the cylinder shown in Fig. 4-4a.   The unit stress on a transverse section perpendicular to the longitudinal axis of the cylinder is called "longitudinal stress."

Solution: Pass an imaginary transverse plane A–A cutting the cylinder into two parts and show one of the two parts as a body in equilibrium, as in Fig. 4-4c.   The forces due to the tensile unit stress on the cut section of the wall of the cylinder must balance the force F.   The area of the cut section of the wall is equal to the thickness of the wall times the mean circumference.   Hence

$$S = \frac{F}{A} = \frac{100\pi \times 80}{21\pi \times 1}$$

$$S = 8{,}000/21 = 381 \text{ psi}$$

Note that this stress would also be the unit stress in a sphere with an inside diameter of 20 in. and walls 1 in. thick.   The method of solution for the sphere would differ only in that the transverse plane would cut the sphere into two equal parts, one of which would be taken as a body in equilibrium.   The force F is the same as for the cylinder.

Example 3.   Calculate the circumferential stress or "hoop tension" in the cast-iron cylinder of Example 1.

Solution: Imagine two transverse planes a short distance L apart and perpendicular to the axis of the cylinder. Between these two planes is a ring or "hoop" shown in Fig. 4-5a. Against the inner surface of this ring are normal forces due to the gas pressure in the cylinder. Next the hoop is cut into two equal parts by a horizontal plane, and the upper half is shown in Fig. 4-5b. This is a body in equilibrium with the vertical force F (the resultant of the gas pressure on the inner surface) and two forces H, due to the circumferential stress in the wall of the cylinder. Equilibrium requires that

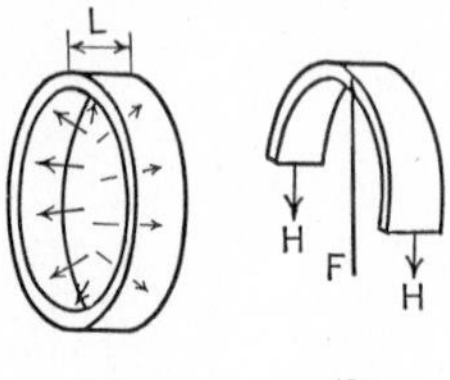

$$2H = F$$

whence

$$2 \times 1 \times L \times S = 20L \times 80$$

from which

$$S = 1{,}600/2 = 800 \text{ psi}$$

(a)   (b)

FIG. 4-5

Note that the longitudinal unit stress calculated in Example 2 is somewhat less than half the circumferential stress. For cylinders with thinner walls in proportion to the inside diameter, the longitudinal stress is more nearly equal to half the circumferential stress. The statement is often made that in "thin cylinders" the longitudinal stress is one-half the circumferential stress, and this is nearly true. For instance, if the wall thickness is one-fiftieth of the inside diameter, the ratio of longitudinal stress to circumferential stress is 0.49.

A formula for longitudinal stress in a thin-walled cylinder will now be derived. Let Fig. 4-4c be the end of a thin-walled cylinder with inside diameter of D in. and wall thickness of t in. The area of the metal cut by the cross-section equals the mean circumference times the thickness, or $\pi (D + t) t$; but, if t is small in comparison to D, a close approximation will be $\pi D t$. Equating the force F due to the internal pressure of R psi with the unit stress in the shell times the cut area,

$$(\pi/4)D^2 R = \pi D t S$$

whence

$$S = RD/4t$$

Note that this formula also gives a value for the stress in a thin spherical shell with the same degree of approximation.

A formula for the "hoop tension" or circumferential stress in a thin-walled cylinder is derived as follows. Let Fig. 4-5a represent a ring cut from a thin-walled tank with internal fluid pressure of R psi. Let L be 1 in. Now consider half this ring, as shown in Fig. 4-5b, as a body in equilibrium. If t is the thickness of the shell, the force H equals $S \times 1 \times t = St$. The force $F = RD$. Equating the upward and downward forces, $2St = RD$, from which

$$S = RD/2t$$

Note that this is exactly twice the value of the longitudinal stress as given by the approximate formula derived just above.

Since the plane dividing the ring into two half rings (Fig. 4-5b) may cut the ring at any two opposite points, it follows that the total tension is the same at all cross-sections of the ring. If for any reason the area of the ring is not the same for all cross-sections, the maximum unit stress will occur at the cross-sections where the area is least.

Tanks and pipes are sometimes made of wooden staves held together by hoops. The construction is somewhat like that of a wooden barrel. The total stress on one hoop may be found much as the force H is found. The maximum unit stress is then determined by dividing the total stress by the minimum cross-section of the hoop. The distance L between the two transverse planes should be taken equal to the distance between the hoops. This same method applies to other types of fastenings which occur at intervals along a pipe or tank.

PROBLEMS

4-1. A fire extinguisher has a copper tank holding 2.5 gal. The inside diameter is 7 in., and the thickness of the shell of the tank is 0.12 in. The extinguisher was tested with a water pressure of 350 psi. What stress did this pressure cause in the shell of the tank?   *Ans.* $S = 10,200$ psi.

4-2. A "blind flange" or cover is used to close the end of a 14-in. (outside diameter, see Table VIII) steam line which is subjected to a pressure of 600 psi at a temperature of 750°F. The "American standard" for this service requires that the flange be held on with twenty $1\frac{3}{8}$-in. alloy steel bolts. (a) What is the maximum stress in each bolt? (b) On this same pipe and flange a hydraulic (non-shock) pressure of 1,100 psi at ordinary temperature is permitted. What is the maximum bolt stress?

4-3. Specifications of the American Water Works Association provide that a 36-in.-diameter Class A (wall thickness 1.15 in.) cast-iron pipe must withstand a hydrostatic pressure of 200 psi. What circumferential unit stress does this pressure cause?

4-4. The inside diameter of a wood-stave pipe is 66 in. (Fig. 4-6). Hoops are steel rods 1 in. in diameter spaced 6 in. center to center. The ends of each rod are threaded so that the hoop can be tightened by turning a nut. What is the maximum unit stress in the hoop when the water pressure in the pipe is 50 psi?

Ans. $S = 17,900$ psi.

4-5. A rectangular tank is 20 in. square by 40 in. long (interior dimensions). It is cast in two sections, as shown in Fig. 4-7. The two halves are bolted together with ten $1\frac{1}{2}$-in. bolts having an ultimate strength of 65,000 psi. Find the factor of safety for the bolts when the pressure in the tank is 210 psi. Is there any shearing stress on the bolt cross-sections? Slope of joint is 45°.

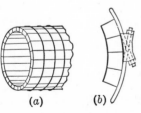

(a)   (b)

Fig. 4-6

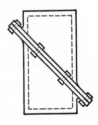

Fig. 4-7

4-6. An air chamber for a pump is shown in Fig. 4-8. For a pressure of 240 psi calculate the number of $\frac{7}{8}$-in.-diameter bolts required at A and also at B. Stress is not to exceed 6,000 psi.   *Ans.* 10 bolts at A.

4-7. A small cylinder subject to high pressure is to be made by brazing a plug p into each end of a steel tube (inside diameter d of 2.00 in.) as shown in Fig. 4-9. Through one of the plugs there is an accurately drilled hole 0.60 in. in diameter. The pressure is produced by filling the tube with a liquid and forcing in the 0.60-in.-diameter plunger with a load F. (*a*) What pressure in pounds per square inch is allowable in the liquid if the allowable shearing stress in the brazing is 1,500 psi? (*b*) What is the load F to produce this pressure? (*c*) The tube is made of metal 0.20 in. thick. What is the maximum unit stress in the tube when this load is applied? (*d*) What is the longitudinal unit stress in the tube?

Ans. (*a*) $R = 3,600$ psi.

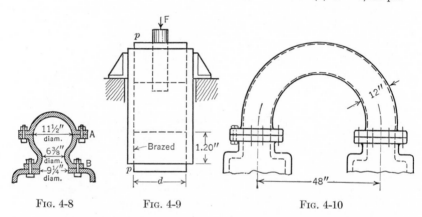

Fig. 4-8   Fig. 4-9   Fig. 4-10

4-8. A bent steam pipe connecting a valve chamber and a cylinder is shown in Fig. 4-10. The pipe is 12 in. in outside diameter and 11 in. in inside diameter. Steam pressure is 450 psi. Determine the total number of bolts required to attach the bent pipe to the two chambers. Bolts are $1\frac{1}{4}$ in. in diameter, and allowable stress in the bolts is 5,000 psi.

4-9. A water tank made of wood staves has an inside diameter of 12 ft and is 18 ft high. Hoops are flat steel bars 2 in. by $\frac{3}{8}$ in., spaced 10 in. center to center. (*a*) What is the unit stress in a hoop 10 in. above the bottom of the tank when the tank is full? (*b*) If instead of fresh water the tank is to hold brine (specific gravity = 1.20), to what should the hoop spacing be reduced for retention of the same factor of safety?

4-10. A welded steel water pipe used as a "siphon" in the Owyhee reclamation project in eastern Oregon has a diameter of 9 ft and is made of $\frac{13}{16}$-in. plate. After fabrication this pipe was tested under a water pressure of 220 psi. What circumferential stress was developed?   *Ans.* $S = 14,600$ psi.

4-11. The Outardes hydroelectric project in Canada includes what is believed to be the largest wooden-stave pipe so far constructed. (See *Civil Engineering*, December, 1937.) This pipe has an internal diameter of 17 ft 6 in. and operates under a maximum head of 113.0 ft. The staves are held together by 1-in. steel bars, threaded. What maximum tensile unit stress does the water pressure cause in these bars where the head is 100 ft and the hoops are spaced 2.5 in. center to center?

4-4. Thick-Walled Cylinders. The relation between unit pressure and circumferential stress developed for "thin-walled" cylinders does not hold for "thick-walled" cylinders. The reasoning applied to the thin-walled cylinder gives a correct value for the *average* circumferential stress in the wall of any circular cylinder subjected to internal pressure. But if the cylinder wall is thick (in comparison with the internal radius) the *maximum* unit stress is higher than the average. If the wall thickness is 2/10 of the inner radius, the maximum stress is 10 per cent above the average stress. For greater relative thicknesses, the maximum stress increases somewhat more rapidly than the thickness.

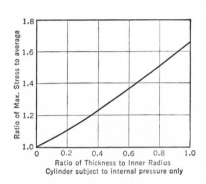

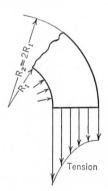

Fig. 4-11   Fig. 4-12

The analysis of stresses in thick-walled cylinders will not be given in this book.[1] However, a curve giving the ratio of the maximum circumferential unit stress to the average unit stress is given in Fig. 4-11. By means of this curve thick-walled cylinders subject to internal static pressure may be designed or investigated. As an example illustrating the variation of circumferential stress, Fig. 4-12 shows the stresses in the wall of a cylinder having a thickness equal to the inner radius. For this case the curve (Fig. 4-11) indicates that the maximum stress is about 1.65 times the average stress obtained by the methods of this chapter. The curve of Fig. 4-11 is so nearly straight that generally satisfactory results can be obtained from a straight line giving a ratio of unity when the thickness is zero and 1.65 when the thickness equals the inner radius.

Example. A chrome-vanadium steel cylinder used in a chemical manufacturing plant has an inside diameter of 24 in. and an outside diameter of 32 in. When the

[1] See Seely and Smith, *Advanced Mechanics of Materials*, 2nd ed., John Wiley & Sons, 1952.

cylinder is in use the inside pressure is 4,200 psi. Calculate the maximum unit stress in the wall.

Solution: The average stress is found by considering a ring between planes 1 in. apart. On half of this ring the force due to the unit tensile stress equals the force due to the interior pressure. Hence $S \times 2 \times 4 = 24 \times 4,200$. Average $S =$ 12,600 psi. The ratio of thickness to interior radius is $4/12 = 0.33$. From the curve of Fig. 4-11 it is seen that for this ratio the ordinate is 1.19. Hence the maximum tensile stress is $1.19 \times 12,600 = 15,000$ psi.

WELDED AND RIVETED JOINTS

4-5. Kinds of Joints. Steel tanks and boilers and the steel frames of buildings are ordinarily made of a number of separate pieces joined together. There are two principal methods of joining pieces of metal in this way. One method is by welding them together, the other by riveting them.

In this chapter joints of both types are described, the stresses resulting in them are discussed, and the accepted methods for calculating the allowable loads for such joints are illustrated.

In the field assembly of structural members there is a trend toward greater use of bolted joints. Special types of high-strength bolts are specified for such work. In such joints the loads are transmitted from one plate to the other by the friction developed due to the great pressure between the plates when the bolts are tightened. The design of such joints is based on empirical methods and will not be discussed here.[2]

The welded and riveted joints considered in this chapter are assumed to be loaded with an axial load, the resultant of which passes through the centroid of the group of rivets or welds. In Chapter 20 welded and riveted joints with eccentric loadings are discussed.

4-6. Welded Joints. The common methods of welding in wide use are arc welding and oxyacetylene welding. In both these methods, fused metal is caused to flow between the parts to be welded, which, in turn, are themselves fused to an appreciable depth where in contact with the fused weld metal. When this fused metal has cooled, the parts are joined by the new metal. If properly made, such welds are as strong as the metal which has been melted to form them. If not properly made, the welds may have little strength.

In these methods of welding the new metal is melted from a slender rod. In arc welding the heat is supplied by an electric arc, generally formed between the metal to be joined and the rod. The arc heats the parts to be welded and fuses the tip of the rod. The weld metal is usually deposited in the form of a "bead" or "fillet." Oxyacetylene

---

[2] See *Civil Engineering*, September, 1952, for a discussion of the present state of this development.

welding differs from arc welding in that the source of heat is a jet of burning oxygen and acetylene gas.

These types of welding are extensively used in repairing breaks in castings and forgings and in making tanks, machine frames, and numerous other products of rolled steel. When such welded machine frames are used in place of castings, there may be considerable saving in weight, increase in strength, and reduction in cost.

Welding of structural steel for bridges and buildings is emerging from the experimental stage and offers great advantages and promises some economies. This use of welding is increasing rapidly at the present time.

4-7. Types of Welded Joints; Allowable Stresses. The two most frequently encountered types of welds are *fillet* welds and *butt* welds These are illustrated in Fig. 4-13. Structural welds are generally of the fillet type (Fig. 4-14*a*). Often the fillet *A* is omitted, only the *fillets B*

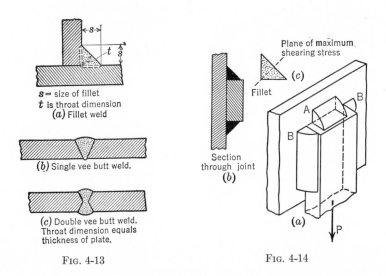

$s =$ size of fillet
t is throat dimension
(*a*) Fillet weld

(*b*) Single vee butt weld.

(*c*) Double vee butt weld.
Throat dimension equals
thickness of plate.

Plane of maximum
shearing stress
(*c*)

Fillet

Section
through joint
(*b*)

(*a*)

Fig. 4-13   Fig. 4-14

being used. In both fillets *A* and *B*, shearing stress limits the allowable load. In *B*, the maximum shearing stress is on the "throat" (Fig. 4-13*a*) of the fillet. In fillet *A* it can be shown that the shearing stress on the throat equals the shearing stress on the vertical face. The specifications of the American Institute of Steel Construction state that "stress in a fillet weld shall be considered as shear on the throat, for any direction of applied load." Therefore, in all fillet welds, shearing stress on the fillet throat is the important stress.

The Specifications of the American Welding Society[3] permit this stress to be 13,600 psi. Based on this unit stress the following values are specified as the allowable load per linear inch of fillet for fillets of different sizes.

Size of Fillet (inch)	Allowable Load (pounds per linear inch)
$\frac{1}{2}$	4,800
$\frac{7}{16}$	4,200
$\frac{3}{8}$	3,600
$\frac{5}{16}$	3,000
$\frac{1}{4}$	2,400

As an example of the way in which these allowable loads per inch are determined, consider a $\frac{1}{2}$-in. fillet. As shown in Fig. 4-14c, the minimum shear area is along the plane bisecting the right angle, and for the $\frac{1}{2}$-in. fillet is $0.5 \times 0.707 = 0.3535$ sq in. This area multiplied by the allowable shearing stress of 13,600 psi gives 4,800 lb per in. of fillet.

Butt welds are used principally in pressure containers, such as boilers, tanks, and standpipes. However, the use of butt welds in structural work is increasing. Since the throat dimension of a butt weld is the thickness of the plates which the weld joins, the allowable pressure in a butt-welded container is affected by the weld only in so far as the metal of the weld, or the metal adjoining the weld, is weaker than the metal at other parts of the container. The Boiler Construction Code of the American Society of Mechanical Engineers[4] provides that a butt weld shall be assumed to have a certain percentage of the strength of un-welded plate. The specified percentage varies from 90 for the highest-grade, most carefully inspected double-vee work, down to a minimum of about 60 per cent for single-vee welds subjected to a much less rigid type of inspection.

For structural butt welds the specifications of the American Welding Society lists as allowable stresses the following:

Tension on section through weld throat, 20,000 psi.

Compression on section through weld throat, 20,000 psi.

The Building Code of the City of New York, 1951, also specifies these values.

[3] "Code for Arc and Gas Welding in Building Construction," American Welding Society, 1950.

[4] This very comprehensive set of specifications, commonly called the A.S.M.E. Boiler Code, has been adopted by law in many cities and states and is widely followed in the design and construction of boilers and other pressure containers.

4-8. Design of Welded Joints or Connections. In connections for members of symmetrical cross-section, the weld fillet should be symmetrically placed with respect to the axis of the member (Fig. 4-15). Connections for unsymmetrical members may be designed by methods equivalent to the following.

Assume that the stress in the member shown in Fig. 4-16 is uniformly distributed over the cross-section, as it must be if the member is to carry the maximum load consistent with a given allowable stress.   Then the resultant of the stress is a force P which acts through the centroid of the cross-section of the member.   If the resultant force exerted by the welds upon the member is collinear with the force P, the load per linear inch of weld will be nearly the same in all parts of the weld, as is explained in Chapter 20.   To insure this, the sum of the moments of the forces

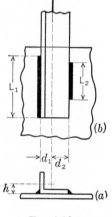

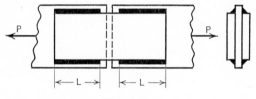

FIG. 4-15   FIG. 4-16

exerted by the welds, with respect to any moment center, must equal the moment of the force P with respect to the same center.   Letting F equal the allowable load per inch of weld and taking a moment center on one weld, $L_2F\,(d_1 + d_2) = Pd_1$; also $L_1 + L_2 = P/F$.   These two equations determine the necessary lengths.

The methods in common use for the design of welded joints involve simplifying assumptions.   It is not strictly true that each linear inch of a fillet weld carries the same load as every other inch of weld.   Furthermore, there are stress concentrations where the weld abruptly changes the cross-sections.   These effects are less serious in ductile materials than in brittle materials and are provided for by the use of allowable stresses well below the ultimate strengths.[5]

PROBLEMS

4-12. A tank is made of $\frac{5}{16}$-in. plates, butt-welded.   The (internal) diameter is 32 in.   If the ultimate tensile strength of the plate is 70,000 psi and if the strength

[5] For a thorough discussion of welded joints see: C. H. Jennings, "Welding Design," *Trans. A.S.M.E.*, Vol. 58, 1936, p. 497.

of the weld is 90 per cent of the strength of the plate, what pressure would burst the tank?   *Ans.* $R = 1,230$ psi.

4-13. In Fig. 4-15 the length L is 6 in.   (*a*) If $P = 80,000$ lb, what is the necessary size of fillet according to the specifications of the American Welding Society? (*b*) If L is 7 in. and the fillet size is $\frac{5}{16}$ in., what is the allowable value of P?

4-14. The angle in Fig. 4-16 is a $6 \times 4 \times \frac{3}{8}$ in. angle.   The fillets are applied to the 6-in. leg.   What are the proper lengths L_1 and L_2 if the stress is to be uniform along the length of the fillets and is not to exceed 2,400 lb per in. when $P = 40,000$ lb?

4-15. A "standpipe" or tall cylindrical tank, having a height of 100 ft and a diameter of 41 ft 8 in., was built in Webster, Mass., in 1939.   The steel plates are butt-welded, and for design purposes the efficiency of the butt welds was assumed as 90 per cent and allowable stress was 15,000 psi.   Calculate the required thickness of the lower ring of plates.   Assume the full depth of 100 ft of water.
                                        Ans. $t = 0.802$ in.

4-16. Calculate the required thickness of the second ring of plates from the bottom of the standpipe in Problem 4-15.   The depth of water is 92 ft 10 in.

4-17. A cylindrical standpipe of d-ft internal diameter contains water.   The allowable stress in the plate is S, and the efficiency of the weld is e.   Calculate the required thickness of the plate at a depth of H ft below the water surface.

4-18. In 1950 two large steel tanks were built at Charlestown, Ind., to store a concentrated solution of ammonium nitrate.   Each tank has a capacity of 80,000 barrels and is 120 ft in diameter and 40 ft high.   Calculate the required thickness of the bottom ring of plates.   Assume that the weight per cubic foot of the solution is 84 lb, use an allowable stress of 16,000 psi, and assume the strength of the welded joint to be 90 per cent of the strength of the plate.

4-19. A steel sphere, 6 ft in inside diameter, for holding helium was made by pressing two $1\frac{1}{2}$-in. plates into half spheres and welding the two together electrically. In a test to failure, the sphere exploded when the internal pressure was 4,500 psi. No breaks occurred in the weld.   Calculate the unit stress in the metal at failure.
                                        Ans. $S = 52,800$ psi.

4-9. Riveted Joints.   To make a simple riveted joint, holes are drilled or punched in each of the plates to be joined.   The plates are then lapped over one another, with the holes matched, and a red-hot steel rivet is inserted in each hole.   A rivet has a head already formed on one end. Pressure is exerted on this head to hold the rivet in place, while the projecting shank of the rivet is hammered with a pneumatic hammer or is pressed to form a head on the other end.   The rivet is cooling off during this process, but is still at a high temperature at its conclusion. Subsequent cooling of the rivet shortens it and thus sets up in it a tensile stress which draws the two plates very tightly together.[6]

4-10. Kinds of Stress in a Riveted Joint.   As an introduction to the stresses which occur in riveted joints, consider the simple example of a

---

[6] "Hot riveting" is the general practice in structural, shipbuilding, and boiler work, but rivets are sometimes driven cold in structural work.   Rivets of metals other than steel and small steel rivets are generally driven cold.

steel plate (Fig. 4-17) to which a weight of P lb is attached.   The plate
is supported, as shown, by means of a round pin projecting from a vertical
wall and fitting in a hole of the same diameter drilled in the plate.   At
any horizontal cross-section of the plate between the pin and the load
there is tension due to the supported weight, and the unit stress due to
this tension is a maximum at the section which passes through the center
of the hole.   This tensile unit stress, considered
uniformly distributed, is equal to the load P
divided by the area at the net section.

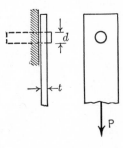

FIG. 4-17

On the part of the plate which is in contact
with the upper half of the cylindrical surface of
the pin, the pin exerts a compressive force.
The variation in the compressive unit stress
that results from this force is very uncertain,
and in practice no attempt is made to determine how the stress varies.   Instead an arbitrarily defined "bearing unit stress" is com-
puted.   This bearing unit stress is the quotient obtained when the
compressive force exerted by the pin is divided by a rectangular area
the dimensions of which are t and d, the plate thickness and the pin
diameter, respectively.

This bearing stress is thus a fictitious stress in the sense that it is not
known to be equal to the compressive stress at any particular point in
the plate.   The use of this bearing stress is quite legitimate, however,
since allowable values for it are determined from a corresponding "ultimate bearing strength" of the plate material.   This bearing strength is
determined by testing to destruction joints which have been so propor-
tioned that they fail by crushing the plate where the highest compressive
stress occurs.   The ultimate bearing strength is defined as the quotient
obtained when the load causing a compressive failure is divided by the
area td.   The allowable bearing stress is then obtained by dividing the
ultimate bearing strength by a suitable factor of safety.

The stresses which have been considered up to this point are those
in the plate. The pin, however, is also stressed by the force which is
exerted on it by the plate, this being equal and opposite to the force
exerted on the plate by the pin. One effect of this force on the pin is to
cause shear on every vertical section between the plane of the wall and
the adjoining face of the plate. The total shearing force is, of course,
equal to the weight of plate and supported load.   On the assumption
that this shearing force is equally distributed over the circular cross-
section of the pin, the shearing unit stress in the pin is the load P
divided by the cross-sectional area of the pin.   The deformations of

the rivet in specimen S5A (Fig. 4–18) indicate high shearing stresses on two planes.

In addition to this shearing stress, the pin is subjected to a bending stress, which is a maximum at the surface of the wall. If the plate is hung close against the wall, this bending stress is not of great importance; and in the ordinary riveted joint, where the plates are actually in contact with one another, the effect of the bending is neglected.

Courtesy, Bethlehem Steel Co.

Fig. 4-18.   Test specimens from two single riveted joints.

Dimensions of plate and load at failure are given.   Rivets, $\frac{7}{8}$-in. diameter.   The joints were identical except that from center of hole to top edge of plate was 2 in. in S5 and $2\frac{1}{2}$ in. in S5A.

Because of insufficient edge distance in S5 the plate failed in front of the rivet before the tensile strength was reached.   Note the evidence of over-stress in bearing above the hole in the plate.   Note also the effect on the rivet of over-stress in shear.

In the plate, in addition to the bearing and tensile stresses discussed, shearing stresses exist on the two planes tangent to the sides of the pinhole (Fig. 4-19). These stresses can be kept as low as desired by making the edge distance m sufficiently large. The actual failure of a plate with insufficient edge distance in front of a rivet is the result of a complex state of stress and is more likely to be somewhat like that of specimen S5 (Fig. 4-18). Specifications for riveted joints include the minimum edge distance (usually $1\frac{1}{4}$ to 2 times the diameter of the rivet). It will be assumed that the edge distance of the joints considered hereafter is sufficient to prevent failure of the plate in front of the rivet.

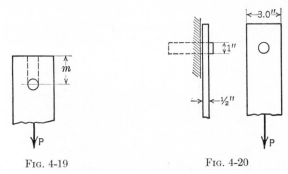

Fig. 4-19   Fig. 4-20

Example. A mild steel pin with a diameter of 1 in. supports a mild steel plate of the dimensions shown in Fig. 4-20. What is the greatest load which the plate can support without causing failure of the joint? The ultimate strengths of the materials are as follows:

Tension, 55,000 psi.
Bearing, 95,000 psi.
Shear,   44,000 psi.

Solution: Shear strength of pin = 44,000 × 0.7854 = 34,600 lb.
Bearing strength of plate above pin = 95,000 × 1 × $\frac{1}{2}$ = 47,500 lb.
Tensile strength of plate of net section = 55,000 × (3 − 1) × $\frac{1}{2}$ = 55,000 lb.
Therefore strength of joint = 34,600 lb, which is the maximum load that can be carried.

In the example just solved, the strength of the joint is limited by the shear strength of the pin. If the pin diameter were made $1\frac{1}{4}$ in. instead of 1 in., its cross-sectional area would be increased in the ratio of 1.25^2 to 1^2, or by 56 per cent, and the shear strength of the joint would be equally increased. At the same time the bearing strength would be increased by 25 per cent. The tensile strength would be decreased, however, by 12.5 per cent, and would become the least strength of the joint.

If, however, with a $1\frac{1}{4}$-in. pin as before, a plate of the same gross cross-sectional area were used, but with half the thickness and twice the width of the original plate, the effect of this difference in the plate dimensions would be to leave unchanged the shear strength of the pin, to increase the tensile strength of the plate, and to halve the bearing strength. With these dimensions the bearing strength of the plate above the pin would become the limiting strength of the joint; failure would occur by crushing the plate above the pin before the pin itself sheared or the plate failed in tension at the net section.

From this discussion it is evident that the type of failure of a joint of this sort depends on the relative dimensions of pin and plate.

PROBLEMS

4-20. In Fig. 4-20 let the pin and pin-hole diameters be $\frac{3}{4}$ in., and the plate dimensions $2 \times \frac{3}{8}$ in. What is the maximum weight which can be supported if the following unit stresses are not to be exceeded: tension, 18,000 psi; bearing, 27,000 psi; shear, 13,000 psi?   *Ans. P = 5,750 lb.*

4-21. A $\frac{7}{8}$-in.-diameter pin fits closely in a hole in a plate of $4 \times \frac{3}{8}$ in. cross-section arranged as in Fig. 4-20. What are the unit tensile, bearing, and shearing stresses in plate and pin when a load of 10,000 lb is supported by the plate?

4-22. If the two plates shown in Fig. 3-5 are each $\frac{5}{8}$ in. thick and the diameter of the pin is $2\frac{3}{8}$ in., calculate the bearing stress between the pin and plates.

4-11. Single-Riveted Lap Joint. The simplest possible riveted joint is illustrated in Fig. 4-21; it consists merely of two narrow plates or bars joined by means of a single rivet. The stresses in this joint, when it is used to transmit tension from one plate to another, are similar to the stresses in the plate and pin which have been discussed.

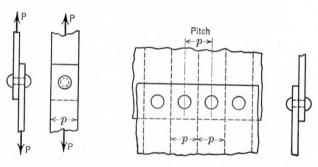

FIG. 4-21   FIG. 4-22.   Single-riveted lap joint.

The ordinary *single-riveted lap joint* differs from the joint just discussed in that it has more than one rivet to hold the bars or plates together, the rivets being in a single row. The rivets are equally spaced, and the distance between them is called the "rivet pitch," generally represented by the symbol p. Such a joint may be considered as equivalent to several joints with one rivet each, placed side by side as in Fig. 4-22.

Many joints or "seams" in tanks, pipes, and boilers are more complicated than the single-riveted lap joint here considered. Whether simple or complicated, the joint may be divided into unit sections or "repeating sections," every one of which is exactly like each of the others. In investigating a continuous joint or seam, it is not necessary to deal with more of the joint than a single repeating section, since the stresses are the same in each repeating section and since the strength of all repeating sections is the same.

Example. A single-riveted lap joint has the following dimensions: plate thickness, $\frac{1}{4}$ in.; rivet pitch, $1\frac{3}{4}$ in.; diameter of rivet holes, $\frac{11}{16}$ in. What is the allowable load on the repeating section of the joint if allowable stresses are: tension, 11,000 psi; bearing, 19,000 psi; shear, 8,800 psi?

Solution: Length of repeating section = $1\frac{3}{4}$ in.

Allowable load as limited by tension = $(1\frac{3}{4} - \frac{11}{16}) \times \frac{1}{4} \times 11,000 = 2,920$ lb.

Allowable load as limited by bearing = $\frac{11}{16} \times \frac{1}{4} \times 19,000 = 3,270$ lb.

Allowable load as limited by shear = $(\pi/4) \times (\frac{11}{16})^2 \times 8,800 = 3,260$ lb.

Therefore the allowable load on a repeating section is 2,920 lb.

4-12. Efficiency of a Joint. By the efficiency of a joint is meant the ratio of the strength of a repeating section of the joint to the strength of the same length of the unpunched plate. This ratio is expressed as a percentage. Instead of using ultimate strengths, the efficiency of a joint can also be found by dividing the *allowable load* on a repeating section of the joint by the *allowable load* on an equal length of the unpunched plate and multiplying by 100 to express the ratio as a percentage.

Example. What is the efficiency of the joint considered in the preceding example?

Solution: Allowable load on joint = 2,920 lb.

Allowable load on $1\frac{3}{4}$-in. length of $\frac{1}{4}$-in. plate = $1\frac{3}{4} \times \frac{1}{4} \times 11,000 = 4,810$ lb.

Efficiency = $(2,920/4,810) \times 100 = 60.7$ per cent.

The efficiency of a riveted joint can never be as great as 100 per cent, since the tensile strength of the repeating section can never be as great as the tensile strength of the same length of the unpunched plate, and since the strength of the joint can never be more than the tensile strength of the joint. The higher the efficiency of a joint, the more nearly can the full strength of the plates at sections between the joints be developed. For instance, in the foregoing example, when the joint is carrying its allowable load, the tensile stress in the plate at any section away from and parallel to the joint is only 60.7 per cent of the allowable tensile stress. Hence it is important that the efficiency of joints be kept as high as is compatible with economy of fabrication. This requirement results in the frequent use of more complicated joints than single-riveted lap joints, the efficiency of which is seldom higher than 60 per cent.

PROBLEMS

4-23. A single-riveted lap joint is used to join two plates $\frac{3}{8}$ in. thick. The rivet pitch is $1\frac{7}{8}$ in., diameter of rivet holes $\frac{13}{16}$ in. Find the allowable load per repeating length of joint if the ultimate strengths of plates and rivets are: tension, 70,000 psi; bearing, 105,000 psi; shear, 60,000 psi; and if the joint is to have a factor of safety of 4. What is the efficiency of this joint?   *Ans.* Eff. = 56.7 per cent.

4-24. What are the stresses in the joint of Problem 4-23 when it is subjected to a load of 2,000 lb *per in. length of joint?*

4-25. A single-riveted lap joint is used to connect two plates $\frac{7}{16}$ in. thick. The rivet pitch is $2\frac{1}{8}$ in., and rivet holes are $\frac{15}{16}$ in. in diameter. What is the efficiency of the joint if the material is the same as in Problem 4-23?

4-26. Calculate the allowable load on a repeating section and the efficiency of a standard single-riveted lap joint having the following dimensions: $t = \frac{1}{2}$ in., $p = 2\frac{1}{2}$ in., $d = 1\frac{1}{16}$ in. The allowable stresses are: tension, 16,000 psi; shear, 12,000 psi; bearing, 24,000 psi.

4-27. Solve Problem 4-26 if $t = \frac{5}{16}$ in., $p = 2$ in., $d = \frac{13}{16}$ in.

$\qquad\qquad\qquad\qquad\qquad$ *Ans.* $P = 5,940$ lb.

4-28. Solve Problem 4-26 if $t = \frac{3}{8}$ in., $p = 2\frac{1}{4}$ in., $d = \frac{15}{16}$ in.

4-13. Riveted Joints in Boilers and Tanks.

A riveted tank, boiler, or pipe, is made of bent plates fastened together by continuous joints or "seams." It will be seen that the plates composing the tank shown in

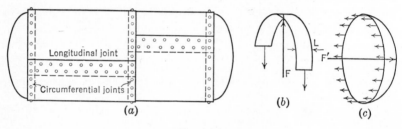

Longitudinal joint

Circumferential joints

(a)

(b)

(c)

F<small>IG.</small> 4-23

Fig. 4-23*a* are fastened together by "longitudinal" or lengthwise joints and also by joints which coincide with a circumference of the tank and are called "circumferential" joints.

The longitudinal joints are investigated by considering a half hoop as shown in Fig. 4-23*b*, in which the dimension L is equal to the repeating section of the longitudinal joint. The force F equals twice the load on a repeating section.

An entire circumferential joint resists the force F' due to the internal pressure acting on one end of the tank as shown in Fig. 4-23*c*. The force that the circumferential joint exerts is equal to the force exerted by a repeating section multiplied by the number of repeating sections in the joint. This number is found by dividing the circumference by the length of a repeating section.

Example 1. The single-riveted lap joint of the example of Art. 4-11 is a longitudinal joint in a boiler 24 in. in diameter. What unit pressure is permissible if the stresses are not to exceed the allowable stresses in the example?

Solution: Consider a half hoop of the boiler with a length equal to the length of the repeating section. This is shown in Fig. 4-24. The rupturing force on this hoop caused by a pressure of R psi is $1\frac{3}{4} \times 24 \times R$ lb. This force is resisted by the two tensions in the hoop, which can each equal 2,920 lb as calculated in Art. 4-11. Therefore

$$1\tfrac{3}{4} \times 24 \times R = 2 \times 2,920$$
$$R = 139 \text{ psi}$$

Example 2. If this same single-riveted lap joint is a circumferential joint in a boiler 24 in. in diameter, to what steam pressure does it limit the boiler?

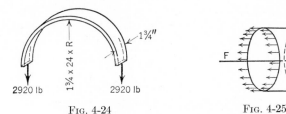

FIG. 4-24   FIG. 4-25

Solution: Imagine the boiler to be cut in two by a *transverse* plane and consider one of the two parts (Fig. 4-25) as a body in equilibrium. Since the allowable load for the $1\frac{3}{4}$-in. repeating section of this joint is 2,920 lb, it is evident that 2,920 lb can act on each $1\frac{3}{4}$-in. length of the circumference without causing excessive stresses in the circumferential joints.

Therefore the total longitudinal force on the entire circumference can equal $2,920 \times 24\pi/1\frac{3}{4} = 126,000$ lb.

But the total force developed on the head of the boiler by the steam pressure of R psi is $\pi \times 12^2 \times R$. Hence

$$R = \frac{126,000}{\pi \times 12^2} = 278 \text{ psi}$$

It will be seen from these two examples that the given joint used as a longitudinal joint allows only half the internal pressure that is permitted by the same joint used as a circumferential joint. Evidently a more efficient longitudinal joint would make a higher internal pressure permissible without increasing the thickness of the boiler plates and therefore without raising greatly the cost of the boiler.

4-14. Allowable Stresses in Riveted Boiler and Tank Joints. Boilers and tanks are now made of plates rolled from many different carbon steels, alloy steels, and non-ferrous metals. Rivets are also made from a number of different metals. Consequently there are many different allowable stresses for boiler and tank joints listed in the American Society of Mechanical Engineers Boiler Code (1952). As examples, there are listed specified strengths for one grade of rivet steel and one grade of boiler plate, the resulting allowable stresses based on a factor of safety of 5, and also stresses based on a factor of safety of 4. All values are pounds per square inch.

MATERIAL	Specified Ultimate Strength	Allowable Stresses	
		F.S. = 5	F.S. = 4
		A	B
Rivets SA–31 (shearing)	44,000	8,800	11,000
Plates SA–285 (tension)	55,000	11,000	13,750
Plates SA–285 (bearing)	95,000	19,000	23,750

For many years a factor of safety of 5 was specified by the A.S.M.E. Code for Boilers and was almost universally used in boiler design. The allowable stresses in group A of the table have been known for many years as the "A.S.M.E. Boiler Code stresses." Higher stresses than those corresponding to a factor of safety of 5 are coming into use and are specified in some codes for work designed and fabricated in accordance with the highest standards of design and workmanship.

PROBLEMS

4-29. A water main 32 in. in diameter is made of $\frac{3}{8}$-in. plates. Longitudinal joints are single-riveted lap joints with a rivet pitch of 2 in. Rivet holes are $\frac{13}{16}$ in. Assuming the rivets have a shearing strength of 60,000 psi and plate a tensile strength of 70,000 psi and a bearing strength of 105,000 psi, what head of water is allowable? What is the efficiency of the joint? Factor of safety is 5.

4-30. A steam boiler 52 in. in diameter is made of $\frac{1}{2}$-in. plates and has single-riveted circumferential joints. These joints have a rivet pitch of $2\frac{1}{8}$ in. and rivet holes $\frac{15}{16}$ in. in diameter. When the boiler pressure is 180 psi, what is the factor of safety of the circumferential joints? Assume strengths as in Problem 4-29.

4-31. What is the efficiency of the joint in Problem 4-30 using the Boiler Code stresses given in group B, Art. 4-14?   *Ans.* 52.0 per cent.

4-32. A boiler 36 in. in diameter is made of $\frac{3}{8}$-in. plates. Longitudinal joints are triple-riveted butt joints with an efficiency of 86 per cent. Circumferential joints are single-riveted lap joints with 1-in.-diameter rivet holes and 3-in. pitch. What is the allowable steam pressure? Allowable stresses are: shearing, 12,000; tension, 14,000; bearing, 21,000 psi.

4-15. Double-Riveted Lap Joints. To secure higher efficiencies and greater tightness than can be secured with single-riveted lap joints, double-riveted lap joints are often used. Such a joint is illustrated in Fig. 4-26. The repeating length of joint is again equal to the rivet pitch. The pitch is defined as the distance from one rivet to the next rivet in the same row. The distance between the two rows of rivets is made great enough so that, if the plate fails in tension, it will tear between the holes of one row and not along a zigzag line between rivets in both rows. In a double-riveted joint the tensile strength is the same as in a single-riveted joint with the same pitch, plate thickness, and rivet diameter. The shear and bearing strengths are twice as great as for the single-riveted joint.

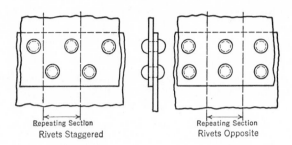

Repeating Section   Repeating Section
Rivets Staggered   Rivets Opposite

Fig. 4-26.   Double-riveted lap joints.

PROBLEMS

4-33. Calculate the allowable load on a repeating section and the efficiency of a standard double-riveted lap joint having the following dimensions: $t = \frac{1}{2}$ in., $d = 1\frac{1}{16}$ in., $p = 3\frac{3}{8}$ in. Allowable stresses: shearing, 8,800; tension, 11,000; bearing, 19,000 psi.   *Ans.* $P = 12{,}710$ lb.

4-34. Solve Problem 4-33 but let $t = \frac{7}{16}$ in., $d = 1\frac{1}{16}$ in., $p = 3\frac{3}{8}$ in.

4-35. Solve Problem 4-33 if $t = \frac{3}{8}$ in., $d = \frac{15}{16}$ in., $p = 3$ in.

4-36. Solve Problem 4-33 if $t = \frac{5}{16}$ in., $d = \frac{13}{16}$ in., $p = 2\frac{5}{8}$ in.

4-37. A small compressed-air tank has an inside diameter of 26 in. and a plate thickness of $\frac{3}{8}$ in. Its longitudinal joints are double-riveted lap joints with the rivets staggered. The pitch of the rivets in each row is 3 in., and the rivet holes are $\frac{15}{16}$ in. in diameter. What are the stresses in the longitudinal joints when the internal unit pressure in the tank is 220 psi?   *Ans.* $S_b = 12{,}200$ psi.

4-38. The ultimate strengths of the tank plates and rivets in Problem 4-37 are 95,000, 55,000, and 44,000 psi for bearing, tension, and shear, respectively. What is the greatest internal unit pressure which can be developed in the tank, if its factor of safety is to be 5?

4-39. For circumferential joints this tank has single-riveted lap joints with a rivet pitch of $2\frac{1}{4}$ in. and a rivet-hole diameter of $\frac{15}{16}$ in. Which have the greater factor of safety, the longitudinal or the circumferential joints, for any given internal unit pressure?

4-40. Calculate the efficiencies of the longitudinal and circumferential joints, respectively, of the tank referred to in Problems 4-37 to 4-39.

4-41. A spherical gas holder 36 ft in inside diameter is made of $\frac{3}{8}$-in. steel plate. The joints are double-riveted lap joints, with rivet holes $\frac{7}{8}$ in. in diameter and pitch of $2\frac{3}{4}$ in. Find the allowable internal pressure if the allowable stresses are: tension, 14,000 psi; shear, 10,000 psi; bearing, 24,000 psi. All riveted joints are in great circles of the spherical surface.   *Ans.* $R = 33.2$ psi.

4-16. Butt Joints. In a lap joint, in addition to the stresses that have been discussed, there is bending stress in the plates, which results from their natural tendency to assume such a position that the tensile forces become collinear. This is illustrated in Fig. 4-27. The stresses that result from this bending are not ordinarily taken into consideration in the design and investigation of lap joints. In large tanks and boilers, however, these stresses are often obviated by using butt joints in which the bending effect is not present.   The A.S.M.E. Boiler Code provides, for instance, that butt joints must be used for the longitudinal joints of all power boilers having diameters greater than 36 in.   In tanks, butt joints are recommended for joining plates of $\frac{1}{4}$-in. thickness and greater.

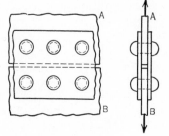

If a tensile force is applied to plate A (Fig. 4-28), it is transmitted from A

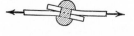

Fig. 4-27.   Fig. 4-28.   Single-riveted butt joint.

to the rivets that pass through A, thence to the cover plates, thence to the rivets that pass through plate B, and thence to B.

It is seen that the tensile unit stress in the main plates is greatest along the lines of rivets, where the net section occurs.   In the cover plates, the greatest tensile unit stress occurs along the same lines.   If the thickness of each cover plate is one-half the thickness of the main plate, the area which supports this tension in the cover plates is equal to the area supporting it in the main plates.   Under this condition, the tensile unit stress in the cover plates would be the same as in the main plates. Actually, to guard against failure in the cover plates, they are made more than one-half as thick as the main plates, and the tension in the cover plates need not be calculated.   For the same reasons the maximum bearing stress in the joint may be found by finding the bearing stress in the main plates.

In a lap joint a shear failure necessitates that each rivet be sheared through once at the section where the faces of the two plates are in contact with one another.   In a butt joint, however, if a shear failure occurs, it involves pulling the main plate out from between the cover plates, and this cannot be done without shearing each rivet at two sections.

Single-riveted butt joints are not widely used in boilers and tanks because of low efficiency in comparison with other butt joints.

PROBLEMS

4-42. A single-riveted butt joint is used to connect two $\frac{9}{8}$-in. plates.   Cover plates are $\frac{7}{16}$ in. thick, rivet holes $1\frac{1}{16}$ in. in diameter, rivet pitch 3 in.   Determine the allowable load on a repeating length of the joint and its efficiency, using stresses in group B, Art. 4-14.   *Ans.*   Load = 15,760 lb.

4-43. Determine the diameter of the largest boiler in which the joint in Problem 4-42 could be used longitudinally if the steam pressure is to be 100 psi.

4-17. Double-Riveted Butt Joints. In butt joints, as in lap joints, the joint efficiency can be increased by the addition of another line of rivets to each side of the joint, making a double-riveted butt joint. Most double-riveted butt joints have only half as many rivets in the outside rows as in the inside rows (see Fig. 4-29). This arrangement increases the tensile strength of the joint. A butt joint is usually much stronger in bearing and in shear than it is in tension when the rivet spacing is the same in all rows of rivets. Hence the removal of alternate rivets in the outside rows, by increasing the tensile strength, increases the strength of the joint.

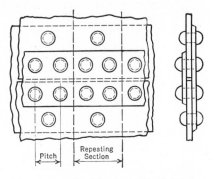

Fig. 4-29.   Double-riveted butt joints.

In double-riveted butt joints it is common practice to use one wide and one narrow cover plate. The rivets in the outer lines are therefore in single shear. A narrow cover plate ordinarily does not reduce the strength of the joint below what it would be with two wide plates.[7]

Example. In the double-riveted butt joint shown in Fig. 4-29 the thickness of the main plate is $\frac{1}{2}$ in., the thickness of splice plates is $\frac{7}{16}$ in., the diameter of rivet holes is $\frac{15}{16}$ in., the "short" pitch is $2\frac{1}{2}$ in. (these are dimensions of a standard double-riveted boiler joint for $\frac{1}{2}$-in. plate). Calculate the allowable load on a repeating section and the efficiency of this joint, using allowable stresses in group A, Art. 4-14.

Solution: Before proceeding with the calculations for allowable load on the joint, it is convenient to have available the following values:

Allowable load in single shear on one rivet $= \pi/4 \times (\frac{15}{16})^2 \times 8,800 = 6,080$ lb.

Allowable load in bearing on $\frac{1}{2}$-in. plate $= \frac{1}{2} \times \frac{15}{16} \times 19,000 = 8,910$ lb.

Allowable load in bearing on $\frac{7}{16}$-in. plate $= \frac{7}{16} \times \frac{15}{16} \times 19,000 = 7,790$ lb.

The allowable load on the repeating section may be limited by any one of several combinations of the above values.

1. The two rivets in the inner row are each stressed in shear on two planes, and the rivet in the outer row is stressed in shear on one plane, making a total of five cross-sections.

Allowable load as limited by shearing $= 5 \times 6,080 = 30,400$ lb.

---

[7] The narrow cover plate is desirable from the standpoint of joint tightness. Calking is more effective if applied to the edges of the narrow plate, since the rivets are closer together and consequently hold the edge of the cover plate more tightly against the shell plate.

2. Three rivets bear against the $\frac{1}{2}$-in. plate, but it will be observed that the least value of the outer rivet is determined by shear, rather than by bearing against either the main plate or the cover plate.

Allowable load on repeating section as determined by bearing of two inner rivets and shearing of outer rivets is

$$2 \times 8,910 + 6,080 = 23,900 \text{ lb}$$

3. Allowable load as determined by tension in plate at outer row (one hole in 5-in. width) = $(5 - \frac{15}{16}) \times \frac{1}{2} \times 11,000 = 22,350$ lb.

4. The tensile strength of the plate is less at the inner row, where two holes occur in the 5-in. width, but it will be observed that this failure cannot occur without simultaneous failure of the rivet in the outer row. The allowable load for this combination is

$$(5 - \tfrac{15}{8}) \times \tfrac{1}{2} \times 11,000 + 6,080 = 23,280 \text{ lb}$$

5. Allowable load as determined by tension in the two splice plates at the inner row is

$$(5 - \tfrac{15}{8}) \times 2 \times \tfrac{7}{16} \times 11,000 = 30,100 \text{ lb}$$

6. Allowable load as determined by bearing of two rivets of inner row against the splice plates plus the shearing of the rivet in the outer row is

$$4 \times 7,790 + 6,080 = 31,160 + 6,080 = 37,240 \text{ lb}$$

The allowable load for the joint is 22,350 lb.

The efficiency of the joint is $\dfrac{22,350}{5 \times \frac{1}{2} \times 11,000} \times 100 = 81.3$ per cent.

PROBLEMS

4-44. The double-riveted butt joint in the preceding example is used as a vertical joint in a standpipe which is 22 ft in diameter and is made of plate with a tensile strength of 60,000 psi. If allowable stresses are 12,000, 8,800, and 19,000 psi for tension, shear, and bearing, respectively, to what height above the joint may the standpipe be filled with water?   *Ans.* $H = 83.8$ ft.

4-45. What change in the efficiency of the joint of the preceding example and problem result from changing the allowable tensile stress from 11,000 to 12,000 psi?

4-46. Standard dimensions for a double-riveted butt joint joining plates $\frac{3}{8}$ in. in thickness are: splice-plate thickness, $\frac{5}{16}$ in.; diameter of rivet holes, $\frac{13}{16}$ in.; "short" pitch, $2\frac{1}{4}$ in.; "long" pitch, $4\frac{1}{2}$ in. Find the allowable load on a repeating length, and the joint efficiency, using stresses in group B, Art. 4-14.

4-47. A standard double-riveted butt joint for $\frac{7}{16}$-in. plates has $\frac{15}{16}$-in. rivet holes, $2\frac{1}{2}$-in. short pitch, and 5-in. long pitch; the splice plates are $\frac{3}{8}$ in. thick. Calculate the allowable load on a repeating section and the efficiency of the joint. Use stresses in group B, Art. 4-14.   *Ans.* Eff. = 81.5 per cent.

4-18. Triple-Riveted and Quadruple-Riveted Butt Joints.

In boilers, tanks, or pipes which are subject to very heavy pressures and which therefore require heavy plates, the saving in material which results from increased efficiency in the joints justifies the use of triple- and even quadruple-riveted butt joints. In every case, determination of the strength of the joint or of the stresses caused in the joint by a given pressure, involves determination of the repeating length of the joint and then determination of the areas of metal which resist each possible method of failure of the joint, as was done in the preceding example.

4-19. Riveted Joints in Structural Work. All the joints that have been discussed so far have been used to transmit tensile stress from one plate to another. In a building frame the typical joint is one used to

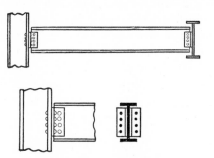

FIG. 4-30. Riveted beam connections.

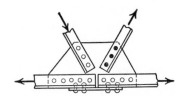

FIG. 4-31. Riveted joint in small truss.

connect floor beams to each other or to the columns which support them. This joint, *or connection* as it is frequently called, is made by riveting short lengths of steel angles to both sides of the web of the beam, as shown in Fig. 4-30, and riveting the outstanding legs of the angles to the column. The angles are usually riveted to the beam in the fabricating shop and to the column in the field as the building is erected.[8]

Another important type of structural joint is that used to connect the different members of a truss. Figure 4-31 shows such a joint. In a truss joint usually there are both tension and compression members connected to the gusset plate.

Important differences exist between the fabrication of structures such as buildings and the fabrication of boilers and other pressure containers. In boiler work the rivet holes are *drilled*, with the plates bolted in position, so that a perfect matching of holes is secured. Drilling does not injure the plate metal adjoining the rivet holes, and the matching of the holes results in the driven rivet being a cylinder every cross-section of which equals the area of the rivet hole. Therefore the diameter of the rivet hole is used in computing tensile, bearing, and shear-

[8] In shop drawings for structural steel, shop rivets are shown as circles, representing the outlines of the rivet heads, and field rivets are shown as smaller black circles, representing open holes, as in Fig. 4-30.

ing stresses.   In ordinary structural work, however, most rivet holes are *punched* (the punch being $\frac{1}{16}$ in. larger than the diameter of the rivet), and the punching of each part is done separately.   Consequently, when the various parts are assembled, the matching of the rivet holes is somewhat imperfect.   Since this is so, the driven rivet is likely not to be a single cylinder but to consist of two or more cylindrical portions with axes not collinear.   Hence, at the planes separating poorly matched rivet holes, the cross-section of the rivet is likely to be less than the cross-section of the rivet holes.   For this reason it is customary to use the diameter of the *undriven* rivet in figuring the shearing stresses in structural joints.   The same diameter is used in computing bearing stress, which in structural work is therefore definable as the load on a rivet divided by the area td, where d now represents the diameter of the rivet before driving.   In figuring stress in a structural member transmitting tension, however, the practice is to deduct for a rivet hole having a diameter $\frac{1}{8}$ in. greater than that of the undriven rivet.   This deduction allows not only for the fact that the hole is $\frac{1}{16}$ in. larger than the rivet, but also for damage done to the plate in the punching operation and for reaming mismatched holes.

In calculating the load that can be transmitted safely through a riveted structural connection, it is customary to assume that each rivet in a group of n rivets, as, for example, the eight field rivets that connect the beam to the column in Fig. 4-30, carries $1/n$ of the load transmitted by the rivet group.   This assumption is not rigidly true at low stress values but becomes more nearly true, because of yielding, as ultimate loads are approached, and it is a satisfactory working assumption.

Various specifications covering the allowable stresses in riveted structural joints have been prepared at different times and by different authorities.   Specifications for steel railway bridges adopted by the American Railway Engineering Association (1952) permit the following unit stresses (pounds per square inch):

ALLOWABLE STRESSES FOR STRUCTURAL RIVETING,
A.R.E.A. SPECIFICATIONS, 1952

	Shear	Bearing
Power-driven rivets	13,500	27,000
Pins	13,500	24,000
Turned bolts	11,000	20,000

These specifications permit a tensile stress of 18,000 psi in structural steel.

The specifications of the American Institute of Steel Construction for the design of steel buildings allow higher bearing values for rivets in double shear than for rivets in single shear. A summary of these allowable stresses is given in Table IX, Appendix C.

PROBLEMS

4-48. In Fig. 4-32, $w_1 = 8$ in. and $t_1 = \frac{1}{2}$ in., $w_2 = 6$ in. and $t_2 = \frac{3}{8}$ in. Rivets are $\frac{7}{8}$ in. (*a*) Calculate the allowable tensile load P if allowable stresses are: tension 18,000 psi, shearing 13,500 psi, and bearing 27,000 psi. (*b*) Indicate on a sketch how the plates may be joined by welding instead of riveting, and state the total length of weld required to carry the load P found in (*a*). Use $\frac{1}{4}$-in. fillet and the same splice plates.   *Ans.* $P = 47,200$ lb.

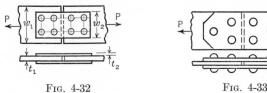

FIG. 4-32   FIG. 4-33

4-49. Same as Problem 4-48 but rivets are $\frac{3}{4}$ in. in diameter.

4-50. Same as Problem 4-48 but $w_1 = 7$ in. and $t_1 = \frac{5}{8}$ in., $w_2 = 6$ in. and $t_2 = \frac{3}{8}$ in. Rivets are $\frac{7}{8}$ in.

4-51. Solve Problem 4-48 but $w_1 = 7$ in., $t_1 = \frac{5}{8}$ in., $w_2 = 6$ in. and $t_2 = \frac{3}{8}$ in. Rivets are $\frac{3}{4}$ in.

4-52. Two steel bars 5 in. wide and $\frac{1}{2}$ in. thick are connected as shown in Fig. 4-33. Splice plates are 5 in. wide and $\frac{3}{8}$ in. thick. Diameter of rivets is $\frac{7}{8}$ in. Calculate the allowable load P. Use A.R.E.A. allowable stresses. Note that the tensile stress must be investigated at more than one section through the connection.
                                               Ans. $P = 35,450$ lb.

4-53. Same as Problem 4-52 but diameter of rivets is $\frac{3}{4}$ in.

4-54. Same as Problem 4-52, but main plates are $6 \times \frac{5}{8}$, and splice plates are $6 \times \frac{3}{8}$.

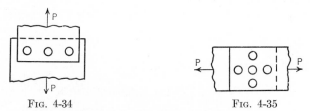

FIG. 4-34   FIG. 4-35

4-55. Two plates, one $8\frac{1}{2}$ in. wide and $\frac{1}{2}$ in. thick, the other 10 in. wide and $\frac{7}{16}$ in. thick, are connected by rivets as shown in Fig. 4-34. The rivets are $\frac{7}{8}$ in. in diameter. What load P is allowable? Use A.R.E.A. stresses.   *Ans.* $P = 24,330$ lb.

4-56. Two plates, one 8 in. wide and $\frac{1}{2}$ in. thick, the other 9 in. wide and $\frac{7}{16}$ in. thick, are connected by rivets as shown in Fig. 4-34. Diameter of rivets is $\frac{3}{4}$ in. What load P is allowable? Use A.R.E.A. stresses.

4-57. Two plates, each 8 in. wide and $\frac{3}{8}$ in. thick, are connected by the lap joint shown in Fig. 4-35. Rivets are $\frac{3}{4}$ in. Calculate the allowable load P. Use A.R.E.A. stresses

4-58. Two plates, each 9 in. wide and $\frac{1}{2}$ in. thick, are connected by the lap joint shown in Fig. 4-35. Rivets are $\frac{7}{8}$ in. Calculate the allowable load P. Use A.R.E.A. stresses.   *Ans. P* = 40,550 lb.

4-20. Allowable Loads on Beam Connections.

Because of the loads on a beam, the beam pushes down on the shop rivets (Fig. 4-30), causing shearing stresses in the rivets and bearing stresses in the rivets, in the web of the beam, and in the connection angles. The field rivets, in turn, transmit the load from the connection angles to the column or other supporting member. This develops shearing stresses in the field rivets and bearing stresses in the rivets, in the connection angles, and in the supporting member. The design or investigation of a beam connection includes consideration of these various shearing and bearing stresses. There are no tensile stresses that require consideration.

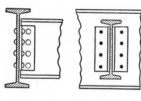

Example. Calculate the allowable end reaction for a 15-in., 42.9-lb I-beam connected to the web of a 20-in., 65.4-lb I-beam by two $4 \times 3\frac{1}{2} \times \frac{3}{8}$ in. angles, as shown in Fig. 4-36. The rivets are all $\frac{3}{4}$ in. Rivet stresses are those in the specification for steel railway bridges given in Art. 4-19. The rivets attaching the connection angle to the 15-in. beam are shop rivets; the others are field rivets. Web thickness of the 20-in. beam is 0.50 in.; of the 15-in. beam, 0.410 in.

Fig. 4-36

Solution: Consider first the eight field rivets connecting the angles to the web of the deeper beam and assume the reaction to be divided equally among the eight rivets. The load which these rivets can carry will be limited by either shearing of the rivets, bearing of the rivets against the $\frac{3}{8}$-in.-thick angles, or bearing of the rivets against the 0.500-in.-thick web. The last of these need not be computed.

The allowable loads, as limited by the first two considerations, are as follows:
Shearing of eight field rivets is

$$P = 8 \times \frac{\pi}{4} \times (\tfrac{3}{4})^2 \times 13{,}500 = 8 \times 5{,}950 = 47{,}600 \text{ lb}$$

Bearing of eight field rivets against $\frac{3}{8}$-in. angles is

$$P = 8 \times \tfrac{3}{8} \times \tfrac{3}{4} \times 27{,}000 = 60{,}700 \text{ lb}$$

Consider next the four shop rivets connecting the angles to the web of the 15-in. beam. Assume these four rivets to be equally loaded. Each rivet bears against two angles (total thickness of $\frac{3}{4}$ in.) and against the web of the beam (thickness of 0.410 in.). Consequently bearing against the angles will not limit the allowable load for the connection.

The allowable load, as limited by bearing on the web of the 15-in. beam, is

$$P = 4 \times \tfrac{3}{4} \times 0.410 \times 27{,}000 = 33{,}200 \text{ lb}$$

Each rivet is in double shear, making eight cross-sections in shear, which is the same number of shears as for the field rivets. The unit stress allowed on the shop rivets is 13,500 psi, which is the same as is allowed on the field rivets, and consequently the shearing value of the shop rivets will not limit the allowable load.

It follows from the foregoing considerations that the allowable load for the joint is limited by bearing of the shop rivets against the web of the 15-in. beam. The allowable load is therefore 33,200 lb.

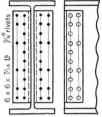

PROBLEMS

4-59. In the beam connection just discussed, replace the $\frac{3}{4}$-in. rivets with $\frac{7}{8}$-in. rivets and find the allowable reaction, using A.R.E.A. stresses.

4-60. Where very heavy end reactions are to be resisted, the connection shown in Fig. 4-37 is specified by the handbook of the A.I.S.C. for wide-flanged beams 36 in. deep. A 36 WF 160-lb beam has a web thickness of 0.653 in. If this connection is used to attach the beam to a column flange 0.99 in. thick, what is the allowable reaction in accordance with A.R.E.A. stresses?

FIG. 4-37

Ans. $R = 246,500$ lb.

GENERAL PROBLEMS

4-61. A boiler is 80 in. in diameter and has longitudinal joints in which the repeating section is $7\frac{3}{4}$ in. long. The safe load (factor of safety = 5) for the repeating section is computed and found to be 32,000 lb. (*a*) What steam pressure is safe for this boiler? (*b*) If the plate of which the boiler is made is $\frac{7}{16}$ in. thick, what is the efficiency of the joint? Allowable tensile stress is 11,000 psi.

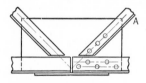

FIG. 4-38

4-62. Member A, made of two $5 \times 3\frac{1}{2} \times \frac{7}{16}$ in. angles as shown in Fig. 4-38, carries a load of 98,000 lb. How many $\frac{7}{8}$-in. rivets are required to connect it to the gusset plate, which is $\frac{5}{8}$ in. thick? (A.R.E.A. stresses.) Assume all rivets are equally loaded. *Ans.* 7 rivets required.

4-63. In Problem 4-62, if the member is welded to the gusset plate, to what thickness may the angle be reduced below $\frac{7}{16}$ in.? What saving in weight of the member (per foot of length) results? Using the stresses of Art. 4-7, determine how many inches of $\frac{5}{16}$-in. weld should be used along each edge of each of the two angles which compose A.

4-64. A tank is 42 in. in diameter and 90 in. long. It is made of $\frac{3}{8}$-in. steel plates the allowable tensile stress for which is 12,000 psi. The efficiency of the longitudinal joints is 80 per cent and of the circumferential joints, 56 per cent. What internal pressure is allowable?

4-65. Loads are supported by 14-in. WF 68-lb beams which are riveted to 21-in. WF 62-lb beams as shown in Fig. 4-39. Using A.R.E.A. allowable stresses, calculate the allowable load P. Rivets are $\frac{7}{8}$ in., and the connection angles are $4 \times 3\frac{1}{2} \times \frac{3}{8}$ in. *Ans.* $P = 56,700$ lb.

4-66. A spherical gas holder 36 ft in diameter is made of $\frac{3}{8}$-in.-thick plates. Plates are joined by double-riveted lap joints. Rivet holes are $\frac{15}{16}$ in. in diameter, and rivet pitch is 3 in. Calculate the allowable gas pressure if allowable stresses are: tension 16,000, shearing 13,000, bearing 24,000 psi.

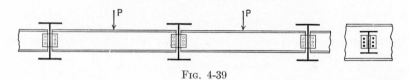

FIG. 4-39

4-67. A column in a bridge is made of two 10-in., 30-lb channels, latticed together. It is supported on a steel pin 3 in. in diameter. The maximum load exerted on the pin by the column is 95 tons. To reduce the bearing stress set up in the webs of the channels, each channel has a "pin plate" riveted to it as shown in Fig. 4-40. After riveting, the pin hole is bored through the plate and web, so as to get an even bearing on both. (a) If bearing in the web and plates is limited to 27,000 psi, what is the required thickness of each pin plate? (b) Available plates have thicknesses varying by sixteenths of an inch ($\frac{1}{4}$, $\frac{5}{16}$, etc.). What plate should be selected for

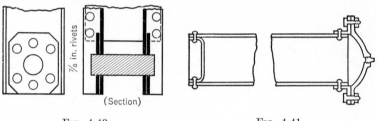

FIG. 4-40   FIG. 4-41

use? (c) Using this plate and assuming that the same load comes on each rivet, are the six rivets shown adequate to transfer to the column the load that comes on the pin plate? Allowable stresses are 13,500 psi and 27,000 psi in shear and bearing, respectively.

4-68. A piece of standard 16-in. pipe (inside diameter 15.25 in. and outside diameter 16.00 in.) 12 ft long is to be made into a gas container by riveting a head into one end and a flange $\frac{3}{4}$ in. thick onto the other end, to which a cast cover is bolted, as shown in Fig. 4-41. Allowable stresses are: tension, 12,000 psi; shearing, 10,000 psi; bearing, 16,000 psi. What gas pressure is allowable for the pipe, assuming that the ends will be made strong enough? With this pressure how many $\frac{15}{16}$-in. rivets should be used to attach the flange to the pipe? How many $1\frac{1}{4}$-in. bolts should be used to attach the cover to the flange?   *Ans.* 22 rivets required.

FIG. 4-42

4-69. A tensile load of 72,000 lb is applied along the centroidal axis of an 8 × 6 × $\frac{7}{16}$ in. angle, which is welded to a plate as shown in Fig. 4-42. To minimize the lengths L_1 and L_2, a fillet is applied along the 8-in. end of the angle. What lengths of L_1 and L_2 will result in a load of 3,000 lb per in. of fillet?

4.-70. A cylindrical standpipe has a diameter of 30 ft. At a short distance above the bottom of the tank the vertical joints are double-riveted lap joints. Plate thickness is $\frac{1}{2}$ in.; diameter of rivet holes is 1 in.; pitch is $3\frac{3}{8}$ in. The allowable stresses are: tension, 18,000; shearing, 12,000; bearing, 24,000 psi. What depth of water above this joint is allowable? *Ans.* $H = 71.6$ ft.

4-71. Same as Problem 4-70 except that diameter of rivet holes is $\frac{7}{8}$ in.

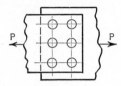

Fig. 4-43

4-72. Two plates are connected by the lap joint shown in Fig. 4-43. One plate is $8\frac{1}{2}$ in. wide and $\frac{9}{16}$ in. thick. The other plate is 10 in. wide and $\frac{1}{2}$ in. thick. Diameter of rivets is $\frac{3}{4}$ in. Calculate the allowable load P. Use A.R.E.A. stresses.

4-73. Same as Problem 4-72 but diameter of rivets is $\frac{7}{8}$ in.

4-74. Same as Problem 4-72 but one plate is $8\frac{1}{2}$ in. wide and $\frac{1}{2}$ in. thick and other plate is 10 in. wide and $\frac{7}{16}$ in. thick. *Ans.* $P = 35,760$ lb.

5

Stresses Due to Axial Loads
Additional Cases

5-1. Introduction. In the preceding chapters numerous problems have been presented in which stresses have been determined by applying the conditions of equilibrium to a segment of a body on which external forces are balanced by the force resulting from stresses on the plane cutting the body.

In this chapter some less obvious applications of this method will be made and also some cases will be presented in which deformations must be considered in determining stresses.

The topics in this chapter are selected because of their usefulness at this time and include the following:

Statically indeterminate structures.

Temperature stresses.

Shearing stresses caused by tension or compression.

Shearing stresses on mutually perpendicular planes.

Stress concentrations due to abrupt changes in cross-section.

In discussing all these topics it will be assumed that the resultant force acting on the cross-section of a stressed member passes through the centroid of the cross-section. This condition is known as axial loading and, in general, results in uniform distribution of stress on the cross-section.

In the discussion of *stress concentrations* it will be pointed out that under certain conditions axial loading does not result in uniformly distributed stress.

Axial loading is assumed in discussing these topics merely to simplify the discussion; the methods used and the results obtained are applicable to cases of non-axial loading which will be considered later.

5-2. Statically Indeterminate Structures. So far, in problems involving unknown forces and stresses, the forces have been found by using one or more of the equations of statics. In problems involving bodies held in equilibrium in which all external forces act in a single plane, there are three available equations of equilibrium, and a maximum of three unknowns can be found. In many problems one or two of the three equations cannot be used, and consequently, the number of unknowns

ART. 5–2   STATICALLY INDETERMINATE STRUCTURES   77

that can be found by statics is reduced to two and sometimes to only one. Problems involving more unknowns than can be found by the equations of statics are known as *statically indeterminate problems*.

Frequently the deformations that occur in the body or bodies may be used as the basis for additional equations that, together with the available equations of statics, permit the solution of problems in which the conditions of statics are not sufficient to find the unknown forces.

Structures in which more forces must be found than can be found by statics are called statically indeterminate structures. Such structures are important in present-day engineering. The examples and problems given in this chapter deal with statically indeterminate arrangements rather than structures. Other statically indeterminate problems occur in later chapters of this book.

Example 1. The prism AB (Fig. 5-1) is of steel 2 in. square and 10.00 in. long. Prism BC is of cast iron 3 in. square and 12.00 in. long. E for the cast iron is 12,000,000 psi. When a load W is applied to the top of AB and is supported by the two prisms the dimension L decreases 0.0085 in. Calculate W and the compressive unit stress in A.

Solution: The last condition of the problem may be stated algebraically as follows:

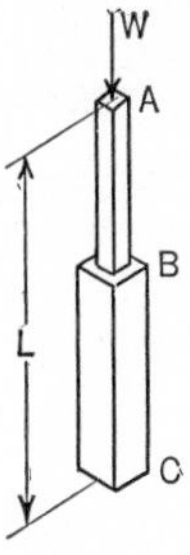

$$\Delta_{AB} + \Delta_{BC} = 0.0085$$

Since $\Delta = PL/AE$,

$$\frac{W \times 10}{4 \times 30,000,000} + \frac{W \times 12}{9 \times 12,000,000} = 0.0085$$

Multiplying by 1,000,000,

$$0.0833W + 0.111W = 8,500$$

whence

$$W = 43,700 \text{ lb} \quad \text{and} \quad S_{AB} = 43,700/4 = 10,925 \text{ psi}$$

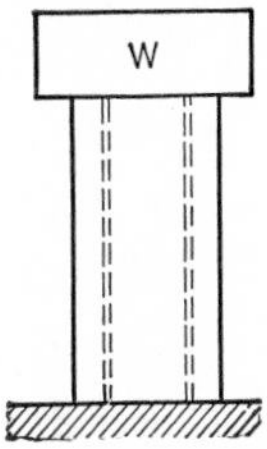

FIG. 5-1

FIG. 5-2

Example 2. A solid cylinder of brass with a cross-sectional area of 5 sq in. is placed inside a steel tube having a cross-sectional area of 8 sq in. Each is 8.500 in. long at 60°F. They stand on end on a flat, rigid surface, and a rigid block rests on top of them. A load W of 130,000 lb is applied to the block as shown in Fig. 5-2. Calculate the unit stress in the brass. Assume E for brass to be 16,000,000 psi.

Solution: Let F be the number of pounds carried by the brass cylinder. Then the load carried by the steel tube is $(130,000 - F)$ lb as required by statics.

Both the brass cylinder and the steel tube must shorten the same amount, or $\Delta_{br} = \Delta_{st}$. If values are written for these deformations in terms of F, this equation results:

$$\frac{F \times 8.500}{5 \times 16,000,000} = \frac{(130,000 - F) \times 8.500}{8 \times 30,000,000}$$

$$\frac{F}{80} = \frac{130,000}{240} - \frac{F}{240}$$

whence $F = 32,500$ lb and $S = 32,500/5 = 6,500$ psi.

Example 3. Let the conditions be the same as in Example 1, except that the brass cylinder has a length of 8.505 in.

Solution: If it is assumed that some of the load is carried by the steel tube, the brass cylinder will shorten 0.005 in. more than the steel tube. Hence

$$\Delta_{br} = \Delta_{st} + 0.005$$

Letting F equal the number of pounds carried by the brass,

$$\frac{F \times 8.505}{5 \times 16,000,000} = \frac{(130,000 - F) \times 8.500}{8 \times 30,000,000} + 0.005$$

Multiplying by 1,000,000,

$$0.1063F = 4,600 - 0.0354F + 5,000$$
$$0.1417F = 9,600$$

whence $F = 67,700$ lb and $S = 67,700/5 = 13,540$ psi. Note that, since brass and steel have different coefficients of thermal expansion, the cylinder and tube of Example 2 would be of unequal lengths at any temperature other than 60°. Hence changes in temperature would cause changes in stress in both these examples. This is a characteristic of many indeterminate structures.

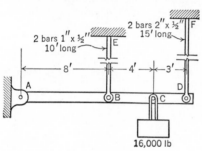

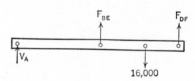

FIG. 5-3   FIG. 5-4

Example 4. The beam AD shown in Fig. 5-3 is supported by a hinge at A and by steel bars at B and D. Calculate the tensions in the bars and the amount of the reaction of the pin at A caused by a load of 16,000 lb applied at C. Assume that deformations of the beam due to bending are negligible.

Solution: A free-body diagram of the beam is shown in Fig. 5-4. First the conditions of statics will be applied. If $\Sigma H = 0$ is used, it is evident that $H_A = 0$. If $\Sigma M = 0$, with A as a center of moments, is used, there results this equation:

$$-16,000 \times 12 + 8F_{BE} + 15F_{DF} = 0 \qquad (1)$$

The equation $\Sigma V = 0$ becomes

$$V_A + F_{BE} + F_{DF} - 16,000 = 0 \qquad (2)$$

This exhausts the help that statics can give. There are three unknowns and only two equations, and hence the problem is statically indeterminate. The beam will rotate slightly about the pin at A as a center; and, since the beam remains straight, the relative elongations of BE and DF must be such that

$$\Delta_{BE}/\Delta_{DF} = 8/15$$

or
$$\Delta_{BE} = 8\Delta_{DF}/15$$
But
$$\Delta = SL/E$$
hence
$$120S_{BE}/E = 8 \times 180S_{DF}/15E$$
whence
$$S_{BE} = 0.8S_{DF}$$

Equation 1 may now be written in terms of S_{DF}, giving
$$8 \times 1 \times 0.8S_{DF} + 15 \times 2 \times S_{DF} = 192,000$$
$$36.4S_{DF} = 192,000$$

Hence
$$S_{DF} = 5,270 \text{ psi} \quad \text{and} \quad S_{BE} = 0.8S_{DF} = 4,220 \text{ psi}$$
$$F_{BE} = 1 \times 4,220 = 4,220 \text{ lb} \quad F_{DF} = 5,270 \times 2 = 10,540 \text{ lb}$$
$$V_A = 16,000 - 4,220 - 10,540 = 1,240 \text{ lb}$$

PROBLEMS

5-1. A weight of 3,200 lb is picked up by two steel wires as shown in Fig. 5-5. Each wire has a cross-sectional area of 0.10 sq in. One wire is 80.0 ft long, and the other wire is 80.04 ft long. The pull P increases gradually until it equals 3,200 lb. What load is the short wire carrying when the weight is carried by the wires?

Ans. Load = 2,350 lb.

FIG. 5-5

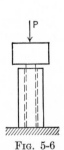

FIG. 5-6

5-2. The aluminum alloy bar shown in Fig. 5-6 has a cross-section of 3 sq in. and a length of 10.0015 in. when unstressed.   The steel pipe has a cross-section of 4 sq in. and a length of 10.0000 in. when unstressed. E equals 11,000,000 psi for aluminum alloy.   What axial load P will cause the same unit stress in each material?   (Assume rigid supports.)

5-3. A steel pipe having a cross-sectional area of 5 sq in. and a length of 8.000 in. is shown in Fig. 5-6.   Inside of the pipe is a solid cylinder of bronze with a cross-sectional area of 4 sq in. and a length of 8.004 in. The pipe and cylinder rest on a smooth rigid surface as shown. A load P of 40,000 lb is applied by the rigid block

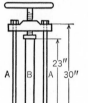

shown. Calculate the stress in the steel and the stress in the bronze caused by this load. For the bronze, E = 12,000,000 psi.

5-4. A screw press has the dimensions shown in Fig. 5-7. The rods marked A are of steel 1.20 in. in diameter. The pitch of the screw thread is 0.125 in. A brass tube B with outside diameter 2.50 in. and inside diameter 1.50 in. is placed in the press. What part of one turn is required for each increase of 4,000 psi stress in the brass tube? (Assume no deformation of the upper and lower heads of the press, nor of the screw. Take E for brass as 16,000,000 psi.)   *Ans.* 0.0904 turn.

Fig. 5-7   **5-5.** Solve Problem 5-4 if the diameter of each steel rod is 1.5 in. and the cross-sectional area of the brass tube is 4 sq in.

5-6. Solve Example 4 of this article if EB is 12 ft long and FD is 18 ft long, 2 in. wide, and $\frac{3}{8}$ in. thick (two such bars).

5-7. The bar AB of Fig. 5-1 is of steel 2.5 in. square and 12 in. long. The bar BC is made of an aluminum alloy and is 3.5 in. square and 14 in. long. The load W causes the dimension L to decrease 0.006 in. Calculate the value of W if the E for the aluminum alloy is 10,500,000 psi.

5-3. Temperature Stresses. Most substances expand when they are heated and contract when they are cooled. The rate at which this change in dimension takes place as the temperature changes is expressed by a number called the *coefficient of thermal expansion,* for which the symbol C is used.

This quantity is the unit change in dimension per degree change in temperature, temperature usually being expressed on the Fahrenheit scale in this country.

Commonly used values of the coefficients of thermal expansion (per degree Fahrenheit) for a few materials are as tabulated. For a more comprehensive list see American Institute of Steel Construction, *Steel Construction,* or other handbooks.

Aluminum	0.0000128
Steel	0.0000065
Cast iron	0.0000062
Copper	0.0000093
Concrete	0.000006
Wood	0.000003

In many forms of construction allowance must be made for this expansion and contraction. For instance, a concrete road slab should be laid with joints at intervals. Otherwise, as it cools and contracts in winter weather, the contraction will set up tensile stresses in the material which may cause it to crack.

When constraint prevents all the deformation normally accompanying change in the temperature of a body, the resulting stress equals $E \times \delta$, where δ is the unit deformation which is prevented from occurring.

Example 1. A steel bar 1 in. square is held between rigid supports exactly 10 ft apart. There is no stress in the bar when its temperature is 50°F. What is the unit stress in it when its temperature is 0°F?

Solution: The change in temperature while the bar is constrained = 50°. C = 0.0000065. Therefore δ = 0.0000065 $\times$ 50 = 0.000325 in. per in. Since $S = E\delta$, S = 30,000,000 $\times$ 0.000325 = 9,750 psi tension.

It should be noted that, in a body in which *all* temperature deformation is prevented, the unit stress set up by a change in temperature is wholly independent of the length of the body. Nor is the total force which the body exerts on the constraints at its ends affected by its length, but only by its cross-sectional area, its modulus of elasticity, and its temperature change. However, in a body which undergoes some change in dimension with change in its temperature, but not the entire change which would normally occur, the stress is affected by the length of the body.

Example 2. A railroad track is laid in winter at a temperature of 15°F, with gaps of 0.01 ft between the ends of the rails. The rails are 33 ft long. If they are prevented from buckling, what stress will result from a temperature of 110°F?

Solution: The normal change in length of a 33-ft rail when its temperature increases 95° = 0.0000065 $\times$ 95 $\times$ 33 = 0.0204 ft. The change in length prevented = 0.0204 − 0.01 = 0.0104 ft. Therefore the unit deformation which is prevented is δ = 0.0104 ÷ 33 = 0.000315 ft per ft. Since $S = E\delta$, S = 30,000,000 $\times$ 0.000315 = 9,450 psi.

Example 3. An aluminum tube A with an inside diameter of 2.1 in. and a cross-sectional area of 3.52 sq in. is shown in Fig. 5-8a. Within the tube is a steel bolt B, 2 in. in diameter. The nut of the bolt is tightened until the head of the bolt and the nut are tight against the ends of the tube but exert no appreciable pressure on the tube when the temperature of the bolt and tube is 60°F. Calculate the stress in tube when the tube and bolt are both heated to 150°F. For steel C = 0.0000065; for aluminum C = 0.0000128, E = 10,000,000 psi.

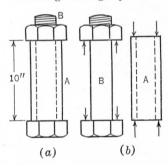

(a)   (b)

Fig. 5-8

Solution: Imagine that the tube and bolt are separated and that the rise in temperature then takes place.

The increase in length of A = 90 $\times$ 0.0000128 $\times$ 10 = 0.01152 in.
The increase in length of B = 90 $\times$ 0.0000065 $\times$ 10 = 0.00585 in.
Excess length of tube over bolt   = 0.00567 in.

Actually there is a tensile force F on the bolt and the same compressive force F on the tube of such magnitude as to make their lengths the same.

It will be seen from Fig. 5-8b that A and B will be the same length when F is such as to make the *sum* of the shortening of A and the lengthening of B equal to 0.00567 in. Hence

$$\Delta_B + \Delta_A = 0.00567$$

$$\frac{F \times 10}{3.142 \times 30,000,000} + \frac{F \times 10}{3.52 \times 10,000,000} = 0.00567$$

Multiplying by 10,000,000,

$$1.062F + 2.84F = 56,700$$

$$F = 56,700/3.902 = 14,500 \text{ lb}$$

$$S = 14,500/3.52 = 4,120 \text{ psi}$$

An alternative solution may be based on the fact that the change in length of A equals the change in length of B.

$$90 \times 0.0000128 \times 10 - \frac{F \times 10}{3.52 \times 10,000,000} =$$

$$90 \times 0.0000065 \times 10 + \frac{F \times 10}{3.142 \times 30,000,000}$$

It will be seen that this solution contains exactly the same elements as the one above and therefore leads to the same answer.

PROBLEMS

5-8. A surveyor's steel tape is 0.050 in. thick and 0.320 in. wide and is exactly 100.000 ft long at 70°F with a pull of 15.0 lb. What pull will be required to make it 100.000 ft long at 25°F? *Ans.* $P = 155.5$ lb.

5-9. A copper bar, 20 ft long, is cooled from 200°F to 32°F. At 120° the ends are suddenly gripped, and further contraction is prevented. What is the stress in the bar when 32° is reached? ($E = 17,000,000$ psi; $C = 0.0000095$.)

5-10. A rod of Invar steel 5 sq in. in cross-section and 18.000 in. long at 32°F and a rod of brass which has the same cross-section and is 22.000 in. long at the same temperature are placed end to end. Their temperature is then raised to 212°F while pressure is exerted on their ends to keep them exactly 40.000 in. apart. (a) At 212°F what is the total force exerted on the end of each rod? (b) What is the length of each rod? (C for Invar steel = 0; for brass = 0.0000104; E for Invar steel = 29,000,000 psi; for brass = 14,500,000 psi.)

5-11. Solve Problem 5-10, substituting ordinary steel for Invar steel.

5-12. For "shrunk-link-joints," as illustrated in Fig. 5-9, Kent's *Mechanical Engineers' Handbook* recommends that the length of the link be 0.999 of the sum d, of the thicknesses of the two parts to be joined by the link. If the link is steel and if the material of the flywheel is assumed to be *absolutely rigid*, what unit stress results in a link made in accordance with this recommendation? How many degrees Fahrenheit must the temperature of the link be above that of the flywheel castings in order to place it in the slot? *Ans.* 154°F.

5-13. A steel link (Fig. 5-10) has side bars A each 1×1.25 in., and the distance L is 8.000 in. at 50°F. A bronze rod B having a cross-sectional area of 1.20 sq in. and a length of 8.000 in. at 50°F is placed within the link. Calculate the stress in the bronze rod when the temperature of rod and link is 180°F. For this bronze, $E = 12,000,000$ psi and $C = 0.000010$.

5-14. The carbon steel link shown in Fig. 5-10 has side bars A each 1.5 in. square. The bar B is of Invar steel with a cross-sectional area of 2.50 sq in. The length L

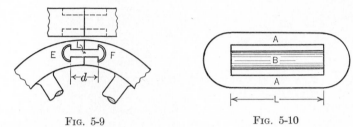

FIG. 5-9   FIG. 5-10

is exactly 9.00 in. for both the link and the bar at 100°F. Calculate the unit stress in B when the temperature is 30°F. For both steels E is 30,000,000 psi. For carbon steel C is 0.0000065 and for Invar steel $C = 0$. *Ans.* $S_B = 8,790$ psi.

5-15. Three wires, each having a cross-sectional area of 0.20 sq in. and the same unstressed length of 200 in. at 60°F hang side by side in the same plane. The middle wire, equidistant from each of the others, is steel. The outer wires are copper. (*a*) If a weight of 1,000 lb is gradually picked up by the three wires, what part of the load is carried by each? (*b*) What must the temperature become for the entire load to be carried by the steel wire? E for copper is 15,000,000 psi; C for copper = 0.0000095.

5-16. A locomotive driving wheel without a steel tire has an outside diameter of 70.60 in. To what inside diameter should the tire be machined so that its unit stress will not exceed 14,000 psi after being shrunk on? (Assume that the diameter of the inside of the tire after shrinking will be 70.58 in.)

5-4. Shearing Stresses Caused by Tension or Compression.

In a body subject to tensile or compressive stress in one direction there will be shearing stress on any plane neither parallel nor perpendicular to the normal stress. The maximum value of this shearing stress is one-half the normal stress, and it occurs on planes inclined 45° to the normal stress.

Proof: The body shown in Fig. 5-11*a* is a prism subject to tensile stress, the resultant force being P. In Fig. 5-11*b*, is shown one segment of this prism cut off by a plane m–n making an angle θ with a plane perpendicular to the direction of the tensile stress. This segment is in equilibrium, one force being the external load P and the other force

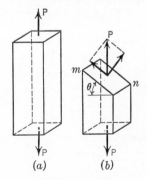

FIG. 5-11

being the equal and opposite force P exerted by the rest of the body on the inclined face. This force on the inclined face has one component parallel to the face and equal to $P \sin \theta$, and one normal to the inclined face and equal to $P \cos \theta$. The area of the inclined face is $A/\cos \theta$ if A is the area of the cross-section of the prism.

The parallel component causes shearing stress, the unit stress being

$$S_s = \frac{P \sin \theta}{A/\cos \theta} = \frac{P}{A} \sin \theta \cos \theta = \frac{P}{A} \frac{\sin 2\theta}{2}$$

The maximum value of S_s occurs on a plane for which $\sin 2\theta$ is a maximum. The maximum value of $\sin 2\theta$ is its value when $\theta = 45°$ or $135°$ and is 1.

When $\sin 2\theta = 1$, $S_s = P/2A$, which is one-half of the normal unit stress. There is also normal stress (tensile or compressive) on any inclined plane, its value being

$$S_n = \frac{P \cos \theta}{A/\cos \theta} = \frac{P}{A} \cos^2 \theta$$

S_n is a maximum when $\theta = 0$.

The two formulas derived above are not essential for determining shearing and normal unit stresses on inclined planes when the inclination

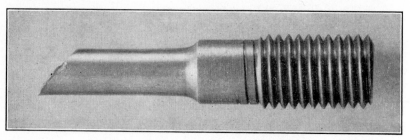

Fig. 5-12.   Failure of Duralumin under tension.

is given. Such problems are best treated as problems in statics in which the normal and shearing components are found in the usual way. The area of the inclined section is computed and the unit stresses found by $S = P/A$.

Example. A specimen of Duralumin, 0.500 in. in diameter (Fig. 5-12), failed under a tensile load of 11,500 lb. The plane of failure was found to be at $48°$ with the cross-section. What was the shearing unit stress at failure? What was the tensile stress on a cross-section?

Solution: Area of cross-section $A = \pi(0.5)^2 = 0.196$ sq in.

Area of inclined section $= A/\cos 48° = 0.196/0.669 = 0.293$ sq in.

Shearing component $= P \sin 48° = 11,500 \times 0.743 = 8,540$ lb.

$S_s = P'/A = 8,540/0.293 = 29,100$ psi.

$S_t = P/A = 11,500/0.196 = 58,700$ psi.

The tensile strength of a material is defined as the tensile unit stress on a cross-section of the material when failure occurs, irrespective of whether the failure is due directly to tension on a cross-section or to shear on an oblique plane. The tensile strength of the above specimen of Duralumin would therefore be said to be 58,700 psi. Brittle materials

FIG. 5-13.   Failures of concrete and cast iron under compression.

ordinarily have shearing strengths much less than the compressive strength, so that, when compressive loads are applied, they fail in oblique shear (Fig. 5-13). The compressive strength, however, is defined as the value obtained by dividing the ultimate load by the area of the cross-section.

In the example worked out above, the specimen (shown in Fig. 5-12) failed on a plane not quite at 45° with the axis because of some condition of the material that made it a little *weaker* on the 48° plane than on the 45° plane. The unit stress, of course, was slightly greater on the 45° plane, where it was 58,700/2, or 29,350 psi.

The propositions stated and proved in this article illustrate the important fact that at any point in a body subject to stress there are different stresses or combinations of stresses on planes in different directions. The relationships between these different stresses and applications of the relationships will be considered in Chapter 15. In ductile materials or brittle materials under tensile loads, however, the stresses on planes perpendicular or parallel to the loads are generally more serious than any others. Most of the cases considered in the earlier chapters of this book are of that sort.

PROBLEMS

5-17. Table I, Art. 3-5, gives the following allowable stresses for southern pine, prime structural grade, in a dry location: compression on end of grain, 1,450 psi; compression on side of grain, 455 psi; shear parallel to grain, 120 psi. (*a*) What is the allowable load on the end of a $5\frac{1}{2} \times 5\frac{1}{2}$ in. (actual size) post? (b) If this load is placed on the end of a post in which the grain of the wood makes an angle of 20° with the axis of the post, what is the resulting shearing unit stress along the grain? Compressive unit stress on the side of the grain? Are these within the specified values?   Ans.   (a) $P = 43,900$ lb.

5-18. A brass bar 0.60×0.60 in. in cross-section has grooves 0.1 in. deep on opposite faces in a plane which makes an angle θ of 40° with the other two faces of the member, as shown in Fig. 5-14. (a) What load P will cause a shearing stress of 8,000 psi? (b) If $\theta = 45°$, calculate P.

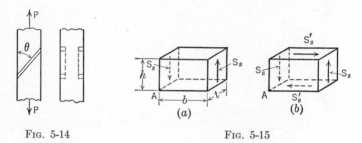

FIG. 5-14   FIG. 5-15

5-5. Shearing Stresses on Mutually Perpendicular Planes.
If, at a point within a body subject to stress, there exists a shearing unit stress along one plane, there must also be an equal shearing unit stress along a perpendicular plane through that point.

Proof: Figure 5-15a shows a small rectangular particle taken from a point in a stressed body where a shearing unit stress of S_s psi is known to exist along vertical planes. This small body will then have shearing stresses of S_s psi on two opposite vertical faces, as shown in Fig. 5-15a.

Since the body is in equilibrium, the sum of the moments of the forces acting on the body is equal to zero, and other forces than those shown in Fig. 5-15a must be acting on the body. Such additional forces do exist and are supplied by shearing unit stresses of S'_s psi acting on the horizontal faces of the body as shown in Fig. 5-15b.

Putting the sum of the moments of all the forces on the body with respect to A equal to zero,

$$(S_s \times ht) \times b - (S'_s \times bt) \times h = 0$$

whence $S_s = S'_s$, as was stated at the beginning of this article.

The presence of uniformly distributed tensile or compressive stresses on the faces of the block does not affect the soundness of the above reasoning, nor does the presence of non-uniformly distributed tensile or compressive stresses, provided the dimensions of the block are infinitesimal.

The existence of equal shearing unit stresses on mutually perpendicular planes will be further discussed in connection with shafts and beams.

5-6. Stresses in Members of Variable Cross-Section; Localized Stress. When a prism of rectangular cross-section is loaded axially, it is believed that the stress distribution is very nearly uniform over sections which are some distance away from the points where the loads are applied. The assumption of uniformity of distribution of such stress is always made.

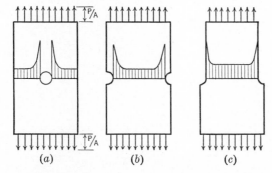

FIG. 5-16.   Ordinates of curves are unit stresses on reduced sections.

Suppose, however, that at some cross-section of the bar there is a cylindrical hole, as in Fig. 5-16a. In this case the stress is not uniformly distributed over the cross-section through the hole but reaches a maximum value immediately adjacent to the hole, as shown. The stress decreases rapidly so that the average stress on the cross-section is reached not far away from the hole. A similar situation exists in a bar notched at the sides, as shown in Fig. 5-16b, or in a bar in which two portions of different widths are joined with a "fillet," as in Fig. 5-16c.

The ratio of the maximum stress to the average stress is affected by the ratio of the radius of the hole, notch, or fillet to the width of the bar. For a circular hole in a plate of indefinitely great width (or an indefinitely small hole in a bar of finite width) it can be shown mathematically that the maximum stress in an "ideal" material is three times the average. If the diameter of the hole bears a finite relation to the width of the bar, the ratio of maximum to average stress is less. The same situation exists with respect to notches in the side of a bar.

In cases of this sort where, because of a change in the shape of the member, the maximum stress over a small area is above the average stress, the ratio of maximum to average stress on the most highly stressed section is called the *stress-concentration factor* for that change in shape.

The mathematical analysis of cases of this sort frequently becomes very complex.   For this reason a number of experimental procedures for the study of stress concentrations and the determination of stress-concentration factors have been developed.   Figure 5-17 shows graphs giving stress-concentration factors for three types of change in cross-section.[1]   These stress-concentration factors were determined by the experimental procedure known as photoelastic analysis.

Inspection of Fig. 5-17 shows that for each of the changes in cross-section a very small hole, notch, or fillet causes a much larger stress

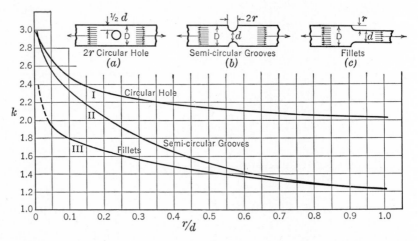

FIG. 5-17.   Stress concentration factors (flat bars).   The ordinate of a curve is the ratio of the maximum stress to the average stress on the minimum net section.

concentration than a hole, notch, or fillet of somewhat greater radius. In the member with a hole, for example, if the hole has a diameter of only one-tenth the width of the "net" cross-section through the hole $(r/d = 0.05)$, the maximum stress immediately adjacent to the hole is 2.7 times the average on a net section through the hole.   If, however, the diameter of the hole equals the net width $(r/d = 0.5)$, the maximum stress is only 2.1 times the average.   In the cases of the notch and the fillet, the gain in stress uniformity as r increases with respect to d is even more pronounced.   In all these situations, however, it is evident that the stress as calculated from $S = P/A$ is much too low.

In some situations this fact is important; in others it is not.   In a

[1] M. M. Frocht, "Factors of Stress Concentration Photoelastically Determined," *Trans. A.S.M.E.*, Vol. 57 (1935), p. A-67. For a discussion of stress concentrations and methods by which they may be determined see F. B. Seely and J. O. Smith, *Advanced Mechanics of Materials*, 2nd ed., John Wiley & Sons, 1952, Chapter 12.

member made of material with a pronounced yield point and subjected to gradually applied or steady loading, the maximum stress on the reduced cross-section is much above the average so long as the maximum stress is below the yield point. However, as the load is increased, this stress differential diminishes. The maximum stress reaches the yield point of the material long before the average stress does, but an increase in load thereafter causes no increase in the maximum stress. Instead there is only a flow of metal in a region adjacent to the hole. As this region is very small, the plastic deformation of the member is without serious consequences. Before the "usable strength" (Art. 3-2) of the material is approached, most of the inequality of stress has disappeared; when the full usable strength has been developed, all the stress inequality has disappeared. Consequently, in structural practice no allowance is made, for example, for the stress concentration immediately adjacent to the root of the thread of a bolt subjected to tension or adjacent to holes in axially loaded steel tension and compression members. In this situation the minute deformation is unimportant, and most of the stress inequality disappears before a dangerous load is reached. Generally speaking, therefore, in designing in the milder grades of steel or other ductile materials, and for loads which do not fluctuate rapidly, no account is taken of such local stresses.

In using more brittle materials, stress concentrations are much more serious. Under high local stress, a crack is likely to start because of the inability of the brittle material to deform plastically. Under repeated loads, also, localized stresses are important, because under such loads a stress above the endurance limit, even though it exists only on a very small area, tends to start a fatigue crack. Therefore, in designing members of brittle materials and members subject to reversals of stress, where changes in dimension are unavoidable the effort is made to minimize the non-uniformity of stress distribution by means of fillets, the avoidance of sharp notches, and similar means and to employ the stress-concentration factor in making proper allowance for such localized stress as remains.

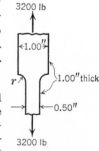

Fig. 5-18

Example. A steel bar of rectangular cross-section and subjected to complete alternations of tensile and compressive stress has a reduced portion as shown in Fig. 5-18. The endurance limit of the steel is 40,000 psi, and the maximum computed stress in the bar is not to exceed one-fourth of the endurance limit. If the load on the bar is 3,200 lb, what is the minimum size of fillet that may be used?

Solution: Area of reduced section = 0.5 sq in. Average stress on reduced section = 6,400 psi. Allowable computed stress = 10,000 psi. Therefore allowable stress-concentration factor $= 10,000/6,400 = 1.56$.   From Fig. 5-17, required $r/d = 0.35$, whence required radius of fillet $= 0.175$ in.

PROBLEMS

5-19. The head of a standard structural-steel eyebar is joined to the shank by a fillet the radius of which is equal to the width of the shank.   Assuming the graph given in Fig. 5-17 for stress concentration due to fillets to apply to this case, calculate the maximum stress that occurs in an eyebar when the average stress is 20,000 psi. If the radius were equal to only one-half the width of the shank, what would be the maximum stress?

5-20. Three flat bars each 0.25 in. thick and with a drilled hole as shown in Fig. 5-19 are used as tension members.   Dimensions in inches are: for bar a, $D = 1.00$, $2r = 0.25$; for bar b, $D = 1.25$, $2r = 0.50$; for bar c, $D = 1.75$, $2r = 1.00$.   The load on each bar is 1,250 lb.   What maximum stress occurs in each of the bars as a result of stress concentrations?   *Ans.* (*b*) $S = 14,750$ psi.

5-21. Each block in Fig. 5-20 has the same minimum cross-section.   The blocks are of soft steel, the proportional limit being 25,000 psi and the yield point 30,000 psi. Using the curve of Fig. 5-17, find the maximum stress in A and in B when P equals (*a*) 6,000 lb, (*b*) 24,000 lb, (*c*) 12,000 lb.

5-22. Figure 2-1 shows a standard form of static tensile test specimen of mild steel.   Figure 2-5 shows a tensile test specimen of cast iron.   From the standpoint of stress concentration, discuss the difference in their shapes.

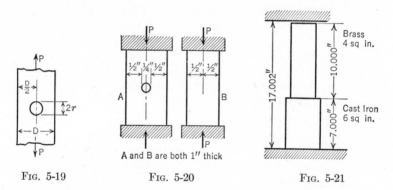

FIG. 5-19   FIG. 5-20   FIG. 5-21

GENERAL PROBLEMS

(In all these problems disregard the effect of stress concentration.)

5-23. Lengths of the cylinders (Fig. 5-21) are exact as shown at 16°F.   The dimension 17.002 in. remains fixed.   What is the unit stress in the brass at 110°F?
For brass: $C = 0.000010$, $E = 16,000,000$ psi.
For cast iron: $C = 0.0000062$, $E = 12,000,000$ psi.
(Assume uniform stress distribution throughout each cylinder.)
                                     Ans. $S_{br} = 11,320$ psi.

5-24. Solve Problem 5-23 except that upper cylinder is of an aluminum alloy ($E = 10,000,000$ psi and $C = 0.000013$) and the lower cylinder is steel ($C = 0.0000065$).

5-25. The rod A in Fig. 5-22 is of steel 2.50 in. in diameter, and the rods B are of cast brass 2.00 in. in diameter ($E = 16,000,000$ psi). If the supports are rigid and the load is applied by means of a rigid block, what load W will cause a stress of 12,000 psi in A?

5-26. Using the data in Problem 5-25, calculate the unit stress in rod A caused by a load of 90,000 lb. *Ans.* $S = 9,400$ psi.

5-27. The rod A in Fig. 5-22 is of steel 2.20 in. in diameter and 13.9980 in. long, and the rods B are of cast brass 1.80 in. in diameter and 10.000 in. long ($E = 16,000,000$ psi), so that there is a gap of 0.002 in. between rod A and the block before the load is applied. Calculate the stress in the brass rods when a load of 100,000 lb is applied.

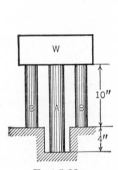

Fig. 5-22

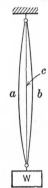

Fig. 5-23

5-28. Three steel wires, a, b, c, each 0.040 sq in. in cross-sectional area, connect two rings as shown in Fig. 5-23. The lengths of the wires, unstressed, are: $a = 100.00$ ft, $b = 99.950$ ft, $c = 99.900$ ft. The lower ring is attached to a 3,000-lb weight resting on the floor, and the upper ring is gradually raised by a crane hook until the weight is lifted from the floor and is supported by the wires. Calculate the unit stress in wire a and the elongation of wire a.

5-29. A weight of 4,000 lb. is slowly lifted from the floor by three wires, each 50 ft long and each having a cross-sectional area of 0.20 sq in. One wire is steel, one is brass ($E = 15,000,000$ psi), and one is aluminum alloy ($E = 10,000,000$ psi). Calculate the stress in the steel wire and its elongation. *Ans.* $S_{\text{steel}} = 10,900$ psi.

5-30. Solve Problem 5-29 if the areas of the wires are: steel, 0.20 sq in.; brass, 0.25 sq in.; aluminum alloy, 0.30 sq in.

5-31. Solve Problem 5-28, with the following changes in data: wire a is copper, b is steel, and c is Duralumin, and the load lifted is 1,800 lb. (E for copper is 17,000,000 psi, and E for Duralumin is 11,000,000 psi.)

5-32. The steel forging AB shown in Fig. 5-24 is hinged at A. The prisms C and D fit accurately between the rigid platform and the forging when there is no load on AB. C is steel 2 in. square and 8 in. long; D is cast iron 2.2 in. square and 8 in. long. Dimensions m and n are both 15 in. Calculate

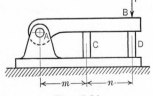

Fig. 5-24

the load on each prism and the reaction at A when a load of 40,000 lb is applied to A directly above D as shown. Assume that AB does not bend. For cast iron, $E = 12,000,000$ psi. *Ans.* $P_c = 27,000$ lb.

5-33. Solve Problem 5-32 but with cylinders C and D interchanged.

5-34. Solve Problem 5-32 but make $m = 14$ in. and $n = 16$ in.

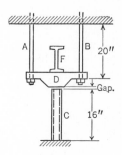

FIG. 5-25

5-35. The rigid block D (Fig. 5-25) is supported by two round steel rods A and B each 1 in. in diameter which are attached to a rigid overhead support as shown. The 3-in. steel pipe C rests on a rigid surface with a gap of 0.003 in. between the pipe and D when there is no load on D. Calculate the unit stress in C when a vertical load of 20,000 lb is applied to D by the beam F. *Ans.* $S_c = 3,720$ psi.

5-36. A tension member in a 352-ft railroad bridge consists of eight eyebars, each 12×2 in. in cross-section, placed side by side. The panel length is 32 ft 0 in. center to center of the pins. Because of a mistake made when drilling the holes, one of the bars has the pin holes drilled 0.025 in. too close together. The total load on the tension member equals 3,120,000 lb when the bridge is fully loaded. (*a*) What is the unit stress in the short bar? (*b*) In the other bars? (*c*) What would be the unit stress if all bars were exactly the same length? *Ans.* (*b*) $S = 16,000$ psi.

5-37. A tension member or a short compression member made of two materials, for example, a steel pipe filled with concrete, carries an axial load P. The cross-sectional area and modulus of elasticity for material 1 are respectively A_1 and E_1, and for material 2 they are respectively A_2 and E_2. Show that the part of the load carried by material number 1 is $P_1 = \dfrac{A_1 E_1}{A_1 E_1 + A_2 E_2} P$.

6

Torsional Stress, Shafts, and Helical Springs

6-1. Introduction. In all the stressed bodies considered up to this point, the equation

$$\text{Unit stress} = \text{Force/Area}$$

has been used to give the stress intensity. In some of the situations considered, this equation gives very nearly the true stress at any point of the stressed area; that is, the stress is very nearly uniform. It holds, for instance, for an eyebar at a section well away from the "heads." In other situations the assumed relationship is not true, but in connection with appropriate allowable stresses it forms a practical basis for satisfactory design. Bearing stresses in riveted joints illustrate this. There are, however, many important situations where the stress is known to vary from nothing at all at some point or points of the cross-section of a member to a maximum value at some other point or points. As applied to situations of this sort, the foregoing equation has no useful meaning, and some other relationship must be developed.

The torsional stress that occurs on the cross-section of a round bar subjected to twisting moments or torques is an example of this non-uniform stress distribution.

Let AB in Fig. 6-1 represent a round bar of steel rigidly fastened to a fixed support at A so that it cannot turn and with a square end at B on which is fitted a bar CD. If the two forces marked

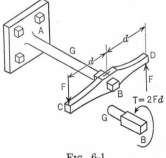

Fig. 6-1

F are equal and opposite, they do not bend AB, but they apply a torque to the bar and twist it. Torque may be applied to a shaft by any one of several different devices, the most common of which are pulleys and gears. The torque applied by a pulley equals the difference in the belt pulls multiplied by the radius; the torque applied by a gear is the product of the tooth pressure and the radius of the pitch circle. Pulleys and gears may be shrunk onto the shaft, attached by set screws, or made in two parts that are bolted together and grip the shaft firmly when the nuts are tightened. A "key" fitting in a slot in the shaft and in the pulley or coupling is one of the most widely used fastenings.

Shafts often have several pulleys, one of which drives the shaft and the others are turned by the shaft and drive machines. In such shafts there are different torques on different cross-sections of the shaft.

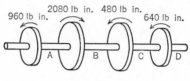

FIG. 6-2

The amount of torque, or torsional moment, existing on any cross-section of a shaft equals the algebraic sum of the torques applied to that part of the shaft on one side of the cross-section in question. For example, for the shaft shown in Fig. 6-2 the torques on the cross-sections A, B, C, and D are 960 lb-in., 1,120 lb-in., 640 lb-in., and 0 lb-in., respectively.

6-2. Torsional Stress. An analysis of the stresses resulting from torque can be made by the free-body method, but it is necessary to consider the deformations to determine the distribution of the stresses that exert the balancing forces.

Imagine a plane perpendicular to the axis of AB (Fig. 6-1) cutting AB at any point G between A and B. Consider the part of the bar from B to this plane as a free body in equilibrium. The body is subjected to a torque of $2Fd$ with respect to its geometrical axis. Since the body is in equilibrium, an opposite torque must be exerted on the body. This torque must be exerted by forces which act on the cut surface of the bar and which act *in the plane* of the cut surface. Therefore these forces result from shearing stresses. The name *torsional stress* is given to shearing stress caused in this way. The moment of the torsional stresses is called a *resisting torque*. From the equilibrium of the free body it is evident that

Resisting torque = External torque

This relationship holds true whether the shaft to which the torque is applied is stationary, as shown in Fig. 6-1, or whether it is rotating at uniform speed under equal and opposite torques applied to it by driving and driven pulleys or equivalent mechanisms.

It has been stated that the stress distribution in torsion is not uniform over the cross-section; that is, the unit stress in pounds per square inch is not the same at all points. The truth of this statement, and the way in which the unit stress varies, will be evident from the discussion which follows.

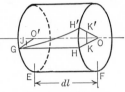

FIG. 6-3

Let the cylinder shown in Fig. 6-3 be part of a shaft between two transverse planes E and F. GH is an element of the cylindrical surface extending from plane E to plane F. Now, if the shaft is subjected to a torque, stresses and deformations result, and each of these planes will rotate relative to the other. If plane E is regarded as being fixed, plane F will rotate slightly so that the radius OH will assume a position OH' and the element GH will become GH', part of a helix. If GH is a "fiber" of the material in the shaft, this fiber has been given a shearing distortion, and the unit deformation is HH'/dl. Consider a fiber JK parallel to the axis and half way between the axis and the surface. It has been shown by experiment and by analysis based on the theory of elasticity that any radius such as OH *remains a straight line* as the shaft is twisted, provided the maximum stress in the shaft does not exceed the proportional limit. Therefore the distortion of fiber JK' is half as much and the unit deformation half as great as that of GH'. If the material obeys Hooke's law, and if all the stresses are below the proportional limit, the shearing unit stress in the fiber JK is half as great as the shearing unit stress in the fiber GH. By this reasoning the conclusion is reached that the shearing unit stress is proportional to the distance from the geometrical axis of the cylinder. Therefore the law of distribution of stress caused by torsion in a shaft of circular cross-section may be stated thus:

The shearing unit stress on a cross-section is zero at the geometrical axis of the shaft and increases in direct proportion to the distance from the geometric axis. It is, therefore, a maximum in the fibers at the outer surface of the cylinder.

Starting with this law of stress variation, it is possible to establish a relation between the shearing unit stress in the outermost fibers, the torque, and the size of the cross-section. With such a relation, it will be possible to compute any one of the three quantities if the other two are given.

Consider a short length of a shaft as a free body. Figure 6-4 shows the circular cross-section at one end of this part. The resisting torque of the stresses on this cross-section is equal to the torque T exerted by the external forces twisting the shaft. Let the unit stress in any fiber at the surface of the shaft $= S_s$. Let dA be an ele-

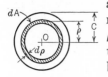

FIG. 6-4

mentary area in the form of a narrow ring of radius ρ. If the above law of stress variation is applied, the unit stress at $dA = (\rho/c)S_s$. The force exerted by the stress over the area $dA = (\rho/c)S_s\, dA$. The moment of this force with respect to the axis of the shaft $= \rho \times$ the force, $= (\rho^2/c)S_s\, dA$. The sum of the moments of all the stresses on the entire cross-section is

$$\int_0^c \frac{\rho^2}{c} S_s\, dA = \frac{S_s}{c}\int_0^c \rho^2\, dA$$

The value of the integral $\int \rho^2\, dA$ for a given area is called the polar moment of inertia of the area and is represented by the symbol J. An explanation of moment of inertia of an area is given in Appendix B.

Substituting J for the integral in the above equation

$$\text{Resisting torque} = (S_s/c)J$$

But the resisting torque equals the external torque T. Consequently

$$T = \frac{S_s J}{c} \qquad \text{or} \qquad S_s = \frac{Tc}{J} \tag{6-1}$$

in which S_s is the maximum shearing unit stress in the cross-section (pounds per square inch); T is the torque on the shaft (pound-inches); c is the outside radius of the shaft (inches); J is the polar moment of inertia of the cross-section (inches^4). These formulas apply to solid or hollow circular shafts. J for the cross-section of a hollow shaft is found by subtracting J for a circle of the inside diameter from J for a circle of the outside diameter. The polar moment of inertia for a circle with respect to an axis through the center is $\pi r^4/2$ or $\pi d^4/32$ in.^{4}

If the torque and allowable stress in extreme fibers are given and the size of shaft is to be determined, the value of J/c is calculated. J/c is a function of the dimensions of the cross-sections, and the size of a solid or hollow shaft having the required J/c may be computed.

It should be kept in mind that the stress given by the above formula is that due to torsion alone. Shafting is usually subject to other forces besides axial torque at the ends. Transverse loads (such as weight of shaft itself and of pulleys, and tensions in belts) cause bending stresses which may be serious. Sometimes axial stresses are also present; the torsional stress must then be computed and combined with other stresses. The combination of these stresses is treated in Chapter 15.

Example: What torque will cause a stress of 10,000 psi in the extreme fibers of a shaft 5 in. in diameter?

Solution: The polar moment of inertia of a circle is $\pi r^4/2$.

$$T = \frac{S_s J}{c} = \frac{10,000(2.5^4 \pi/2)}{2.5} = 245,500 \text{ lb-in.}$$

PROBLEMS

6-1. Solve the foregoing example if the shaft is hollow with an inside diameter of 2.4 in. What is the stress at the inner surface of the shaft?

6-2. Calculate the diameter of a solid steel shaft to transmit a torque of 24,000 lb-ft, with a unit stress of 8,000 psi.   *Ans.* D = 5.68 in.

6-3. Solve Problem 6-2 but let the torque be 8,000 lb-ft and let the unit stress be 12,000 psi.

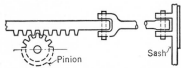

Pinion   Sash

FIG. 6–5

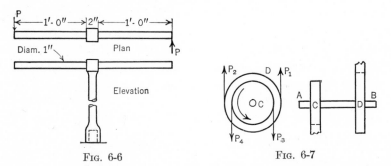

FIG. 6–6   FIG. 6–7

6-4. A heavy monitor window is to be opened by a rack-and-pinion device shown in Fig. 6-5. The maximum force which the pinion must exert is 250 lb applied at a distance of 2.5 in. from the axis of the shaft. The pinion and the hand wheel at the lower end of the shaft will be "shrunk" onto the shaft, there being no keyways or other devices to weaken the shaft. What should the shaft diameter be if the torsional stress is not to exceed 10,000 psi?

6-5. What should be the diameter of the stem of the wrench shown in Fig. 6-6 if the maximum torsional stress in it is not to exceed 8,000 psi, each of the forces P being 60 lb.   *Ans.* d = 1.00 in.

6-6. In Fig. 6-7 pulleys C and D are attached to the shaft AB, which is supported on bearings not shown. The shaft is driven at a uniform speed by pulley D and turns pulley C. Belt pulls are $P_1 = 360$ lb; $P_2 = 80$ lb; $P_4 = 60$ lb. Calculate the tension P_3. The diameter of the shaft is 2.5 in. Calculate the maximum unit stress in the shaft. Diameters of pulleys are 30 in. and 38 in.

6-7. Same as Problem 6-6 except that $P_1 = 400$ lb, and diameter of D is 40 in.

6-8. In Fig. 6-2 if the torque of 640 lb-in. is increased to 720 and the 2,080 lb-in. is changed to keep the shaft in equilibrium, calculate the maximum shearing stress that occurs in the shaft. Diameter of shaft is $2\frac{1}{4}$ in.   *Ans.* $S_s = 536$ psi.

6-9. Show that the weight of a hollow shaft with an internal diameter equal to five-tenths of the external diameter is only 78.1 per cent of the weight of a solid shaft which will transmit the same torque with the same maximum stress.

6-3. Angle of Twist.

In the design of certain types of machinery it is important to be able to calculate the angle of twist that is caused in a shaft of given length by the torque.

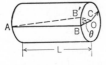

FIG. 6-8

The cylinder shown in Fig. 6-8 is part of a shaft subject to a torque which is the same for all sections. AB represents an element of the cylindrical surface of the untwisted shaft, and AB' the curve (part of a helix) which this same element assumes after the torque is applied. A horizontal radius OB on the end which rotates assumes a position OB' after the torque is applied. The angle BOB' is the angle of twist for which a value will be found.

Let this angle of twist, expressed in *radians*, be θ.

The deformation of a fiber at the surface of the shaft is shearing deformation. For the fiber represented by AB the total deformation in the length L inches is BB'. The unit deformation δ_s is BB'/L. But $BB' = c\theta$ if θ is expressed in radians. If Hooke's law holds, $\delta_s = S_s/E_s$. Hence

$$\frac{c\theta}{L} = \frac{S_s}{E_s} \quad \text{or} \quad \theta = \frac{S_s L}{E_s c} \tag{6-2}$$

which gives the angle of twist in terms of the stress in the extreme fibers. But $S_s = Tc/J$. Then

$$\theta = \frac{TcL}{E_s Jc} = \frac{TL}{E_s J} \tag{6-3}$$

As would be expected, the longer the shaft and the greater the torque, the greater will be the angle of twist. Conversely, the stiffer the material and the larger the cross-section, the smaller will be the angle of twist. For steel E_s is 12,000,000 psi.

PROBLEMS

6-10. Compute the length of a 0.36-in.-diameter steel wire that can be twisted through one revolution without exceeding a torsional stress of 20,000 psi.

6-11. A hollow shaft has a length of 72 in., an inside diameter of 2 in., and an outside diameter of 3 in.   A force of 380 lb with a moment arm of 4 ft twists the shaft through 1°.   (a) Find S_s and E_s.   (b) What torque would be required to stress a solid shaft with 3-in. diameter to the unit stress found in (a), and through what angle would this torque twist the solid shaft if 40 in. long?

Ans.   (a) $E_s = 11,800,000$ psi.

6-12. A bar of hot-rolled steel $\frac{3}{4}$ in. in diameter was tested in a torsion-testing machine.   When the applied torque was 2,690 lb-in., the angle of twist in a length of 8 in. was 3.20°.   Find the shearing modulus of elasticity of the material.

6-13. If a $\frac{3}{4}$-in.-diameter steel rod is used for the shaft in Problem 6-4, through what angle will the shaft be twisted when the 250-lb force acts on the pinion, if the length of the shaft is 50 ft 0 in.?

6-14. A bar of an aluminum alloy of 0.80 in. in diameter was tested in a torsion-testing machine.   When the applied torque was 1,183 lb-in., the angle of twist in a length of 8.00 in. was 3.21°.   Calculate the shearing modulus of elasticity.

Ans. $E_s = 4,200,000$ psi.

6-15. If in Fig. 6-7 $P_1 = 400$ lb, $P_2 = 80$ lb, $P_4 = 70$ lb, and $P_3 = 488$ lb, the distance CD is 6 ft, and the shaft is of steel with a diameter of 3.00 in., calculate the angle of twist in the shaft.   Diameters of pulleys are: $C = 26$ in., $D = 34$ in.

Ans. $\theta = 0.235°$.

6-4. Torsional Stress on Axial Planes.

In Art. 5-5 it was shown that, if a shearing unit stress of any intensity exists on a plane through some point of a stressed body, a shearing unit stress of equal intensity must exist on a perpendicular plane.   Therefore, since there is shearing stress on the cross-section of a shaft sub-jected to torsion, there must also be shearing stresses of the same intensity on all planes that contain the axis of the shaft.

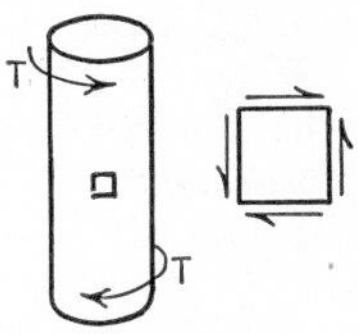

Figure 6-9 shows an enlarged view of a small particle of material taken from the surface of a twisted shaft. On the horizontal faces of this particle there are

Fig. 6-9

shearing forces acting in the directions shown.   For equilibrium of the particle it is therefore necessary that there be shearing forces on the ver-tical faces.   These forces will constitute an opposing couple.

Suppose that a shaft is thought of as being composed of a "bundle" of elements or fibers side by side.   Then, if the shaft is acted on by a torque and undergoes a shearing deformation, these elements *tend* to slide past one another.   This tendency is resisted by the longitudinal shearing stress.

There are situations favorable to the use of shafting of wood.   In such cases the torque would be limited by the allowable shearing stress in the wood along the grain even though the grain of the wood runs lengthwise of the shaft.

PROBLEMS

6-16. In an agitator where chemical action on metal parts would be injurious, a round shaft which must resist a torque of 720 lb-in. is to be made of wood. The allowable shearing stress parallel to the grain is 120 psi. Calculate the required diameter.

6-17. If in Problem 6-16 the torque is 810 lb-in. and the allowable stress is 90 psi, what diameter is necessary?   *Ans.* $D = 3.58$ in.

6-5. Horsepower, Torque, and Speed of Rotation.

If a torque turns a shaft, work is done by the torque. Power is the rate at which work is done. A common unit of power is the horsepower, the value of which is 33,000 ft-lb of work per minute. An expression will now be derived relating torque, speed of rotation, and the horsepower transmitted.

A torque of T lb-in. is equivalent to the torque exerted by a force of $T/12$ lb at a radius of 1 ft. The work done in one revolution is

$$\text{Force} \times \text{Distance} = (T/12) \times 2\pi = \pi T/6 \text{ ft-lb}$$

If the shaft turns N rpm, the work done per minute equals $\pi TN/6$ ft-lb, and the horsepower equals $\pi TN/(33,000 \times 6)$. Note that in this expression T is the torque in *pound-inches*. Hence

$$\textbf{Hp} = \frac{\pi TN}{33,000 \times 6} = \frac{TN}{\textbf{63,000}} \qquad (6\text{-}4)$$

Example. A torque of 18,000 lb-in. is transmitted by a shaft turning 220 rpm. What horsepower is being transmitted by the shaft?

Solution:

$$\text{Hp} = \frac{18,000 \times 220}{63,000} = 62.8$$

PROBLEMS

6-18. A hollow steel shaft has an outside diameter of 4 in. and an inside diameter of 1.5 in. What horsepower does it transmit if, when turning at 100 rpm, it is twisted through an angle of $1.6°$ in a length of 9 ft?

6-19. What is the diameter of a solid shaft which transmits the same horsepower at the same speed and with the same angle of twist as the shaft in Problem 6-18?

6-20. Derive an expression giving the horsepower H transmitted by a solid round shaft of diameter d when turning at N rpm with a maximum shearing stress of S_s psi.
                    Ans. $H = NS_s d^3/321,000$.

6-21. Derive a formula for the diameter D of a solid round shaft to transmit H horsepower at N rpm with a stress of S_s psi.

6-22. A steel shaft 4 in. in diameter transmits 250 hp at a speed of 250 rpm. The length between the driving and driven pulleys is 10 ft. Determine whether the following two requirements are satisfied: (*a*) maximum shearing stress not to exceed 10,000 psi; (*b*) twist of shaft not to exceed $1°$ per 30 diameters of length.

6-23. The hollow steel shafts for the 82,500-kva generators at Boulder dam have a minimum external diameter of 38 in. and an internal diameter of $7\frac{1}{2}$ in. They

transmit 115,000 hp when turning at a speed of 150 rpm. What is the maximum torsional stress developed in the shafts?

6-6. Shaft Couplings. It is often necessary to connect two pieces of shafting end to end so that they act as a single shaft. A common type of connection is known as a "flange coupling." Large-diameter shafting is sometimes forged with flanges at the ends. The flanges at the ends of two lengths of shafting are bolted together by a number of bolts arranged in a circle, as shown in Fig. 6-10.

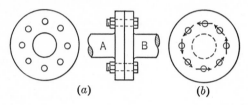

(a)   (b)

Fig. 6-10

Other common types of couplings are not forged as part of the shafts to be joined but may be attached to the ends of two pieces of plain shafting which are to be joined. Descriptions and analyses of these types of couplings may be found in textbooks on machine design.

Suppose that shaft A in Fig. 6-10 resists turning and that shaft B is turned by a motor or engine. Then it will be seen that the bolts will transmit the torque from shaft B to shaft A. The action is much like a riveted or bolted joint between plates except that the forces exerted by the bolts are in directions tangent to the bolt circle, as shown in Fig. 6-10b.

Example. A standard coupling for 5-in.-diameter shafting has six 1-in.-diameter bolts in a 6.75-in.-radius circle. Calculate the shearing stress in the bolts when the torque transmitted is 245,000 lb-in.

Solution: Let F lb be the force exerted by each bolt on one of the flanges. Then $6.75F$ is the torque exerted by each bolt. Hence

$$6 \times 6.75F = 245,000 \qquad \text{and} \qquad F = 6,050 \text{ lb}$$

Making the common assumption that the shearing stress is uniform over the cross-section of the bolt,

$$S_s = 6,050/0.785 = 7,710 \text{ psi}$$

PROBLEMS

6-24. The allowable shearing unit stress in a solid steel shaft 10 in. in diameter is 8,000 psi. (a) What horsepower can it transmit at 160 rpm? The flange couplings of this shaft have twelve $1\frac{3}{4}$-in.-diameter bolts whose centers lie on a circle 20 in. in diameter. (b) What is the shearing stress in the bolts?

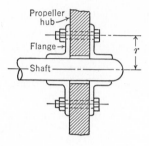

FIG. 6-11

6-25. Solve Problem 6-24 if the diameter of the shaft is 8 in., there are 12 $1\frac{1}{2}$-in. bolts, and the bolt circle has a diameter of 14.5 in. *Ans.* (*a*) 2,045 hp.

6-26. Derive a formula for d, the required diameter of bolts in a coupling, in terms of the following quantities: S_s = shearing stress in bolts and in shaft; D = diameter of shaft; K = diameter of bolt circle; N = number of bolts.

6-27. An airplane engine develops 600 hp at 1,800 rpm. The torque is transmitted to the propeller by six bolts, $\frac{5}{8}$ in. in diameter, which pass through the propeller hub, and two flanges keyed to the engine shaft, so that the bolts are in double shear (Fig. 6-11). Radius r of bolt circle = $3\frac{1}{4}$ in. Find shearing stress in bolts.

6-7. Torsion in Bars of Non-Circular Cross-Section. When a bar of non-circular cross-section is acted on by torsional forces, the section cut by a plane perpendicular to the axis of the untwisted bar does not remain a plane when the bar is subjected to torsion, but becomes a warped surface. This may be demonstrated by scribing on the surface of a square bar a straight line perpendicular to the length of the bar. When the bar is twisted,

From C. Bach

FIG. 6-12. Deformations in a rectangular torsion member.

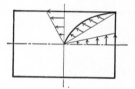

FIG. 6-13. Distribution of shearing stresses on a rectangular section.

the straight line assumes a reversed curvature (Fig. 6-12). The transverse plane section of the untwisted bar which contained this line has become a warped surface.

Figure 6-12 shows how squares marked on a bar are deformed by the twisting. Those adjacent to the edges of the bar are least deformed; those midway between the edges of the face of the bar are most deformed. Since the shearing unit stress is proportional to the shearing deformation, it is evidently greatest along the median line of the face. At the corners of the bar it is zero. If the cross-section of the bar is rectangular but not square, the unit shearing stress at the middle of the wide face is greater than at the middle of the narrow face. In other words, the greatest shearing stress occurs at the point of the surface which is nearest the axis of the bar. (See Fig. 6-13.)

The equation giving the maximum torsional stress in a bar of rectangular cross-section is very cumbersome. An empirical equation proposed by Saint Venant is $S_s = \dfrac{(15h + 9b)T}{5h^2b^2}$, where h and b are the lengths of the long and short sides of the rectangle, respectively.[1] This equation gives values which are correct within 4 per cent. For a square shaft it reduces to $S_s = 24T/5b^3$.

PROBLEMS

6-28. A valve stem with a diameter of $\frac{7}{8}$ in. has its end machined down as shown in Fig. 6-14 to receive the hand wheel. If local stresses due to the change in section are disregarded, what is the maximum torsional stress on the square cross-section when the maximum stress on the round cross-section is 5,000 psi? What is the ratio of the two stresses? *Ans.* Ratio = 2.67.

6-29. Solve Problem 6-28 if the diameter of the stem is $\frac{1}{2}$ in.

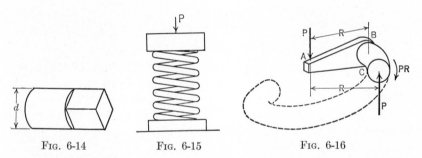

FIG. 6-14　　　　　　FIG. 6-15　　　　　　FIG. 6-16

6-8. Helical Springs. Helical springs are widely used for two purposes: for exerting forces in certain mechanisms and for their "cushioning" effect.

The stress on any cross-section of a helical spring is a shearing stress, and of this shearing stress the greater part is torsional stress. The load on such springs is nearly always axial (the resultant coinciding with the axis of the spring as a whole) as shown in Fig. 6-15.

Helical springs and other types of springs are usually made of metals having high shearing strength. High-carbon steels, alloy steels, bronzes, and brasses are commonly used. For steel springs the allowable stresses are high, frequently from 30,000 to 120,000 psi, depending on the material, size of wire, and type of service.

Figure 6-16 shows a small length of a helical spring and the axial load

[1] A. Morley, *Strength of Materials*, Longmans, Green & Company.

P on the spring. The load is here shown attached to this small length of spring by means of a lever arm AB, although generally the end of the spring itself is bent into a hook, or a plate rests against the end of the spring as in Fig. 6-15. In any case the remainder of the spring must exert on any small length, such as the one here shown, a vertical force P and a torque or couple PR. Both the force and the torque cause shearing stress.

The torsional shearing stress is Tc/J. The shearing stress due to the force P on the cross-section is P/A. The maximum shearing stress on the cross-section is therefore $S_s = P/A + Tc/J$. For springs made of wire of solid circular cross-section $J = \pi r^4/2$ and $c = r$. Since $T = PR$, the equation just above reduces to

$$S_s = (P/A)[1 + (2R/r)]$$

Example. A helical spring is made of $\frac{1}{2}$-in.-diameter steel wire bent into coils with a diameter of 2 in., center to center of wire. What load applied axially to the spring will cause a maximum shearing stress of 40,000 psi? How much will the torsional shearing stress be? The "direct" shearing stress?

Solution: For this spring $A = \pi(\frac{1}{4})^2 = \pi/16$ sq in.

$$P = \frac{A S_s}{1 + (2R/r)} = \frac{40,000\pi/16}{1 + (2 \times 1/0.25)} = 872 \text{ lb}$$

Of the 40,000 psi stress, $\frac{8}{9}$, or 35,560 psi, is due to torsion, and the remaining 4,440 psi is due to the direct shearing effect of the load.

In *this* example a considerable part of the stress is due directly to the load rather than to its torsional effect. In springs where the ratio R/r is larger, however, the direct shearing stress is often negligible in comparison with the torsional shearing stress and is disregarded.

PROBLEMS

6-30. A tension spring made of 1-in.-diameter stock has an outside diameter of 7 in. Calculate the maximum shearing unit stress caused by a tensile load of 3,500 lb applied axially to the spring.   *Ans.* $S_s = 57,900$ psi.

6-31. A handbook gives safe loads for steel springs of various dimensions. For a spring of round stock with diameter $d = 0.75$ in., coiled into a spring with an outside diameter D of 4.00 in., the safe load P is given as 2,210 lb. What unit stress does this load cause?

6-32. Solve Problem 6-31 if $d = 1.00$ in., $D = 4.50$ in., and $P = 4,280$ lb.

6-9. Deflection of Helical Springs. If in Fig. 6-16 the cut cross-section shown at C is assumed to be fixed so that it neither rotates nor moves vertically, the motion of point A will be due to the shearing deformation of the rod between B and C. Practically all this motion will be due to the torsional shearing deformation or twist of the rod and little to the direct shearing deformation caused by the stress P/A.

Therefore, disregarding the movement due to direct shear, if the length BC of the rod is twisted through an angle θ, the vertical movement of A will be $R\theta$.

For a circular shaft

$$\theta = TL/E_sJ$$

If BC is dL,

$$d\theta = PRdL/E_sJ$$

and for a spring made of a number of coils in which the total length of wire is L

$$\theta = PRL/E_sJ$$

and the axial shortening or extension is

$$\Delta = R\theta = PR^2L/E_sJ$$

It is customary to neglect the slope of the wire in calculating the length of a spring of N complete turns. If this is done,

$$L = 2\pi NR \qquad \text{and} \qquad \Delta = 2\pi PR^3N/E_sJ$$

PROBLEMS

6-33. Using the foregoing equations, find the increase in the length of a steel spring with outside diameter of 7 in., which includes seven turns of 1-in.-diameter stock, when loads of 1,500 lb are applied. What is the value of θ for this spring?

6-34. A close-coiled tension spring of eight full turns is made of steel rod, the diameter d of which is 0.75 in. The coils have an outside diameter D of 3.50 in. When the load P is 3,000 lb what is the elongation? What is the maximum shearing unit stress? *Ans.* $S_s = 56,660$ psi.

6-35. Solve Problem 6-34 if $d = 0.50$ in., $D = 2.50$ in., the number of turns $= 10$, $P = 1,000$ lb.

6-36. Solve Problem 6-34 if $d = 0.50$ in., $D = 3.00$ in., the number of turns $= 10$, $P = 1,000$ lb.

6-37. Show that the lengthening (or compression) of a helical spring due to direct as well as torsional shear is given by the equation

$$\Delta = (2\pi PRN/E_sA)[1 + 2(R/r)^2]$$

6-38. Using the equation of Problem 6-37, show what error results from disregard of the effect of direct shear in stretching the spring of Problem 6-33.

GENERAL PROBLEMS

6-39. The hollow vertical shaft connecting the turbine and electric generator in a hydroelectric plant is 16 in. in outside diameter and 9 in. in inside diameter. The speed is 120 rpm. When it transmits 10,000 hp, what is the unit stress? Calculate the diameter required for a solid shaft to transmit the same horsepower at the same speed and with the same unit stress. If the solid shaft costs 24 cents per pound and the hollow shaft costs 31 cents per pound, compare the cost per linear foot of the two shafts.   *Ans.* $D = 15.45$ in.

6-40. In Fig. 6-17 the diameters of pulleys A, B, and C are respectively 40 in., 32 in., and 32 in. The belt pulls P_1 to P_6 are, in order, 300, 3,500, 400, 2,800, 200, 1,800 lb. Length L_1 is 72 in., L_2 is 84 in. Calculate the maximum shearing unit stress and the angle of twist between A and C. The shaft is steel, diameter 4 in.

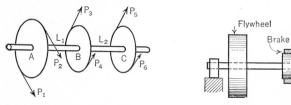

FIG. 6-17   FIG. 6-18

6-41. In Fig. 6-17 the diameters of pulley A, B, and C are, respectively, 40 in., 32 in., and 26 in. Belt pulls P_1 to P_6, in order, are 350, 3,200, 450, 3,200, 350, 1,350 lb. Calculate the necessary diameter of the shaft if the allowable shearing stress is 9,000 psi. Calculate the angle of twist between A and C. $L_1 = 60$ in., $L_2 = 96$ in. The shaft is steel.

6-42. The 4.50-in.-diameter shaft shown in Fig. 6-18 carries a flywheel which has an I of 280 ft^2-slugs and which rotates at 400 rpm. The brake is suddenly applied, stopping the flywheel in 24 revolutions, the machine having been thrown out of gear before the brake is applied. Friction in the bearings may be neglected. What is the maximum torsional stress in the shaft, and where is it found?

6-43. A torque T is applied to a round bar, both ends of which are fixed as shown in Fig. 6-19. Find, in terms of T, a, b, and the diameter d of the bar, the maximum torsional stress produced. In which length of the bar (a or b) is it found? (*Hint:* Evidently the two parts of the bar undergo the same twist.)

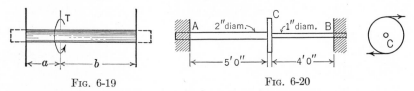

FIG. 6-19   FIG. 6-20

6-44. In Problem 6-43 derive an expression for the angle of twist, θ, in terms of T, E_s, a, b, and d.

6-45. Compare the weights of solid shafts of steel and aluminum alloy designed so that both will have the same angle of twist in a given length when transmitting the same torque. For aluminum alloy $E_s = 3,800,000$ psi.

6-46. A shaft forged of one piece and having two diameters, as shown in Fig. 6-20, is fixed against rotation at both ends. A torque of 16,000 lb-in. is applied at C. Calculate the maximum shearing stress in the 1-in.-diameter section.
                                                        Ans. $S_s = 5,910$ psi.

6-47. Torques applied to pulleys A, B, C, D, Fig. 6-21, are, respectively, 1,600 lb-ft, 4,400 lb-ft, 1,600 lb-ft, and 1,200 lb-ft in the directions shown. (*a*) Calculate the maximum torsional stress in the shaft. The diameter is 3 in. (*b*) Calculate the angle of twist between B and D if $L_2 = 60$ in. and $L_3 = 70$ in. The shaft is steel.

(c) The shaft is driven by a motor belted to pulley B. What horsepower does the motor supply when the shaft turns 100 rpm?

6-48. Torques applied to pulleys A, C, D, in Fig. 6-21, are, respectively, 1,800 lb-ft, 1,500 lb-ft, and 1,400 lb-ft. What torque applied to B will produce equilibrium? (a) Calculate the maximum torsional stress caused by these torques. The diameter of the shaft is 3.2 in. (b) Calculate the angle through which pulley D turns relative to pulley A. The shaft is steel. $L_1 = 40$ in., $L_2 = 50$ in., $L_3 = 60$ in. (c) The shaft is rotated 120 rpm by the belt on pulley B. Calculate the horsepower used by the machine driven by pulley A. $L_1 = 40$ in., $L_2 = 50$ in., $L_3 = 60$ in.

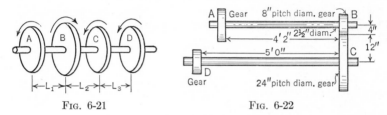

FIG. 6-21   FIG. 6-22

6-49. The gear A (Fig. 6-22) applies a torque to the shaft AB of such magnitude that the maximum shearing stress in the shaft AB is 8,000 psi, and gear D is fixed against rotation. (a) Determine the diameter of the shaft CD if the shearing stress is not to exceed 8,000 psi. (b) Calculate the angle through which gear A rotates. Both shafts are steel.

6-50. The gear A (Fig. 6-22) applies a torque of 28,000 lb-in. to the shaft AB (a) Calculate the stress in the shaft CD if its diameter is 3.00 in. (b) If gear D is held so that it does not rotate, through what angle will gear A rotate? Both shafts are steel.

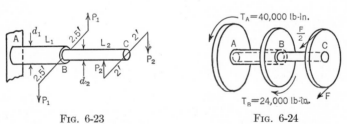

FIG. 6-23   FIG. 6-24

6-51. The steel shaft shown in Fig. 6-23 is of two diameters. Torques are applied at B and C in the directions shown. $P_1 = 300$ lb, $P_2 = 75$ lb. (a) Calculate the maximum shearing unit stress in the shaft. (b) Calculate the angle of twist between A and C. Diameter $d_1 = 3$ in., $d_2 = 2$ in. Length $L_1 = 6$ ft, $L_2 = 5$ ft.

Ans. (a) $S_s = 2,710$ psi.

6-52. Same as Problem 6-51 but $P_1 = 250$ lb and $P_2 = 50$ lb.

6-53. The steel shaft ABC shown in Fig. 6-24 is in equilibrium when subjected to the torques shown. The part AB is hollow, 3 in. in outside diameter, 2 in. in inside diameter, and 10 ft long. The part BC is solid 2 in. in diameter and 6 ft long. Calculate (a) the force F on pulley C; (b) the maximum shearing stress in the shaft; (c) the angle of twist between A and C. Diameter of pulley C is 20 in.

6-54. Figure 6-25 shows two lines of shafting which are driven at 220 rpm by a motor that delivers 20 hp. This power is taken from the shafts as follows: At A and at C, 4 hp; at B and at D, 6 hp. Each shaft is 2 in. in diameter. (*a*) What is the maximum torsional stress in either shaft, and where does it occur? (*b*) What is the maximum torsional stress between C and P? (*c*) What is the maximum torsional stress between A and B? (*d*) What is the maximum torsional stress to the left

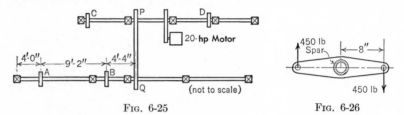

Fig. 6-25   Fig. 6-26

of Q? (*e*) Through what angle is the shaft twisted between Q and the left end of the longer shaft when running at full load? Shafting is steel.

Ans.   (*b*) $S_s = 729$ psi.

6-55. An aileron spar on a certain airplane is an alloy-steel tube 1.50 in. in outside diameter and 0.10 in. in wall thickness (Fig. 6-26). When operating, it rotates a control lever which exerts a pull on a control cable at a radius of 8.00 in. from the axis of the shaft. Calculate the torsional shearing stress in the tube when the pull on the control cable is 450 lb.

Beams—Shear and Bending Moment

7-1. Introduction.   A beam is a structural member or machine part which carries transverse loads.   Most beams are prisms with the loads perpendicular to the axis, and such beams will be considered in this chapter.   A diagrammatic representation of a beam is shown in Fig. 7-1.   The supporting forces of the beams are called "reactions" (indicated by R_L and R_R in the diagram).   The amounts of these reactions are such as to satisfy the conditions of static equilibrium, $\Sigma H = 0, \Sigma V = 0,$ and

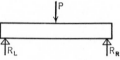

Fig. 7-1.   Simple beam.

$\Sigma M = 0$.   Most beams are horizontal members supporting vertical forces such as occur in floors and roofs.   Such structural elements may be called joists, purlins, stringers, floor beams, or girders to further describe their use.   Many machine members also are subject to transverse loads.

7-2. Types of Beams.   A *simple* beam is one which rests on two supports and carries any system of loads *between* the supports.   The beam in Fig. 7-1 is a simple beam carrying a single concentrated load.

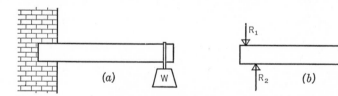

Fig. 7-2.   Cantilever beam.

A *cantilever* beam is one which projects beyond the supports and carries loads which are not between the supports.   Cantilever beams are generally represented as being built into a wall or mass of masonry at one end (Fig. 7-2a).   When they are built into a wall, the wall exerts two reactions which are distributed, but the resultants of which act like R_1 and R_2 in Fig. 7-2b.   Although this is the conventional method of

representing a cantilever beam, it should be noted that the definition
does not limit this type of beam to one built in a wall in this manner.
The reactions may be provided by a wide variety of means. The essential feature is that a cantilever beam projects beyond its support and is
loaded on the projecting part.

Beams may be combinations of simple beams and cantilevers, as
shown in Fig. 7-3. In this figure the part BC is a cantilever, and the

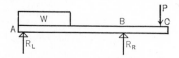

Fig. 7-3.   Overhanging beam.

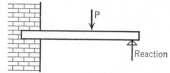

Beam fixed at one end and having a support

beam is said to "overhang the reaction." Such beams are called
over-hanging beams. Beams
may overhang at one or at
both ends. The stresses in the
part BC are the same as if it
were fixed in a wall at B, but
the stresses in the part AB are
quite different from what they
would be were there no part BC
of the beam.

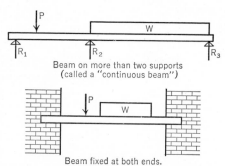

Beam on more than two supports
(called a "continuous beam")

Beam fixed at both ends.

Fig. 7-4.   Statically indeterminate beams.

The beams just described
are called *statically determinate
beams*. Those on two supports are called *statically determinate* because the
values of the reactions can be determined by the conditions of statics,
$\Sigma V = 0$, $\Sigma H = 0$, and $\Sigma M = 0$. Cantilever beams are called statically
determinate because the forces holding the beam in equilibrium, which
generally cannot be determined, are not needed in determining the
stresses due to loads on the beam.

There are also several classes of beams which are said to be *statically
indeterminate* because the reactions cannot be determined by the conditions of equilibrium alone. Among these are beams fixed at one end
and supported at the other, beams on more than two supports (called
continuous beams), and beams fixed at both ends (Fig. 7-4).

In solving problems involving indeterminate beams, the relations
needed in addition to the conditions of equilibrium are found by considering the deflections of the beam. Methods for the determination
of reactions of indeterminate beams are considered in Chapters 11
and 17.

Figure 7-5 illustrates several common ways of supporting beams. In Fig. 7-5a the connection angles are so much less stiff than the beam itself that they restrain the ends very slightly, and such a beam is ordinarily treated as a simply supported beam, with the reaction at the end of the beam

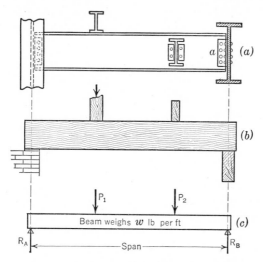

FIG. 7-5.   Distributed and concentrated loads.

7-3. Distributed and Concentrated Loads. Loads on beams are classed as *distributed* and *concentrated*. A distributed load extends over a considerable length of the beam. It is *uniformly distributed* if the load on each unit of the loaded length is the same as on every other unit. Most distributed loads are distributed uniformly or at least sufficiently nearly so to be so considered. The weight of the beam itself is evidently one of the uniformly distributed loads which the beam carries (Fig. 7-5).

A concentrated load is a load which extends over so small a part of the length of the beam that, without appreciable error in the calculated bending and shearing effects of the load, it may be assumed to act at one point on the beam. All "concentrated" loads are actually distributed over a short length of the beam, as when one beam rests on another, or when a post is supported on a beam (Fig. 7-5). In determining *bearing* stresses in a beam, the actual mode of application of the loads must of course be considered.

7-4. Determination of Reactions. Before the stresses in a beam on two supports can be found, the reactions must be known. These are found by applying the conditions of statics, $\Sigma V = 0$, $\Sigma H = 0$, and $\Sigma M = 0$. If the loads and reactions are all vertical, $\Sigma H = 0$ is not used.

Example. Calculate the reactions of the beam shown in Fig. 7-6.

Solution: Use $\Sigma M_A = 0$ (A as moment center).

$$- (300 \times 10) \times 5 - (30 \times 14) \times 7 - 1,800 \times 14 + 12R_B = 0$$
$$12R_B = 15,000 + 2,940 + 25,200 = 43,140$$
$$R_B = 3,595 \text{ lb}$$

Use $\Sigma M_B = 0$ (B as moment center).

$$(300 \times 10) \times 7 + (30 \times 14) \times 5 - 1,800 \times 2 - 12R_A = 0$$
$$12R_A = 21,000 + 2,100 - 3,600 = 19,500$$
$$R_A = 1,625 \text{ lb}$$

Use $\Sigma V = 0$ as a check (the sum of the reactions should equal the sum of the loads).

$$1,625 + 3,595 = 5,220 \text{ lb} \qquad\qquad 3,000 + 420 + 1,800 = 5,220 \text{ lb}$$

It is possible to calculate one reaction by using $\Sigma M = 0$ once, using the other reaction as a moment center, and then to determine the other reaction by using $\Sigma V = 0$. If a mistake is made in the amount of the

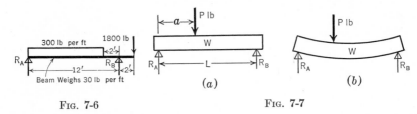

FIG. 7-6   FIG. 7-7

reaction first determined, the second one will also be wrong. It is better to proceed as in the foregoing example and calculate each reaction by means of a moment equation. The calculation may then be checked by seeing that the sum of the reactions equals the sum of the loads.

PROBLEMS

7-1. Calculate the reactions on the beam shown in Fig. 7-12a.

7-2. Calculate the reactions on the beam shown in Fig. 7-23.

7-3. Calculate the reactions on the beam shown in Fig. 7-24.

7-5. Shear and Bending Moment. Consider a simple beam carrying a load of P lb in addition to its own weight (Fig. 7-7a). This beam will be bent somewhat as shown in Fig. 7-7b. If the beam is slender, the bending may be noticeable. If it is short in comparison to the depth, the bending may not be visible but can be detected by accurate measurements.

The bending of the beam involves lengthening of the lower, convex surface and shortening of the upper, concave surface. The bottom fibers are lengthened and are stressed in tension; the top fibers are shortened and are stressed in compression. There is a surface somewhere between the top surface and the bottom surface which remains the original length, and the fibers in this surface are unstressed.   This surface is called the "neutral surface" of the beam.   The line of inter-section of the neutral surface and any vertical cross-section is called the "neutral axis" of the cross-section.   It will be shown later that this axis passes through the centroid of the cross-section.

Since the whole beam is in equilibrium, *any part of it is*.   Consider a segment of the beam to the left of any imaginary vertical plane between the load and the right reaction (Fig. 7-8). W_1 is the weight of the segment.   The forces holding this segment in equilibrium are P, W_1, R_A, and the forces (not shown in Fig. 7-8) exerted by the right segment of the beam on the left segment.   These forces are exerted by the stresses in the beam at the cross section separating the two segments.   For all the forces on the left segment $\Sigma H = 0$, $\Sigma V = 0$, and $\Sigma M = 0$.

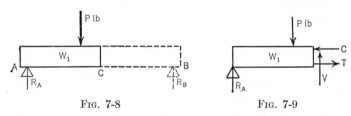

Fig. 7-8   Fig. 7-9

Since the top fibers of the beam are shortened, compressive forces are exerted by the top fibers in the right segment of the beam on the top fibers of the left segment of the beam, which is shown as a free body. Similarly tensile forces are exerted by the bottom fibers in the right segment of the beam on the bottom fibers of the left segment.   In Fig. 7-9 let the resultant of these compressive forces or stresses be C, and the resultant of the tensile stresses be T.   When $\Sigma H = 0$ is applied, it is evident that $C = T$, or the resultant of the compressive stresses equals the resultant of the tensile stresses.

When $\Sigma V = 0$ is applied, it becomes apparent that the rest of the beam must be exerting on the left segment a vertical force V such that $R_A - P - W_1 + V = 0$, or $V = P + W_1 - R_A$; that is, $V =$ the algebraic sum of the external forces on the left segment.   The algebraic sum of the external forces on the segment is called the "external shear" or simply the "shear" at the section.   The force V exerted by one segment on the other is called the *resisting shear* and is the resultant of all the *shearing stresses* on the section.

Applying $\Sigma M = 0$, with a horizontal line on the cut face of the beams as a moment axis (this line is perpendicular to the paper), it is evident that the sum of the moments of C and T must be equal in magnitude and opposite in sense to the algebraic sum of the moments of the external forces R_A, P, and W_1. The algebraic sum of the moments of all the external forces on the segment is called the *bending moment* at the section. The sum of the moments of all the tensile and compressive *stresses* is called the *resisting moment* at the section.   At any section in the beam the resisting moment and the bending moment are numerically equal.

The definitions of shear and bending moment given below should be memorized.

The shear at a section of a beam is the algebraic sum of all the external forces on one side of the section.

Shear is considered positive if the segment of the beam to the left of the section tends to move up with respect to the segment to the right (Fig. 7-10).

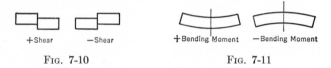

+Shear   −Shear   +Bending Moment   −Bending Moment

FIG. 7-10   FIG. 7-11

The bending moment at a section of a beam is the algebraic sum of the moments of all the external forces on one side of the section.

In calculating the bending moment at a section, each load on one side of the section is multiplied by the distance from the section to the load. The algebraic sum of these products is the bending moment at the section.

The sign commonly given to bending moment is plus if the beam is concave up (or the top fibers are in compression) at the section as shown in Fig. 7-11.   It is frequently stated that the bending moment is positive if the resultant moment of the forces on the left-hand segment is clockwise.

A simple way of arriving at the correct sign in calculating bending moment is to give the moments of upward forces plus signs and the moments of downward forces minus signs.   The algebraic sum of the moments will then have the correct sign whether the right or left segment is used.

A numerical example is given below illustrating the calculation of the shear and the bending moment at a given section of a beam.

Example.   Calculate the shear and the bending moment at a section 6 ft from the left end of the beam shown in Fig. 7-12*a*.

Solution: The reactions are first calculated and are found to be 1,900 lb and 3,100 lb as shown.   The left-hand segment is shown in (*b*).   Applying the definition of shear, $V = 1,900 - 600 = +1,300$ lb.   Applying the definition of bending moment,

$$M = +1,900 \times 6 - 600 \times 3 = 11,400 - 1,800 = +9,600 \text{ lb-ft}$$

To show that either segment may be used, V and M will be calculated using the right-hand segment shown in (c). It will be seen from Fig. 7-10, illustrating the signs for shear, that an upward force on the right segment results in minus shear. Hence

$$V = -3,100 + 3,000 + 1,400 = +1,300 \text{ lb}$$
$$M = +14 \times 3,100 - 7 \times 1,400 - 8 \times 3,000$$
$$= +43,400 - 9,800 - 24,000 = +9,600 \text{ lb-ft}$$

For the section of the beam in this problem the left-hand segment is simpler to use. It is not necessary to make sketches of the segments used as was done in this problem.

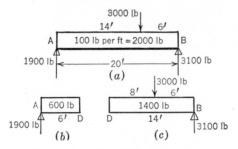

FIG. 7-12

7-6. Shear Diagrams. As will be shown later in this chapter, the maximum bending stress in a beam occurs on the cross-section where the shear is zero. Also the maximum shearing unit stress in a beam occurs at the section where the shear is a maximum. These and other con-

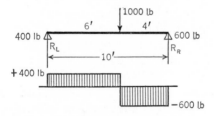

FIG. 7-13

siderations frequently make it desirable to know in what way the shear varies at successive cross-sections along the length of a beam. The most convenient means of determining and representing this variation is through a *shear diagram* (Fig. 7-13).

In a shear diagram the abscissas of successive points on the shear line represent the locations of successive cross-sections of the beam. The ordinate of each point represents the shear at that particular cross-section. It is customary to draw the shear diagram directly below a sketch of the loaded beam and to the same horizontal scale, so that the relationship of the shearing forces to the loads is immediately apparent. As an illustration of the construction of a simple shear diagram, Fig. 7-13 may be considered.   The reactions due to this load are first computed and recorded.   At any cross-section between the left-hand reaction and the load, the resultant of the forces on the left-hand segment is seen to be simply the reaction, and the left-hand segment tends to move up with respect to the right-hand segment.   Therefore, for the length of the beam from the left reaction to the load, there is a positive shear equal in amount to the left reaction.   If a section is taken immediately to the right of the load and the part of the beam to the left of this section is considered, however, it is seen that the resultant of the forces on it is the left reaction minus the load.   This continues to be the amount of the shear at every section until the right-hand reaction is reached.   Since the load is necessarily larger than the left-hand reaction, the segment on the left of the section tends to move *down* with respect to the segment

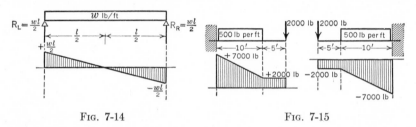

Fig. 7-14   Fig. 7-15

on the right, or the shear is *negative*.   The amount and nature of this shear can also be figured from the segment of the beam that lies to the right of any cross-section, and the same results will be secured.

The shear diagram for a uniformly distributed load on the beam is shown in Fig. 7-14.   If a section is taken any distance x ft from the left reaction, the resultant of the forces on the left-hand segment is $R_L - wx$. Since $R_L = wL/2$, the shear at any section is $wL/2 - wx$.   The amount of shear decreases uniformly with increase in x, becoming zero at the midpoint of the beam, and having its maximum negative value just to the left of the right-hand reaction, where it is $- wL/2$.   It should be noted that for the cantilever beam it is necessary to consider successive lengths measured *from the free end of the beam*, since the forces acting on the fixed end of the beam within the wall are unknown (Fig. 7-15).   It is also useful to note that (1) for all lengths of the beam where there is no distributed load, the shear line is a straight, horizontal line; (2) for all lengths of the beam where there is a distributed load of uniform intensity, the shear line is a straight inclined line, the slope of the line being proportional to the intensity of the load and being downward to the right if the load is a downward load; (3) at each concentrated load, including reactions, the shear line drops (or rises) by an amount equal to the load (or reaction).

7-7. Bending-Moment Diagrams. For determining the deflections of beams, for determining the maximum bending stresses in fixed and continuous beams, and for other purposes it is necessary to know how the bending moment varies throughout the length of the beam. Just as a shear diagram is used to show the amount of shear at any cross-section of a beam, a bending-moment diagram is used to show the amount of bending moment at any cross-section. The abscissa of any point on the diagram indicates the location of a cross-section of the beam, and the ordinate of the point is the bending moment at that section. The bending-moment diagram is drawn directly under the shear diagram.

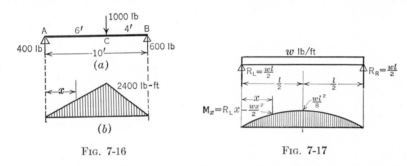

FIG. 7-16   FIG. 7-17

As an example of the construction of a bending-moment diagram, a beam with a single load is shown in Fig. 7-16a. The reactions have been computed and their values are shown. The bending-moment diagram is shown in Fig. 7-16b. The only calculation necessary in this simple case is to determine the bending moment at the load. Applying the definition given for bending moment,

$$M = +400 \times 6 = 2,400 \text{ lb-ft}$$

It will now be shown that the diagram is a straight line between A and C. At any distance x from A, $M = +400x$. Because the ordinate increases as x increases, the diagram is a straight line. The same value for the maximum bending moment could be obtained by using the segment CB.

At any section throughout the length of this beam, the moment is shown as a *positive* moment. This is in accordance with the usual convention (Fig. 7-11).

Figure 7-17 shows the bending-moment diagram for a beam carrying a uniformly distributed load of w lb per ft. For this beam the bending moment at any section distant x from the left-hand reaction is

$$R_L x - wx \cdot x/2 \quad \text{or} \quad M = R_L x - wx^2/2$$

This is the equation of a parabola with its axis vertical and its apex at the midlength of the beam.

The maximum bending moment occurs at the midpoint and is

$$M = \frac{wl}{2} \times \frac{l}{2} - \frac{wl}{2} \times \frac{l}{4} = \frac{wl^2}{8}$$

To construct a moment diagram for a more complex loading, the same procedure is followed. Compute the external reactions. Imagine the beam to be cut into two segments by a transverse plane, and compute the moments, with respect to the plane, of the forces on one segment, the moment of every upward force being considered positive, and vice versa. Plot the resultant of these moments, in pound-feet or pound-inches, as the ordinate of a point (the abscissa is the distance of the cross-section from the end of the beam). Repeat this procedure for as many points as may be necessary to permit the drawing of the curve.

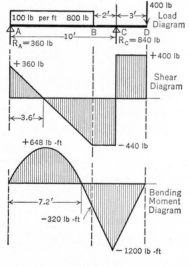

The procedure for a beam carrying both concentrated and distributed loads is outlined in the following example.

Example. Draw shear and bending-moment diagrams for the beam shown in Fig. 7-18.

Solution: The shear diagram is drawn in accordance with the procedure outlined in Art. 7-6. Just to the right of the reaction at A the shear is 360 lb. At cross-sections farther to the right of A the shear equals 360 lb minus the intervening load. Thus, at B, $V = 360 - 800 = -440$ lb and is constant at that value between B and C. The shear to the right of C equals $-440 + 840 = +400$ lb. This value equals the load at the right end, giving a check on the shear calculations. The distance to the point of zero shear is found by noting that to the right of A the shear decreases by 100 lb per ft and becomes zero at a distance $360/100 = 3.6$ ft. The location of sections where shear is zero should be indicated because, as will be shown later, maximum values of bending moment occur where the shear is zero.

After the shear diagram has been drawn, values of the bending moments at selected cross-sections of the beam are computed. In the computations as given below, the subscript after M shows the distance from the left-hand end of the beam to the

Fig. 7-18

section.   Each value of M is calculated by considering the forces either on the left-hand segment or on the right-hand segment of the beam, as may be most convenient.

$$M_0 \ = 0$$
$$M_2 \ = +360 \times 2 - 200 \times 1 \ = \ +520 \text{ lb-ft}$$
$$M_{3.6} = +360 \times 3.6 - 360 \times 1.8 = +648 \text{ lb-ft}$$
$$M_8 \ = +360 \times 8 - 800 \times 4 \ = \ -320 \text{ lb-ft}$$
$$(\text{or } M_8 \ = +840 \times 2 - 400 \times 5 \ = \ -320 \text{ lb-ft})$$
$$M_{10} = -400 \times 3 \ = \ -1{,}200 \text{ lb-ft}$$
$$M_{13} = 0$$

Generally bending moments should be calculated at each load or reaction, at points of zero shear and at the beginning and end of a distributed load.

7-8. Relations between Loads, Shears, and Bending Moments.   The drawing of shear and bending-moment diagrams is greatly facilitated by keeping certain general relations in mind to aid in the intelligent selection of cross-sections at which values are computed and to aid in drawing the curves.   These relations can be derived from the equations which express the shears and bending moments at successive points on the length of a beam.   The foregoing examples illustrate the application of these relations to specific problems.

(a) For any part of a beam where there are no loads, the shear line is a straight horizontal line and the moment line a straight sloping line.

(b) For any part of a beam where there is a uniformly distributed downward load the shear line is a straight line sloping downward to the right and the moment line is a parabolic curve which is concave downward.

(c) The numerical change in bending moment between two sections of a beam equals the area of the shear diagram between those sections, taking into account the sign of the shear.   This statement will be proved in Art. 7-12.

(d) It follows from (c) that at any point where the shear line crosses the zero line there is a maximum ordinate of the moment diagram.   (By maximum is meant that the ordinate is numerically greater than ordinates on either side of it.)

(e) It follows from (c) that the slope of the bending-moment diagram at any section equals the value of the shear at that section.

PROBLEMS

For each of the following beams, Figs. 7-19 to 7-21, draw shear and bending-moment diagrams.   (These should be drawn below a diagram of the beam showing the loading.)   Use a scale of 1 in. = 4 ft for lengths up to 20 ft, and 1 in. = 10 ft for lengths from 20 to 40 ft.   All necessary computations should appear on the sheet beside the diagrams.   Scales for shears and moments should be such as to give diagrams which will go on a single sheet with the diagram of beam.   Values should be written on diagrams at important points as in the example, and dimensions should be given to points of zero shear.

7-4. Fig. 7-19*a*.   **7-5.** Fig. 7-19*b*.   **7-6.** Fig. 7-19*c*.
7-7. Fig. 7-20*a*.   **7-8.** Fig. 7-20*b*.   **7-9.** Fig. 7-20*c*.
7-10. Fig. 7-21*a*.   **7-11.** Fig. 7-21*b*.   **7-12.** Fig. 7-21*c*.

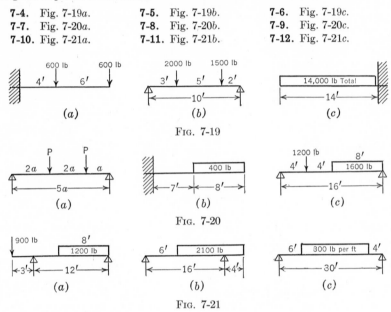

(a)   (b)   (c)

FIG. 7-19

(a)   (b)   (c)

FIG. 7-20

(a)   (b)   (c)

FIG. 7-21

7-9. Shear and Bending-Moment Diagrams by Summation.

Values of shears necessary for drawing a shear diagram may be found by starting at the left end and adding algebraically each load to the shear already calculated to the left of the load. This operation may be tabulated as shown in the example at the end of this article.

Often the principle that the change in the bending moment between two points along the length of a beam is equal to the area of the shear diagram between those points can be advantageously used in drawing moment diagrams. After the shear diagram has been drawn significant values of the bending moment at the successive points are found by cumulatively totaling the areas under the shear line, from left to right. These calculations may also be conveniently tabulated as shown in the example below.

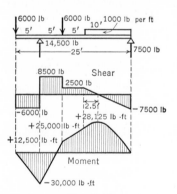

FIG. 7-22

Example. Draw the shear diagram and the bending-moment diagram for the beam shown in Fig. 7-22.

Solution: The reactions are first calculated and the values written in the proper places. As shown below, the shears are computed by successive algebraic additions in the left column. The fact that the final value equals the right reaction is a check on the arithmetic. To the right of the shear calculations the bending moments are found by adding algebraically the successive areas starting at the left end.

SHEARS		BENDING MOMENTS		
V_{0-5}	−6,000 lb	M_5	= −6,000 × 5	= −30,000
	+14,500		+8,500 × 5	= +42,500
V_{5-10}	+8,500	M_{10}	=	+12,500
	−6,000		+2,500 × 5	= +12,500
V_{10-15}	+ 2,500	M_{15}	=	+25,000
	−10,000		+2,500 × 1.25 =	+3,125
V_{25}	−7,500	$M_{17.5}$	=	+28,125
			−7,500 × 3.75 =	−28,125
		M_{25}	=	00,000

Since, in the method used, each moment value was based on the preceding moment value, the correct value secured at the right end of the beam checks the intermediate computed values.

In drawing a moment diagram by summing up the areas under the shear curve, it is to be noted that, following the convention in regard to the algebraic signs of shears and bending moments, the shear areas should be summed up *from left to right.* The bending-moment diagram can be started at the right and carried through to the left end of the beam, but then the sign of each shear area must be reversed.

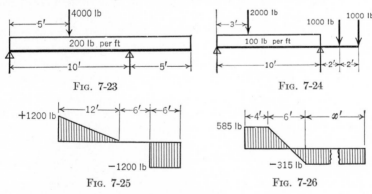

FIG. 7-23   FIG. 7-24

FIG. 7-25   FIG. 7-26

PROBLEMS

Calculate shears and bending moments and draw V and M diagrams approximately to scale.

7-13. Fig. 7-23.

7-14. Fig. 7-24.

7-15. Figure 7-25 shows a shear diagram for a beam on two supports. Draw (*a*) the beam with loads and (*b*) the bending-moment diagram.

7-16. The shear diagram shown in Fig. 7-26 is that of a beam on two supports without overhang. Determine the length x, and draw (a) the beam with its load and (b) the bending-moment diagram.

7-10. Dangerous Section.

In most beams the bending stress is the most serious stress, and this is a maximum at the cross-section of the beam where the greatest bending moment occurs, which, in turn, is at a section of the beam where the shear is (or passes through) zero. Hence sections of zero shear are called *dangerous sections*. Frequently in the design or investigation of a beam it is not necessary to determine any stresses except the maximum bending stress. This requires the determination of the moment at the dangerous section, which necessitates finding where the dangerous section occurs. Where a beam carries large concentrated loads, the shear will generally change sign under one of these loads, and finding the dangerous section in such a case merely requires that the shear on both sides of each load be determined to ascertain at which load the shear changes sign. Where a beam carries both concentrated and distributed loads, it is possible that the dangerous section will occur at some point where there is no concentrated load. The approximate location of such a point may be observed from the shear diagram. Its exact location should not be scaled but should be calculated from the forces on the beam.

7-11. Inflection Points.

An overhanging beam may be concave down throughout part or parts of its length and concave up throughout the remainder, as in Fig. 7-18. In such a beam the points where the curvature reverses are called *inflection points*. They are points of zero bending moment, since they are points where the beam is not bent. They can be located by setting up an expression for the bending moment and equating it to zero.

Example. In the beam of Fig. 7-18, find the distance from the left reaction to point of zero bending moment.

Solution: The bending moment x ft from R_A (if x is not more than 8) may be expressed by this equation

$$M = 360x - 100x^2/2$$

Equating this to zero,

$$(-100x^2/2) + 360x = 0$$

Dividing by $-50x$,

$$x - 7.2 = 0 \quad \text{or} \quad x = 7.2 \text{ ft}$$

If the value of x found by solving this equation had been more than 8, it would not have been the correct distance to the point of zero moment, as the equation written is true only for values of x from zero to 8.

If the shear diagram has been drawn, the inflection point may often be very easily found simply by noting the point for which the positive and negative shear areas on the segment on either side balance.   Thus in Fig. 7-18 the shear diagram shows immediately that the inflection point is at $2 \times 3.6 = 7.2$ ft from the left end of the beam.   Both these methods of finding inflection points should be understood.

PROBLEMS

7-17. A square steel bar 30 ft long and weighing 4 lb per ft rests on two supports 18 ft apart.   The left-hand support is 8 ft from the left end of the bar.   Draw shear and bending-moment diagrams and calculate distances from the left end to the inflection points.   *Ans.* $x_1 = 11.8$ ft.

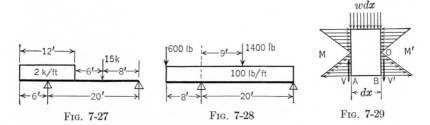

FIG. 7-27   FIG. 7-28   FIG. 7-29

7-18. Same as Problem 7-17 but change 8 ft to 9 ft.

7-19. Draw shear and bending-moment diagrams approximately to scale and locate inflection point in the beam of Fig. 7-27.

7-20. Same as Problem 7-19 but for beam of Fig. 7-28.

7-12. Relation between Shear and Bending Moment.   Consider a segment of a beam between two planes, the distance between which is dx, as shown in Fig. 7-29.   This segment is a body in equilibrium, the forces acting on it being the tensile and compressive forces on the two faces (which constitute the two resisting moments M and M'), the two shearing forces V and V', and a small part of the distributed load, which also includes the weight of the segment.   If the distributed load is w lb per unit of length, the load on this segment is $w\,dx$.   If the moments of these forces are taken with respect to the neutral axis of the right-hand face of the segment and the sum is placed equal to zero,

$$M' - M - V\,dx + w\,dx \times dx/2 = 0$$

Neglecting the term containing the square of dx and noting that $M' - M = dM$,

$$dM = V\,dx \qquad \text{or} \qquad \frac{dM}{dx} = V$$

In the equation $dM = V\,dx$ note that $V\,dx$ is the area of the part of the shear diagram corresponding to the length dx. In a finite length of any beam the change in bending moment is ΣdM, which equals $\Sigma V\ dx$. But $\Sigma V\ dx$ corresponding to a given length of the beam is the area of that part of the shear diagram. Consequently the change in bending moment between any two points in a beam is equal to the area of the shear diagram between those points.

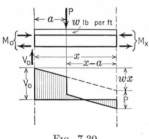

FIG. 7-30

7-13. The General Moment Equation.

Let Fig. 7-30 represent a portion of a beam between two sections x ft apart. Let the bending moments be M_0 and M_x on the left and right ends, respectively, and let the shear at the left end be V_0.

Let the resultant of any system of concentrated loads on the segment be a force P acting at a distance a ft from the left end. Let there be a uniformly distributed load of w lb per ft extending throughout the segment. Then, since the segment is a body in equilibrium, the sum of all the moments about any point on the right-hand end of the segment is equal to zero, or

$$M_0 + V_0 x - P(x - a) - wx(x/2) - M_x = 0$$

This may be written

$$M_x = M_0 + V_0 x - P(x - a) - wx^2/2$$

This is the equation for the bending moment at the right end of the segment shown. Stated in a general way, for any loading on the segment, the equation becomes

$$M_x = M_0 + V_0 x \pm \text{Moments of any forces on the segment}$$

This is called the *general moment equation*. It is applicable to any segment of any beam. When the loads on a beam or segment and the shear and moment at one end are known, the moment at the other end can be found by this equation. When writing the moments of forces on the segment, the moments of upward forces are given plus signs and moments of downward forces minus signs.

PROBLEM

7-21. The shear and bending moment at the left-hand end of a 10-ft segment of a beam are $+1,600$ lb and $+5,200$ lb-ft, respectively. A uniform load of 900 lb per ft extends for 4 ft from the left end of the segment, and 8 ft from the left end there is an upward reaction of 3,600 lb. Calculate the shear and moment at the right end of the segment.   *Ans.* $M_{10} = -400$ lb-ft.

GENERAL PROBLEMS

7-22. (*a*) Calculate the maximum bending moment in a simple beam L ft long carrying a load of P lb at the center.   (*b*) Calculate the maximum bending moment in a simple beam L ft long carrying a uniformly distributed load of w lb per ft.   What does this M equal if the total weight of the distributed load is W lb?

Ans. (*b*) $M = WL/8$.

7-23. Draw, approximately to scale, shear and bending-moment diagrams for the beam shown in Fig. 7-31.   Write shear and moment values on diagrams at significant points. $W_1 = 8$ k, $W_2 = 10$ k, $W_3 = 12$ k.

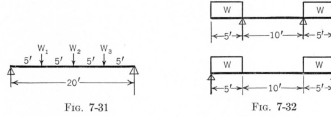

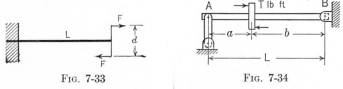

FIG. 7-31   FIG. 7-32

7-24. Draw, approximately to scale, shear and bending-moment diagrams for each of the beams shown in Fig. 7-32.   Write shear and moment values on the diagrams at significant points.

7-25. Draw shear and bending-moment diagrams for the beam shown in Fig. 7-33.

7-26. In Fig. 7-33, $L = 12$ ft, $F = 200$ lb, $d = 3$ ft.   Draw shear and bending-moment diagrams.

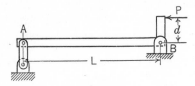

FIG. 7-33   FIG. 7-34

7-27. At a point in a beam a distance of a ft from one end a moment of T lb-ft is applied as shown in Fig. 7-34.   Draw the shear and bending-moment diagrams.

7-28. The beam in Fig. 7-34 is 16 ft long and is supported as shown.   A moment or couple T is applied by two horizontal forces of 600 lb each, 2 ft apart.   The distance a is 5 ft.   Draw shear and bending-moment diagrams.

FIG. 7-35

7-29. The beam AB (Fig. 7-35) is supported at A and B as shown.   Determine the reactions and draw shear and bending-moment diagrams.

7-30. In Fig. 7-35, $L = 12$ ft, $d = 2$ ft, and $P = 900$ lb.   Calculate the reactions, and draw shear and bending-moment diagrams.

7-31. The beam shown in Fig. 7-36 is supported at the ends. It carries no loads but has moments or couples applied to the ends. Assume M_A to be greater than M_B. Draw shear and bending-moment diagrams.

7-32. In Fig. 7-36, $M_A = 1,200$ lb-ft, $M_B = 1,800$ lb-ft, and the length AB is 12 ft. Draw shear and bending-moment diagrams.

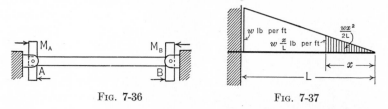

FIG. 7-36   FIG. 7-37

7-33. Triangular loading frequently occurs on beams in airplane frames. A cantilever beam (Fig. 7-37) carries a triangular load varying from an intensity of w lb per ft at the fixed end to 0 lb per ft at the free end. Draw shear and bending-moment diagrams. Note that the total load $W = wL/2$, and that the amount of load in a distance x from the free end equals $Wx^2/L^2 = wx^2/2L$.

Ans. Max $M. = wL^2/6$.

7-34. The loading described in Problem 7-33 is carried by a beam supported at the ends. Draw the shear and bending-moment diagrams locating the point of zero shear. Note the comments in Problem 7-33.

7-35. A beam is supported at the ends, the supports being 24 ft center to center. The beam carries a triangular load over 18 ft nearer the left end. The total load is 3,600 lb, and the heavy end of the load is at the left. Draw shear and bending-moment diagrams. See Problem 7-33 for a hint regarding this loading.

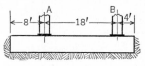

FIG. 7-38

7-36. A concrete footing supports two columns as shown in Fig. 7-38. Load on column A is 55 tons and on column B is 35 tons. Assume that the soil pressure against the under surface is uniform. Draw shear and bending-moment diagrams for the footing, and locate inflection points.

7-37. A wooden beam 12 in. square and 20 ft long floats in water, and a man weighing 200 lb stands on the beam at the midpoint. Assuming the wood to weigh 40 lb per cu ft, draw shear and bending-moment diagrams.

7-38. Pipe lines are put together on the ground beside the trench by welding several segments into a long piece. This piece is then rolled over the trench on two supports symmetrically placed and is placed in the trench by lowering the supports. Taking the length of pipe as L ft and its weight w lb per ft, where should the supports be located to keep the bending moment a minimum? *Hint:* the greatest bending moment will have its least value when the bending-moment at the midpoint is numerically equal to the bending moments at the supports. Why?

8

Stresses in Beams

8-1. Introduction. For the design or investigation of a beam it is necessary to calculate the actual unit stresses (tensile, compressive, and shearing) which occur at certain cross-sections. The greatest unit stress that occurs must not exceed the allowable stress for the material used. For this reason a formula expressing a relation between the bending moment at a given section of a beam, the size and shape of the cross-section, and the maximum tensile or compressive stress is used and will now be derived.[1] Afterwards a formula relating shearing unit stress to the shear on a cross-section will be derived.

8-2. Bending Unit Stress: The Flexure Formula. It was pointed out in Chapter 7 that, as a beam supported at the ends is bent by applied downward loads, the top surface of the beam shortens, the bottom surface lengthens, and in between there is a surface called the neutral surface that is unchanged in length. The shortened fibers are subject to compressive stress, and the lengthened fibers are subject to tensile stress. How these stresses vary and how they are related to the bending moment will now be determined.

Consider a "slice" of the beam between two cross-sections AB and CD, say L in. apart, before the beam was loaded, as shown in Fig. 8-1a. After bending has occurred the length L is unchanged at the neutral surface. In deriving the flexure formula it is assumed that the shortening or lengthening of any fiber extending from one plane to the other is proportional to the distance of the fiber from the neutral surface. This is certainly true if the two planes are still planes after the beam is bent, as may be seen by referring to Fig. 8-1b, where the two planes AB and CD originally parallel and L in. apart are shown as converging planes.

---

[1] In 1638 Galileo published a treatise which contained a number of propositions relating to the behavior and strength of beams. His conclusions were erroneous, but his investigations interested other workers. The problem of the distribution of stress in beams was attacked by many investigators and completely solved for all ordinary cases by the French engineer Navier about 1820. See H. F. Moore, "The History of the Flexure Formula," *Journal of Engineering Education*, Vol. XXI, No. 2 (October, 1930), p. 156.

If a third plane $C'D'$, parallel to AB, is now passed through the intersection of CD and the neutral surface, the distance between AB and $C'D'$ will be the original length of all fibers of the beam between the planes AB and CD in the unbent beam.   It will be seen that the change in length of any fiber is proportional to the distance of the fiber from the neutral surface.   *If the unit stress in no fiber exceeds the proportional limit*, it follows from Hooke's law that the unit stress in any fiber at a given section of the bent beam is proportional to the distance from the neutral axis to that fiber.

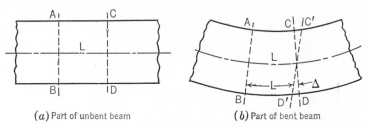

(*a*) Part of unbent beam   (*b*) Part of bent beam

FIG. 8-1

Let $ABCD$ (Fig. 8-2) be any cross-section of a prismatic beam.   One segment of the beam is shown in isometric.   The shaded strip dA is an elementary part of the cross-section, its distance from the neutral axis being y.   This strip represents any elementary area either above or below the neutral axis (y may have any value from $-c'$ to $+c$).

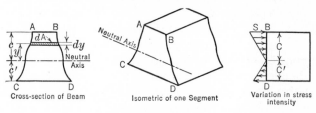

Cross-section of Beam   Isometric of one Segment   Variation in stress intensity

FIG. 8-2

Let S be the unit stress in the fibers farthest from the neutral axis (this will be the maximum unit stress), and let c be the distance to these fibers.   Since the unit stress on any fiber is proportional to the distance of that fiber from the neutral axis, the unit stress on dA is Sy/c.

The force exerted on dA equals the unit stress multiplied by the area, or force on $dA = (y/c)S\,dA$.   The moment of this force on dA about the neutral axis as the axis of moments equals

$$ y \times \frac{y}{c} S\,dA = \frac{S}{c} y^2\,dA $$

The sum of the moments of all the forces on all the elementary areas composing the cross-section is found by integrating and is, of course, the resisting moment M_R at this cross-section.

$$M_R = \frac{S}{c} \int_{-c'}^{+c} y^2 \, dA$$

More than a century ago the value of $\int y^2 \, dA$ for a given area was named "moment of inertia" of the area and was represented by the symbol I. The resisting moment M_R equals the bending moment M. Making these substitutions and solving for S, the following "flexure formula" results:

$$S = \frac{Mc}{I} \tag{8-1}$$

In this formula I is commonly expressed in inches^4, S in pounds per square inch, c in inches, and M in pound-inches.

The tensile stresses and compressive stresses that occur in a beam as a result of the bending moment are often spoken of as "bending stresses" or "flexural stresses." They are sometimes called "fiber stresses."

In the foregoing formula I and c are concerned with the size and shape of the cross-section of the beam regardless of the material of the beam and type of loading. A discussion of moment of inertia of areas is given in Appendix B and should be studied if the meaning of the term and the method of determining this value for a given area are not understood. The quantity I/c for a given cross-section is called the *section modulus of the cross-section*. The relationship expressed by the flexure formula may be stated as follows:

$$\text{Maximum stress on a cross-section} = \frac{\text{Bending moment}}{\text{Section modulus}}$$

The symbol Z is often used for section modulus. Using this notation,

$$S = M/Z$$

The values of I and I/c for the rolled-steel beams and other shapes used in structural work are given in handbooks such as *Steel Construction* published by the American Institute of Steel Construction. Some of this material is given in Tables II to VI inclusive in Appendix C of this book.

8-3. Position of Neutral Axis. It was stated in Art. 7-5 that the neutral axis of any cross-section of a beam passes through the centroid of the cross-section. Its location is fixed by the fact that the sum or resultant of the tensile stresses equals the sum of the compressive stresses. In other words the total horizontal force on the end of any segment of a bent beam equals zero. The unit stress on any elementary area of a cross-section y in. from the neutral axis of the cross-section is $(S/c)y$, and the force exerted by the stress on this elementary area is $(S/c)y\,dA$. The total horizontal force on the cross-section is then

$$\frac{S}{c}\int_{-c'}^{+c} y\,dA = 0.$$ In a bent beam, however, S/c does not equal zero;

hence $\int_{-c'}^{+c} y\,dA = 0.$ But $\int_{-c'}^{+c} y\,dA = \bar{y}A$, where $\bar{y}$ is the distance from the neutral axis to the centroid of the cross-section. Since $\bar{y}A = 0$, and since A does not equal zero, $\bar{y} = 0$, which shows that the neutral axis is a centroidal axis of the cross-section.

8-4. Use of the Flexure Formula. The flexure formula is the basis for all beam design. The following examples and their solutions are given to illustrate the uses of the formula.

Example 1. A wooden beam 3 in. wide, 6 in. deep, and 10 ft long rests on supports at the ends. It carries loads which cause a maximum bending moment of 2,500 lb-ft. Calculate the maximum bending stress.

Solution: The bending moment must be in pound-inches for use in the formula, since all other quantities are in inch units. The moment of inertia of the rectangle is $bh^3/12 = 3 \times 6^3/12 = 54$ in.[4] The distance c is 3 in. Substituting these quantities, $S = Mc/I = 2,500 \times 12 \times 3/54 = 1,665$ psi.

Alternative Solution: For solid rectangular cross-sections an expression for I/c may be found as follows: $I/c = \dfrac{bh^3}{12}\bigg/\dfrac{h}{2} = \dfrac{bh^2}{6}\cdot$ This is a convenient expression to use in dealing with wooden beams, cross-sections of which are generally solid rectangles. For the beam in this problem $I/c = 3 \times 6^2/6 = 18$ and $S = 2,500 \times 12/18 = 1,665$ psi.

Example 2. A steel beam in a machine is to be circular in cross-section. The maximum bending moment is 7,200 lb-in. What diameter is necessary if the allowable stress is 8,000 psi?

Solution: The flexure formula may be written

$$I/c = M/S$$

For a circle the moment of inertia with respect to a diameter is $I = \pi r^4/4$ and $c = r$. Hence for a circle $I/c = \pi r^3/4$. Hence

$$\frac{\pi r^3}{4} = \frac{7,200}{8,000} = 0.90$$

$$r^3 = 1.145 \quad\text{and}\quad r = 1.046 \text{ in.}$$

and

$$D = 2.09 \text{ in.}$$

Example 3. Many steel beams are used which are built up of two or more rolled shapes. The cross-section of a built-up beam is shown in Fig. 8-3. This beam is made by attaching (welding or riveting) a steel plate 10 in. wide and $\frac{1}{2}$ in. thick to the top flange of a 12-in. 35-lb-per-ft American standard I-beam. (a) Calculate the allowable bending moment for this beam if the allowable stress is 18,000 psi. See Table II, Appendix C, for necessary data concerning the I-beam. (b) Calculate the allowable bending moment for the 12-in. 35-lb I-beam without the top plate.

FIG. 8-3

Solution: (a) The distance from the lower edge of the cross-section to the neutral axis is found by

$$\bar{y} = \frac{A_1 y_1 + A_2 y_2}{A_1 + A_2} = \frac{10.20 \times 6 + 5 \times 12.25}{10.20 + 5} = \frac{61.2 + 61.2}{15.2} = 8.05 \text{ in.}$$

It is necessary to calculate the moment of inertia of the cross-section with respect to the neutral axis. For the cross-section of the beam Table II gives the I with respect to its centroidal axis as 227 in.^{4} For the cross-section of plate I is $bh^3/12$ with respect to its centroidal axis. To each of these values must be added Ad^2 to give I with respect to the neutral axis of the entire cross-section.

$$
\begin{aligned}
I \text{ of beam} &= 227 \text{ in.}^4 \\
Ad^2 = 10.20 \times 2.05^2 &= 43 \\
I \text{ of plate} = 10 \times 0.5^3/12 &= 0 \\
Ad^2 = 5 \times 4.20^2 &= 88 \\
\hline
I &= 358 \text{ in.}^4
\end{aligned}
$$

To calculate the allowable bending moment the flexure formula is $M = SI/c$. There are two values for c. The distance to the extreme top of the cross-section is 4.45 in. and to the bottom of the cross-section is 8.05 in. The value of M computed by using $c = 4.45$ in. is the M that would cause a stress of 18,000 psi at the top surface, but, since the stress is proportional to the distance from the neutral axis, the stress at the bottom would be much more than 18,000 psi which is not allowable. Consequently the allowable value for the bending moment is

$$M = 18,000 \times 358/8.05 = 800,000 \text{ lb-in.}$$

Note that for any value of bending moment applied to this beam the resulting tensile stress is greater than the resulting compressive stress because the most stressed tensile fibers are farther from the neutral axis than the most stressed compressive fibers. For this cross-section the section modulus I/c has two values.

(b) In Table II the value of I/c for this beam is found to be 37.8 in. The allowable bending moment for the beam without the plate is therefore

$$M = SI/c = 18,000 \times 37.8 = 680,000 \text{ lb-in.}$$

PROBLEMS

8-1. What bending moment is permissible for a wooden beam 4 in. wide and 10 in. deep, if the allowable stress for this wood is 1,600 psi?

8-2. At a certain point on a beam the bending moment is 14,000 lb-in. The cross-section of the beam is 4×6 in. (6-in. sides vertical). What is the maximum bending stress? What is the stress 1 in. below the top surface?

8-3. What stress will result if the beam in Problem 8-2 is "laid flat" (4-in. dimension vertical)?

8-4. Compute the necessary dimensions for a wooden beam of square cross-section to carry a maximum bending moment of 92,000 lb-in., the allowable stress being 1,600 psi.   What would be a suitable commercial-size beam?

$Ans.$ $b = 7.02$ in.

8-5. Compute the size required for a steel beam of square cross-section to carry the same bending moment as in Problem 8-4, the allowable stress being 18,000 psi.

8-6. Solve Problem 8-4, making the depth of the beam twice the width.

8-7. A load W is to be carried by a piece of 3-in. standard steel pipe (AB, Fig. 8-4) supported by hangers at the ends.   Calculate the allowable value of W if the allowable stress is 12,000 psi.

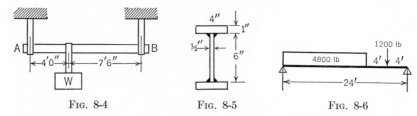

FIG. 8-4   FIG. 8-5   FIG. 8-6

8-8. A welded beam 11 ft long is made of a $6 \times \frac{1}{2}$ in. web plate and two 4×1 in. flange plates.   The cross-section is shown in Fig. 8-5.   The end supports are 10 ft center to center.   What load, uniformly distributed over 10 ft, can the beam carry if the allowable bending stress is 16,000 psi?   Neglect the weight of the beam.

$Ans.$ $W = 28,700$ lb.

8-9. Solve Problem 8-8 if the lower plate is omitted so that the beam is a T-beam.

8-10. What is the longest 1-in.-square bar of steel that can be supported at its midpoint without being stressed above 30,000 psi if (a) sides of the bar are vertical; (b) diagonals of cross-sections are vertical?

8-11. Calculate the maximum bending stress caused by the loads shown in Fig. 8-6 if (a) the beam is a wooden beam $9\frac{1}{2}$ in. square; (b) the beam is 6.5 in. wide and 11.5 in. deep.   What percentage of the weight of the first beam is the weight of the second beam?

$Ans.$ (a) $S = 1,620$ psi.

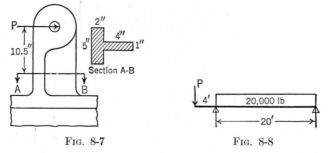

FIG. 8-7   FIG. 8-8

8-12. The short cantilever beam made of cast iron shown in Fig. 8-7 occurs in a large machine.   Calculate the maximum tensile stress and the maximum compressive stress in section A–B if the load P is 9,000 lb.

8-13. The beam shown in Fig. 8-8 is a 10-in. 25.4-lb American standard steel I-beam.   The load P is 7,000 lb.   Calculate the maximum bending stress.   (See table in Appendix C for value of I/c).

$Ans.$ $S = 18,200$ psi.

8-14. The load P in Fig. 8-8 is 4,000 lb. These loads are to be carried by one or more wooden beams 11.5 in. deep. What width is necessary if the allowable stress is 1,600 psi?

8-15. The cross-section of a cast-iron beam is shown in Fig. 8-9. The beam rests on supports 3 ft apart. It overhangs 1 ft at each end and carries two equal downward end loads. Calculate the allowable value of each load if allowable stresses are tension 3,000 psi, compression 16,000 psi, as given in the New York City Building Code.

8-16. The cross-section of a simple beam is a triangle. The base is 6 in. and the altitude 6 in. The beam rests on supports at the ends with the apex up. The maximum bending moment is 64,000 lb-in. What is the maximum compressive stress? Tensile stress?   *Ans.* $S_c = 7,110$ psi.

8-17. A T-shaped steel beam 7 in. deep is subjected to bending. Measurements of deformations are made with two extensometers. In a gage length of 8 in. the top fibers shorten 0.0032 in., and the fibers $\frac{1}{2}$ in. above the bottom lengthen 0.0039 in. (*a*) Calculate the distance from the top of the beam to the neutral axis. (*b*) Calculate the stresses at the top and bottom of the beam.

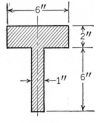

Fig. 8-9

8-5. The Flexure Formula: Assumptions and Limitations. The flexure formula as derived and commonly used is a satisfactory design tool. There are, however, certain limitations to its use. Stresses computed by the formula may in some cases differ more or less from the stresses that really occur in the beam.

The common flexure formula will not give exact values of the bending stresses unless the beam and loading conform to the following conditions:

(*a*) The material of the beam obeys Hooke's law, and the stresses do not exceed the proportional limit. In deriving the formula straight-line stress variation was assumed. However, the formula is often used without serious error for beams of material such as cast iron that do not exactly follow Hooke's law. Beams of materials not following Hooke's law are discussed in Chapter 19.

(*b*) The beam is straight before loading. Curved beams are considered in Chapter 19.

(*c*) The cross-section of the beam has a vertical axis of symmetry, and the resultant of each load lies in the vertical plane containing the axes of symmetry of all cross-sections and is perpendicular to the geometrical axis of the beam. Beams not conforming to these conditions are discussed in Chapters 12 and 19.

(*d*) The beam has sufficient lateral or transverse width relative to its length to prevent "buckling," or is supported transversely so that it does not buckle. No part of the beam is so thin that local wrinkling or buckling occurs as the result of the forces developed. Beams not conforming to these conditions are discussed in Chapter 19.

(e) The longitudinal or "fiber" strains are not affected by the shearing strains which are also present.   They will not be affected by shearing strains in any length of the beam where the shear is constant.   They may be materially affected in a length of beam where the shear is rapidly changing.[2]   This situation exists in short beams subjected to heavy distributed loads, and under certain other conditions.

(f) The material of which the beam is made has the same modulus of elasticity in tension and compression.   Exceptions to this condition are discussed in Chapter 19.

The majority of beams are straight, have cross-sections with vertical axes of symmetry, and have the loads applied substantially in the plane of these axes; most beams have loadings or dimensions such that shear strains do not greatly affect "fiber" strains and have cross-sections such that local buckling cannot occur.   Therefore the flexure formula applies quite satisfactorily to the determination of bending stresses in most beams.   Bending stresses are usually the most important stresses in a beam, although under some conditions shearing stresses or normal stresses on other sections than cross-sections must be considered and may be more significant than bending stresses.   Such stresses will be discussed in later chapters.

SHEARING STRESSES

8-6. Shearing Unit Stresses in Beams.   Articles in Chapter 7 dealt with the determination of the total shearing force on any cross-section of a loaded beam.   The natural assumption might be that this shearing force is uniformly distributed over the cross-section, with a resulting shearing unit stress at any point of the cross-section equal to V/A. This is not true, however, as will now be shown.   The shearing unit stress is zero at those points on the cross-section where the bending stress is a maximum and increases to a maximum value which nearly always occurs at the neutral axis.   For example, in a beam of rectangular cross-section the maximum shearing unit stress at the neutral axis is $1\frac{1}{2}$ times the average stress V/A.

Derivation of the formula for shearing unit stress on a cross-section of a beam involves use of the principle proved in Art. 5-5, that, if a shearing unit stress of any intensity exists on any plane through a point in a stressed body, there is also a shearing unit stress of equal intensity at the same point on a plane at right angles to the first.   The intensity of the vertical shearing unit stress at any point in a beam is most easily determined by finding the shearing unit stress on a horizontal plane

[2] See Maurer and Withey, *Strength of Materials*, 2nd ed., John Wiley & Sons, p. 146.

through the point in question.   Then, by the principle just stated, this horizontal shearing unit stress equals the desired vertical shearing unit stress.[3]

The existence of *horizontal or longitudinal* shear in beams is well demonstrated by the following illustration.   If planks are piled up as shown in Fig. 8-10a, placed on supports at the ends, and loaded with weights between the supports, they will bend as shown in Fig. 8-10b. Consider the upper two planks.   In each of these the top "fibers" are shortened and the bottom fibers lengthened.   This deformation evidently results in a sliding of the top plank over the one beneath it, as is shown by the fact that the originally straight line representing the ends of the planks has become broken.   Now consider a beam (Fig. 8-10c) made of a solid

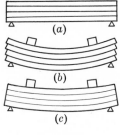

FIG. 8-10

piece of wood with dimensions the same as the four planks together in Fig. 8-10a.   This beam will deflect under the load, though the deflection will be much less than that of the four separate planks. The sliding that occurred between the lower surface of the top plank and the upper surface of the next plank is prevented by longitudinal shearing stresses in the wooden beam.

8-7. Formula for Shearing Stress in a Beam.   Let it be required to determine the shearing unit stress on the cross-section B at a point V_1 in. above the neutral axis in the loaded beam shown in Fig. 8-11a.   The answer to this problem will be a formula for shearing stress at any given point of any given section of a beam.

The body in equilibrium chosen in solving this problem is a block indicated between plane B and a parallel plane A distant dx from B.   The under surface of the block is V_1 in. above the neutral axis. The end view of this block is shown in (d) with forces acting on it.

On the face of this block, in plane A, there is a set of forces (shown as compressive forces) which are the stresses exerted on the block by the part of the beam adjoining it.   These compressive stresses increase in intensity as the distance from the neutral axis increases.   On the face of the block which lies in plane B there is also a set of forces which vary in a like manner with the distance from the neutral axis.

Because the bending moment M_B at plane B of the beam is greater

---

[3] The horizontal shearing unit stress is practically always as important as the vertical shearing unit stress, since the two are of equal intensity.   And in wooden beams, which offer less resistance to shearing forces parallel to the grain, the horizontal (longitudinal) shear is much more important.

than the bending moment M_A at the plane A, the forces on face B of the block will be greater than those on face A. Since this block is in equilibrium, the sum of the horizontal forces acting on it equals zero. Consequently there must be a force acting on the block to the right in addition to these compressive forces. This force is the shearing force on the under surface of the block and is equal to the horizontal shearing unit stress multiplied by the area of the lower surface of the block. It is this shearing unit stress that is to be determined.

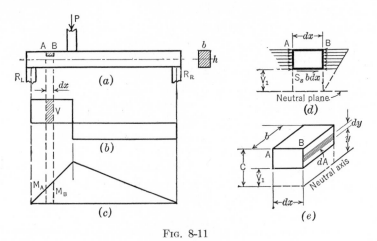

FIG. 8-11

Figure 8-11e is a perspective view of this block. Consider a rectangular area dA parallel to the neutral axis in the face B of this block and having dimensions of b and dy. The compressive unit stress on this area $= M_By/I$, and the force on the area is $(M_By/I)\,dA$. The total force on the face B of the block then is

$$F_B = \int_{v_1}^{c} \frac{M_B}{I} y\, dA = \frac{M_B}{I} \int_{v_1}^{c} y\, dA$$

The quantity $\displaystyle\int_{v_1}^{c} y\, dA$ is the moment of the area of the face of the block with respect to the neutral axis. (The calculation of the moment of an area will be discussed later.) Let the moment be designated[4] as Q. Then $F_B = M_BQ/I$.

[4] The representation of the integral $\displaystyle\int_{v_1}^{c} y\, dA$ by Q is analogous to the representation of the integral $\displaystyle\int_{-c}^{c} y^2\, dA$ by I. See Appendix B.

In the same way the resultant force F_A on the face A of the block is $M_A Q/I$. The difference between the two forces therefore is $F_B - F_A = (M_B - M_A)Q/I$. This value is equal to the force exerted by the shearing stress S_s on the lower surface of the block. This equals $S_s b\, dx$. Hence

$$S_s b\, dx = (M_B - M_A)\frac{Q}{I} \quad \text{or} \quad S_s = \frac{(M_B - M_A)Q}{Ib\, dx}$$

But the change in bending moment between two sections of a beam equals the area of the shear diagram between those sections, shown in Fig. 8-11b. Therefore $M_B - M_A = V\, dx$. Substituting $V\, dx$ for $M_B - M_A$ in the above equation,

$$S_s = \frac{VQ}{Ib} \tag{8-2}$$

in which S_s = the horizontal (and vertical) shearing unit stress at a given point of a given cross-section of the beam.

V = the total shear at the cross-section (may be obtained from a shear diagram for a given loading).

Q = the moment with respect to the neutral axis of the part of the cross-section between the point where the shearing stress is wanted and the top (or bottom) of the cross-section.

I = the moment of inertia of the whole cross-section with respect to the neutral axis (same I as in Mc/I).

b = the width of the cross-section at the point where S_s is being computed.

8-8. Application of the Formula for Shearing Stress. In the formula $S_s = VQ/Ib$, all the terms are familiar through previous use in this book with the exception of Q, which represents $\int_{v_1}^{c} y\, dA$. In the computation of the moment Q for beams of ordinary cross-section, the indicated integration need not be performed. If the area for which Q is wanted is a rectangle or triangle, Q equals the area times the distance from the neutral axis to the centroid of the area. If the area for which Q is wanted is a more complicated shape, it is divided into rectangles or triangles and Q equals the sum of the moments of these rectangles and triangles. For example, let it be required to find the shearing unit stress at a point 2 in. from the top surface of a beam 12 in. by 12 in. in cross-section. The quantity Q would be the area 12 in. by 2 in., times 5 in., the distance from the neutral axis of the beam to the centroid of the area above the point where the stress is being found.

Example. Find the shearing unit stress at the neutral axis of a beam having the cross-section shown in Fig. 8-12, if the total shear at the cross-section is 2,000 lb.

Solution:
$$I = \frac{6 \times 12^3}{12} - \frac{4 \times 8^3}{12} = 693 \text{ in.}^4$$

$$V = 2,000 \text{ lb}$$
$$Q = 6 \times 2 \times 5 + 4 \times 2 \times 2 = 76 \text{ in.}^3$$
$$b = 2 \text{ in.}$$

Therefore

$$S_s = \frac{2,000 \times 76}{693 \times 2} = 109.6 \text{ psi}$$

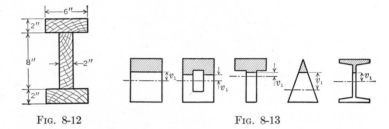

FIG. 8-12   FIG. 8-13

The five diagrams shown in Fig. 8-13 represent the cross-sections of beams. Suppose that the unit shearing stress is to be determined at a distance v_1 from the neutral axis in each case. The quantity Q is the moment of the shaded area. For the first and fourth beams, Q is found by multiplying the shaded area by the distance from its centroid to the neutral axis of the cross-section. For the other beams the shaded area should be divided into rectangles or triangles. The moment is then the sum of the products of each partial area times the distance from its centroid to the neutral axis.

In Fig. 8-13, for each section shown, b is the length of the boundary line between the shaded and unshaded parts of the cross-section, and I is the moment of inertia of the entire cross-section with respect to the neutral axis shown.

When the rectangular cross-section shown in Fig. 8-13 is considered, it is evident that, whatever the value of v_1, there will be no change in any quantity of the expression VQ/Ib except Q, which will increase as v_1 decreases. Q will have a maximum value when $v_1 = 0$, or the maximum shearing stress in the rectangular beam occurs at the neutral axis of the beam. The same line of reasoning shows that the maximum shearing stress will occur at the neutral axis in all beams except those in which the width b is greater at the neutral axis than at some other part of the cross-section. In such beams the maximum shearing stress may occur not at the neutral axis, but at some point where the width is less. For instance, in a beam of triangular cross-section the maximum shearing stress occurs at a distance of one-half the altitude from the base.

For *solid rectangular* cross-sections the maximum shearing stress may be found by a simple relationship that is derived as follows:

$$I = bh^3/12 \qquad Q = b(h/2) \times h/4 = bh^2/8$$

Hence

$$S_s = \frac{VQ}{Ib} = \frac{Vbh^2/8}{(bh^3/12) \times b} = \frac{3V}{2bh} = 1.5\,\frac{V}{A}$$

But V/A is the *average* shearing stress on the cross-section, and therefore the maximum shearing stress on a given cross-section of a beam of solid rectangular cross-section is 1.5 times the average shearing stress.

PROBLEMS

8-18. A wooden beam is 8 in. wide and 12 in. deep. At a cross-section where the total shear is 7,200 lb, calculate the shearing unit stress at 1-in. intervals from top to bottom of the cross-section. Plot these unit stresses as abscissas showing the distribution of the shearing stress.

Ans. $S_s = 34.4$ psi, 1 in. from top.

8-19. A wooden beam has a triangular cross-section, 6-in. base, and 6-in. height. (The apex is turned up.) The total shear on a cross-section is 1,320 lb. Solve for shearing unit stresses, and plot them as directed in Problem 8-18.

8-20. Prove that for a beam of solid circular cross-section the maximum shearing unit stress on any cross-section is $\frac{4}{3}$ times the average shearing stress.

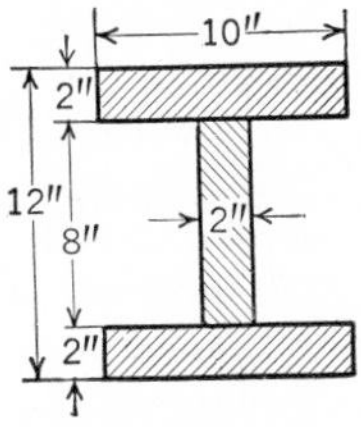

Fig. 8-14

8-21. Figure 8-14 shows the cross-section of a beam made of three planks securely fastened together. Calculate the total vertical shear which will cause a maximum shearing unit stress of 120 psi. Calculate shearing unit stresses at intervals of 1 in. from top to bottom, and plot as directed in Problem 8-18.

GENERAL PROBLEMS

8-22. The maximum bending moment in a certain beam is 4,600 lb-ft, and the maximum shear is 2,800 lb. Determine the minimum dimensions of a square wooden beam if allowable stresses are: 1,600 psi in bending; 110 psi in shearing.

Ans. $b = 6.18$ in.

8-23. Five hundred glued, laminated wooden beams were used in constructing a naval store house in Seattle. Some were 19 in. wide, 41 in. deep, and 30 ft long, and others were 19 in. wide, 43 in. deep, and 40 ft long. The beams were made of Douglas fir planks 2 in. thick glued with casein glue. (See *Engineering News-Record*, June 3, 1943, p. 114.) During tests made on some of the 30-ft beams, each beam carried a total load of 251,200 lb uniformly distributed, which was 38 per cent more than the design load. The deflection at the midpoint was $\frac{7}{8}$ in. (a) Calculate the maximum bending stress. (b) Calculate the maximum shearing stress in a glued joint. Assume 29 ft as distance center to center of bearings.

8-24. Find the maximum fiber stress in the beam of Fig. 7-18 if it is a piece of 3-in. standard pipe. *Ans.* $S = 8,350$ psi.

8-25. A wooden beam is made of two planks, each 2 in. thick and 6 in. wide, fastened together to form a T-beam, and loaded and supported as shown in Fig. 8-15.

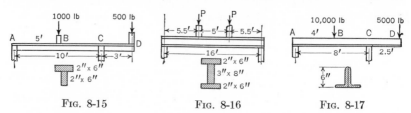

Fig. 8-15

Fig. 8-16

Fig. 8-17

(*a*) Draw shear and bending-moment diagram. (*b*) Calculate maximum tensile bending stress. (*c*) Calculate maximum compressive bending stress. (*d*) Show on the diagram of the beam exactly where each of these stresses occurs. Neglect weight of beam.

8-26. A beam is made of three planks fastened together (Fig. 8-16). It is loaded and supported as shown. Calculate the allowable load P. Neglect weight of beam. Allowable stresses are: bending, 1,750 psi; shearing, 120 psi.

8-27. A beam is made of two $6 \times 4 \times \frac{1}{2}$ in. angles and is loaded and supported as shown in Fig. 8-17. (*a*) Calculate the maximum tensile bending stress. (*b*) Calculate the maximum compressive bending stress. (*c*) Show on a diagram of the beam exactly where these stresses occur. *Ans.* $S_T = 17,300$ psi.

8-28. A beam of T-shaped cross-section is made of a 2×6 in. plank with the 6-in. dimension horizontal, adequately spiked to the top edge of another 2×6 in. plank (6-in. dimension vertical). Calculate the allowable total shear and the allowable bending moment. Allowable stresses are: bending, 1,750 psi; shearing, 120 psi.

8-29. Four planks 2×10 in. (actual dimensions) are spiked together to make a box beam the cross-section of which is a rectangle with outside dimensions 10×14 in. (14 in. vertical). Calculate the maximum allowable bending moment and maximum allowable shear. Allowable stresses are: bending, 1,750 psi; shearing, 120 psi.

8-30. When a dock was being constructed, 4×12 in. (nominal size) wooden sheet piling 28 ft long was used. The resident engineer was asked whether one of these planks could be used as a temporary footwalk to enable workmen to reach an isolated part of the work. The span would be 24 ft. The wood appeared to be fir or hemlock free from defects of any sort. Would you permit its use (laid flat)? If so, would you restrict its use to one man at a time?

8-31. A steel reinforcing bar is 1 in. square and is 30 ft long. It weighs 3.4 lb per ft. If it is picked up at the midpoint of its length, it may be considered to be two cantilever beams, each 15 ft long. What is the maximum bending stress in the bar when it is so held? *Ans.* $S = 27,540$ psi.

8-32. Two men are to carry a square steel reinforcing bar $1\frac{1}{8}$ in. on a side (weight is 4.31 lb per ft) and 34 ft long. (*a*) If they pick it up at the ends, what will be the maximum bending stress in the bar? (*b*) If it is assumed that each man takes hold of the bar at the same distance from the end, between what points can this be done in order that the bending stress in the bar may not exceed 20,000 psi? *Ans.* (*a*) $S = 31,500$ psi.

8-33. A floor and the ceiling below it together have a weight of 16 lb per sq ft, and the floor is to be designed to carry a live load of 75 lb per sq ft. The span of the 2 × 10 in. (nominal size) joists supporting the floor is 14 ft, and the joists are spaced 16 in. on centers. Calculate the maximum bending and shearing stresses.

8-34. A 7-in. 15.3-lb American standard beam rests on supports 12 ft center to center and carries a load of 3,300 lb 4 ft from one end. Calculate the maximum bending stress (a) if the weight of the beam is neglected; (b) if the weight of the beam is considered.   *Ans.*   (a) $S = 10{,}150$ psi.

9

Design of Beams

9-1. Design of Beams. In Chapters 7 and 8 the kinds of beams and loads were enumerated, the shears and bending moments caused by the loads were discussed, and the flexure formula and the shearing stress formula were derived. In this chapter all these principles and relationships will be applied to the *design* of beams.

Beams resist both bending stresses and shearing stresses. In the very large majority of cases, the bending stress is the stress that limits the allowable load on the beam. That is, when the load is such as to stress the beam to the full value of the allowable bending stress, it will usually be found that the allowable shearing stress has not been developed. For this reason, in designing a beam to carry given loads on a given span, it is customary to select a beam which will support the required loads with safe *bending* stresses. If it then appears possible that the shearing stresses in the selected beam may be excessive, they are investigated. If it is found that they are excessive, a new beam is selected which combines the requisite shearing strength with the requisite bending strength.

This article will be limited to the design of beams from the standpoint of bending stresses.

In designing a beam, the following steps are usually necessary:[1]

(*a*) Preparation of a sketch giving locations of loads and reactions and amounts of loads.

(*b*) Calculation of reactions. (This step is not necessary for a cantilever beam.)

(*c*) Drawing of a shear diagram. (For simple problems this may not be necessary.)

(*d*) Calculation of bending moments at cross-sections where shear changes sign or is equal to zero.

(*e*) Calculation of required section modulus, I/c, from $I/c = M/S$. (The greatest numerical value of M should be used, regardless of sign.)

---

[1] For the simplest cases, for example, a beam with a single concentrated load at the midpoint, the maximum bending moment may be computed in terms of the load and length, and the necessary section modulus found without other steps.

(*f*) Selection of a beam the section modulus of which is slightly larger than that computed as necessary to carry the required load. (This excess is to provide for the additional moment caused by the weight of the beam itself.)

(*g*) Calculation of the moment caused by the weight of the beam itself *at the point where the bending moment caused by the given loads is a maximum.*

(*h*) Addition of this moment to the moment previously computed for the given loads, and calculation of the I/c required for the total bending moment.[2] This figure should not be more than the actual value of I/c for the beam which was selected. If it is more, it will be necessary to select a larger beam and repeat steps (*g*) and (*h*).

9-2. Effect of Weight of Beam. Sometimes the weight of the beam is so small compared with the given loads that it may be entirely neglected. Until experience and good judgment have been acquired, however, it is safer to go through steps (*g*) and (*h*).

In general it is true that, for a beam of a given cross-section loaded so as to cause a given unit stress, the longer the span the greater is the proportion of the total load which is due to the weight of the beam. As an example take a 12-in. 65-lb wide-flange beam with a uniformly distributed load such as to cause a stress of 18,000 psi. For a span of 9 ft this load is 117,400 lb. The beam weighs 585 lb, which is about $\frac{1}{2}$ of 1 per cent of the total load. If the span is 18 ft, the total load can be 58,600 lb. This beam weighs 1,170 lb, which is about 2 per cent of the total load. If the span is 27 ft, the load can be 39,100 lb. This beam weighs 1,755 lb, which is $4\frac{1}{2}$ per cent of the total load.

If the weight of the beam does not add more than 2 or 3 per cent to the stresses, it can generally be neglected. For example, in selecting a steel beam to carry 117,000 lb (distributed) on a span of 9 ft, the weight of the beam is negligible; but in selecting a beam to carry 39,000 lb (distributed) on a span of 27 ft, the weight of the beam adds more than 4 per cent to the required section modulus, and this is not negligible.

9-3. Design of Beams for Bending. When the maximum bending moment has been found, and with the allowable stress specified or chosen, the necessary section modulus, I/c, is computed. I/c is a function of the dimensions of the cross-section of the beam and is independent of the material. For structural steel "shapes," such as

---

[2] The maximum bending moment with the weight of the beam included may not occur at exactly the section at which the maximum bending moment neglecting the weight of the beam occurs. In some cases when the weight of the beam is large compared with the loads upon it, the true maximum bending moment should be computed after the weight of the beam is known.

beams, channels, and angles, values of I/c are given in the steelmakers' handbooks, in the tables usually designated "Elements of Sections." (See Tables II to VI.)

It sometimes happens that more than one size of steel beam has a suitable value of I/c. The lightest of these should be used unless there is some reason for using a heavier one.

For shapes not found in tables, such as beams of rectangular cross-section, it is necessary to compute I/c. It should be kept in mind that I is the moment of inertia of the cross-section with respect to the neutral axis (through the centroid of the cross-section). If the neutral axis is not midway between the top and bottom surfaces of the beam, there are two values of I/c corresponding to the stresses at the two "extreme fibers."

Wooden beams are generally rectangular in cross-section. For a rectangle I is $bh^3/12$ and c is $h/2$. Hence $\dfrac{I}{c} = \dfrac{bh^3/12}{h/2} = \dfrac{bh^2}{6}$. This simplified expression for I/c is convenient to use in solving for the dimensions of beams with solid rectangular cross-sections.

Example 1. A beam is to rest on two supports 12 ft center to center and is required to carry a uniformly distributed load of 1,000 lb per ft and a concentrated load of 1,500 lb 4 ft from the left support. Select a satisfactory southern pine beam, using 1,600 psi as the allowable bending stress and 125 psi as the allowable shearing stress.

Solution: The reactions are computed, and the shear and bending-moment diagrams are drawn and are shown in Fig. 9-1. This procedure covers steps (a) to (d) inclusive as outlined in Art. 9-1.

Step (e). Calculation of required section modulus:

$$I/c = M/S = (21{,}125 \times 12)/1{,}600 = 158.5 \text{ in.}^3$$

For a rectangular cross-section $I/c = bh^2/6$. Hence

$$bh^2/6 = 158.5 \qquad \text{and} \qquad bh^2 = 951 \text{ in.}^3$$

There are numberless values of b and h which would make $bh^2 = 951$. It is economical to make the depth greater than the width, and a cross-section with a depth of about twice the width might be assumed. In that case $bh^2 = h^3/2$. Hence

$$h^3 = 1{,}902 \qquad \text{and} \qquad h = 12.4 \text{ in.}$$

Nominal sizes[3] of large timbers are multiples of 2 in., and the next deeper beam will have a nominal depth of 14 in. The actual depth of such a timber is 13.5 in. The necessary width can be calculated from $bh^2 = 951$,

$$b = 951/13.5^2 = 5.22 \text{ in.}$$

A beam nominally 6 in. wide has an actual width of 5.5 in. Hence a beam with nominal dimensions of 6 in. by 14 in. is large enough to resist bending stresses satisfactorily.

[3] Actual sizes of lumber corresponding to nominal sizes are given in Table X.

The weight of the beam should be considered. There are 7 board ft per linear foot in a 6 × 14 in. beam. The weight of the beam (at 4 lb per board foot) is 28 lb per ft, which is provided for by the slight excess width of the beam. (The suitability of this beam from the standpoint of shear will be discussed in Art. 9-5.)

Example 2. A steel beam is required to rest on supports 24 ft center to center and to carry a distributed load of 4,000 lb per ft extending over 14 ft at one end and a concentrated load of 30,000 lb 8 ft from the other end. Select a suitable beam so that the bending stress does not exceed 18,000 psi.

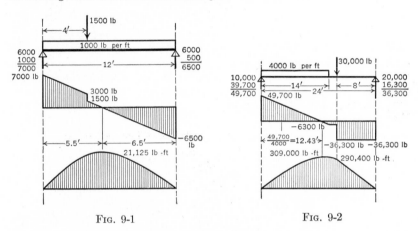

FIG. 9-1   FIG. 9-2

Solution: The sketch showing dimensions and loading is drawn in Fig. 9-2. Below are the shear and bending-moment diagrams. The maximum bending moment occurs 12.43 ft from the left end and is 309,000 lb-ft.

The required section modulus is $I/c = (309,000 \times 12)/18,000 = 206$ in.[3] Turning to the tables, it will be noticed that the 18-in. WF 114-lb beam has a section modulus of 220.1 in.[3], which is ample. But the 21-in. WF 112-lb beam and the 24-in. WF 94-lb beams also have adequate section moduli and would therefore be better beams to use in the absence of any condition making a shallow beam desirable. The table contains no beam lighter than the 24-in. WF 94-lb with a sufficient section modulus.

PROBLEMS

9-1. It is desired to support the loads shown in Fig. 9-3 with a piece of steel pipe. What size of standard steel pipe is necessary if the allowable stress is 15,000 psi?
    Ans. $2\frac{1}{2}$-in. pipe.

9-2. In Fig. 9-4 $P = 12,000$ lb, $w = 120$, $L = 24$ ft, $a = 8$ ft, $S = 18,000$ psi. Select the lightest wide-flange beam. (Neglect weight of beam.)

9-3. In Fig. 9-4 $P = 3,600$ lb, $w = 80$, $L = 12$ ft, $a = 5$ ft, $S = 18,000$ psi. Select the lightest American standard beam. (Neglect weight of beam.)
    Ans. 6 in. 17.25 lb, I-beam.

9-4. In Fig. 9-4 $P = 20,000$ lb, $w = 200$, $L = 20$ ft, $a = 9$ ft, $S = 20,000$ psi. Select the lightest wide-flange beam. (Neglect weight of beam.)

9-5. A wooden beam is to rest on supports 16.0 ft center to center and to carry a load of 1,600 lb 6 ft from the left end, and 1,800 lb 7 ft from the right end. Select a suitable Douglas fir (structural grade) beam, assuming continuously dry conditions. Make depth about three times the width.

9-6. A steel beam is to rest on supports 30 ft center to center and to support a uniform load of 1,000 lb per ft and three loads of 8,000 lb, one at the midpoint and

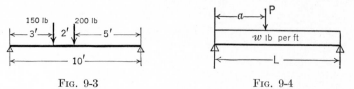

FIG. 9-3   FIG. 9-4

one at each quarter-point. Select the lightest steel beam to carry these loads if the allowable stress is 20,000 psi.   *Ans.* 21-in. WF 73-lb beam.

9-7. What percentage of the allowable bending moment for a beam 8 in. wide and 12 in. deep is the allowable bending moment for a commercial 8 × 12 in. beam? What percentage is the allowable shear?

9-4. Design of Beams with Unsymmetrical Cross-Sections.

For various reasons it is sometimes desirable or necessary to use a beam having a cross-section not symmetrical with respect to the neutral axis. Cast-iron beams, for instance, are often designed with the tension side wider than the compression side in order to reduce the tensile stress, since cast iron is weak in tension. The design consists in assuming a cross-section which seems suitable and then investigating this cross-section to determine whether it is large enough but not excessive.

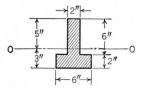

FIG. 9-5

Example. A cast-iron beam is required in the frame of a machine, the loads and lengths being such that the maximum bending moment is +130,000 lb-in. and the maximum shear is 30,000 lb. Allowable stresses are tension, 3,000 psi; compression, 12,000 psi; shearing, 3,000 psi.

Solution: Assume the section shown in Fig. 9-5, and investigate it. The first steps are to calculate y and I_0. The neutral axis is found to be 5 in. from the top. I with respect to this axis is 136 in.[4] Since the neutral axis is not midway between the top and bottom of the beam there are different values of c corresponding to the extreme fibers in tension and compression. Allowable bending moment as limited by compressive stress is

$$M = \frac{SI}{c} = \frac{12,000 \times 136}{5} = 326,000 \text{ lb-in.}$$

As limited by tensile stress,

$$M = \frac{SI}{c} = \frac{3,000 \times 136}{3} = 136,000 \text{ lb-in.}$$

The formula for shearing stress $S_s = VQ/Ib$ may be written

$$V = S_s Ib/Q$$

The allowable shear is

$$V = \frac{3,000 \times 136 \times 2}{5 \times 2 \times 2.5} = 32,600 \text{ lb}$$

A beam of this cross-section will therefore carry the given loads with stresses below the allowable stresses.

It might be possible to save some material without exceeding the allowable stresses by slightly narrowing the web of the beam.

PROBLEMS

9-8. The maximum cross-section of a certain cast-iron beam has the dimensions shown in Fig. 9-6. Calculate the allowable bending moment if allowable stresses are: tension, 4,000 psi; compression, 18,000 psi.   *Ans.* $M = 614,000$ lb-in.

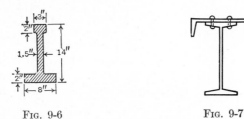

Fig. 9-6   Fig. 9-7

9-9. A beam is built up of a 12-in. 40.8-lb American standard I-beam and a 10-in. 25.0-lb channel (Fig. 9-7). Calculate the allowable bending moment if the allowable stress is 20,000 psi. Compare with the allowable bending moment for the I-beam alone.

9-5. Investigation for Shearing Stress.

In the beam that was selected in Example 1, Art. 9-3, the maximum shearing unit stress resulting from the given loads is found, from the equation $S_s = VQ/Ib$, to be 141 psi. The specified allowable stress, however, is only 125 psi. Therefore the selected beam, though satisfactory from the standpoint of bending stress, is not satisfactory from the standpoint of shear, and a beam of larger section must be used.

For a rectangular section the value of Q/Ib is $1.5/A$, where A is the area of the cross-section. The maximum shearing stress in a beam of rectangular section therefore is $S_s = 1.5V/A$. This shows that, as far as shearing unit stress is concerned, the shape of the rectangle is of no importance. The necessary strength can be obtained by increasing either the depth or the width of the section. The area of the cross-section must be made equal to $1.5V/S_s$, which in this case is 10,500/125 or 84 sq in. If the nominal 14-in. depth is retained, a width of 84/13.5 or 6.22 in. is necessary. To secure this width, a nominal 8-in. dimension must be used. This results in a one-third increase in nominal cross-section over what was required for bending. If the nominal 6-in.

width is retained, the depth must be at least 84/5.5 or 15.3 in. This
requires a nominal 16-in. depth. It will evidently be more economical
to increase the depth than to increase the width, and a 6 × 16 timber
would be used, unless it were desirable to conserve headroom through
the use of the shallower beam.

9-6. Shearing Stresses in Steel Beams.   For steel I- and wide-flange
beams it is standard practice to use a slightly approximate method in
connection with shearing unit stresses. Specifications ordinarily provide that the total shear V on any cross-section must not exceed the
area of the *web* of the beam (which is considered to extend through
the flanges) multiplied by a constant which is somewhat analogous
to an average shearing unit stress acting *on the web only*. The American
Institute of Steel Construction, for example, specifies that the maximum shear on a steel beam must not exceed 13,000 times the web area
th, the thickness of the web times the depth of the beam.

For the 24-in. WF 94-lb beam of Example 2, Art. 9-3, this specification
would permit a maximum shear of $V = 24.29 \times 0.516 \times 13{,}000 =$
163,000 lb. Since the maximum shear caused by the load in that ex-

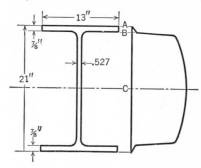

ample is only 49,700 lb, the beam
selected in accordance with the
requirements of bending stress will
be entirely satisfactory from the
standpoint of shear also.

This method of dealing with
shears is purely empirical. Its justi-
fication rests on the fact that the
shearing unit stress in the web of a
steel beam is much more nearly uniform than in a beam of rectangular
cross-section. Figure 9-8 illustrates

FIG. 9–8.   Variation of shearing stress
in wide-flange beam.

this fact for the 21-in. 112-lb WF
section. The shearing stress is very small at any point between A and
B. At B, however, because of the sudden decrease in width, there is a
large increase in unit stress. For successive points between B and C
the value of Q increases very slowly, so that the stress at C is not materially greater than that at B. The A.I.S.C. specification allows a
maximum shearing force of 143,000 lb on this beam, obtained by
multiplying the web area by 13,000. With this shear on the beam the
maximum shearing unit stress, as given by $S_s = VQ/Ib$, is 14,300 psi,
which is a reasonable value. The empirical procedure gives satisfactory
results.

9-7. When Shearing Stresses Are Important.   The bending moment
in a beam is usually a function jointly of the length of the beam and the

loads on it. The shear V, however, depends only on the loads, and is independent of the length. From the standpoint of bending stresses, as the length of the beam decreases, the amount of load can increase correspondingly without causing any increase in bending moment and therefore in bending unit stress. As the load increases, however, the maximum shear V increases proportionately. In a long beam, therefore, bending stresses are likely to be more serious; but in a short beam, shearing stresses may be more serious than bending stresses.

As a numerical example, consider two wooden beams each 6 × 10 in. in cross-section and with lengths of 15 ft and 5 ft, respectively. Let the allowable bending stress be 1,600 psi, and the allowable shearing stress be 90 psi. Then the uniformly distributed load which each of the beams can carry without exceeding the shearing stress will be $\frac{4}{3}S_sA$, or 7,200 lb.

The flexure formula shows that a maximum bending stress of 1,600 psi in the longer beam would be caused by a load of 7,100 lb. Therefore a load which would develop the allowable bending stress in the beam would be permissible from the standpoint of shear.   On the other hand, the uniformly distributed load which would produce the allowable bending stress of 1,600 psi in the short beam is 21,300 lb. But this load would cause a shearing unit stress of 266 psi, which is almost three times what is permissible.   Shearing stress is important in short beams carrying heavy, uniformly distributed loads.   It is also important in beams of any length that carry heavy concentrated loads near the supports, since the effect of such loads is to cause shearing stresses disproportionately large in comparison with the bending stresses produced.

Also, shear is more likely to be of importance in wooden than in steel beams because of the low strength which wood possesses for resisting shearing stresses parallel to the grain.

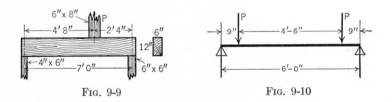

Fig. 9-9   Fig. 9-10

PROBLEMS

9-10. Using the cross-section and unit stresses specified in the example of Art. 9-7, find the minimum length of beam in which the allowable uniformly distributed load is determined by bending stress.   *Ans.* $L = 14.8$ ft.

9-11. In Fig. 9-9 what is the greatest allowable load P? The members are Douglas fir. Allowable stresses are: shearing, 120 psi; bending, 1,700 psi; bearing on side of grain, 415 psi. Neglect weight of the beam.

9-12. The beam shown in Fig. 9-10 is a 6-in. 12.5-lb I-beam. Find safe loads P: (a) as limited by bending stress of 18,000 psi; (b) as limited by allowable average shear on web of 12,000 psi. *Ans.* (a) $P = 14,600$ lb.

9-13. Solve Problem 9-12 using A.I.S.C. allowable stresses (20,000 psi bending, and 13,000 psi average shear on web).

9-14. In Fig. 9-10, P is 20,000 lb. Select the lightest I-beam that will carry the load. Allowable stresses are 20,000 psi bending and 13,000 psi average web shear.

Ans. 7-in. 15.3-lb I-beam.

9-15. Solve Problem 9-11 if load P is 4 ft 4 in. from the left end and 2 ft 8 in. from the right end.

9-16. Solve Problem 9-12 for an 8-in. WF 20-lb beam.

9-8. Economical Sections of Beams.

Where the necessary size of a beam is determined by *bending* stresses, depth is of special importance, since I/c increases much more rapidly with increase in the depth of a cross-section than with increase in its width. This fact was illustrated by Example 2, Art. 9-3, which showed that an 18-in. WF 114-lb beam and a 24-in. WF 94-lb beam have section moduli of about the same amount. If there is no limitation on the depth of beam that may be used, the deeper sections will be more economical where bending stresses are the important stresses.

When shearing stresses, rather than bending stresses, determine the size of a beam, the total *web area* is the only consideration, and a heavy shallow web usually has some advantages over a deep thin web which may "buckle."

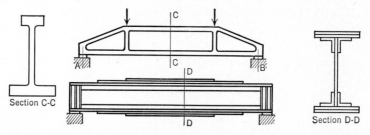

Section C-C

Section D-D

FIG. 9–11. Cast beam and built-up beam (plate girder) of variable cross-section.

Because of their relatively low cost most beams have the same cross-section from end to end. However, it is sometimes economical to use beams with varying cross-sections. In Fig. 9-11 two examples of such beams are shown.

In a beam made of a material such as steel, which is equally strong in tension and in compression, it is logical to make the cross-section symmetrical with respect to the neutral axis. Steel beams usually have cross-sections of this sort. On the other hand, with a material such as cast iron, which is much stronger in compression than in tension, economy is gained by making the compression flange smaller than the tension flange (Fig. 9-11).

When bending stresses determine the necessary cross-section of a beam, any beam which has the same cross-section throughout its length will have an excess of strength at sections other than the dangerous section. In certain beams, such as rolled-steel beams, to vary the cross-section of the beam would cost more than any resulting economy of material would warrant. There are situations, however, in which it is practicable to vary the cross-section of the beam approximately in accordance with variation in the bending moment (Fig. 9-11). If this could be done perfectly, a beam of uniform flexural strength throughout its length would result. Beams of uniform strength are considered briefly in Chapter 16.

9-9. Ways in Which Beams May Fail. Commonly used types of beams designed by the methods discussed in this chapter are, in general, safe if not overloaded. However, there are a number of ways in which beams may fail, depending on the type of cross-section and the manner in which the loads and supports are applied. Some of these are given here.

1. The tensile or compressive bending stress becomes equal to the yield point of the material if ductile or becomes equal to the ultimate strength of the material if brittle.

2. The shearing stress becomes equal to the shearing ultimate strength.

3. The compression flange may buckle sidewise if the flange is too narrow relative to the length of the beam and if the flange is not adequately stayed against bending horizontally.

4. The web of the beam may buckle where reactions or concentrated loads are applied if the web is too thin relative to the depth of the beam.

5. The edge of the compression flange of a beam may "wrinkle" locally if the thickness of the flange is too small relative to the projecting width of the flange. This local wrinkling may occur even though the compressive unit stress is below the allowable compressive stress for the material.

6. In a built-up beam (such as a steel beam made of a web plate and four angles) the parts may become separated if the welding or riveting holding them together is inadequate.

The first two methods of failure are avoided by using adequate factors of safety in selecting the allowable bending stress and the allowable shearing stress. The design of beams for bending and shear has already been discussed.

The method of failure mentioned in 3 above is somewhat difficult to describe.   Tensile stress in the flange of a beam tends to *straighten* the flange; compressive stress, however, tends to cause the flange to "bow" out of line.   When conditions are such that this sidewise deflection can occur, the beam may fail under a load much less than that which the beam could carry in the absence of any lateral deflection of the compression flange.   Most beams with cross-sections of such form as to make this lateral deflection a possibility are used in ways that restrain the compression flange against sidewise motion.   When this is not the case, however, proper allowance for lateral deflection is an essential part of the beam design.

In the use of beams with deep and thin webs, danger exists that, where large concentrated loads (or reactions) are applied, the web may buckle under the load, this part of the web acting like an overloaded column. It might be supposed that the type of failure mentioned in 4 above would be avoided by the rule that the web area must be enough so that the total shear does not exceed 13,000*th*.   For a shear of 65,000 lb, 5 sq in. of web area are required.   A web 10 $\times$ $\frac{1}{2}$ in. would be substantial and would not buckle, but a web 20 in. deep and $\frac{1}{4}$ in. thick might buckle over the reaction unless steps were taken to prevent buckling. The methods of failure mentioned in 3, 4, 5, and 6 above are discussed in Chapter 19, with a number of additional topics concerning beams.

Consideration of the way in which a load is applied to a beam is not essentially a part of the design of the *beam*.   It may well be noted at this point, however, that all concentrated loads and reactions should be applied to beams in ways that will not cause excessive local compressive or bearing stresses.   For steel beams with loads applied through riveted connections, this topic was discussed in Chapter 4. With wooden beams, which are much weaker in resisting compression perpendicular to the grain than compression parallel to the grain, the area over which a concentrated load is applied must often be increased by use of a *bearing plate*.   The necessary area of this plate is determined by the relationship $A = P/S_c$, where P is the load and S_c is the allowable compressive unit stress perpendicular to the grain. The minimum length of bearing that a beam must have on the support on which it rests is also sometimes determined by the sidewise compressive stress.

9-10. Modulus of Rupture.   If a beam is loaded until failure occurs and the maximum bending moment M to which the beam was subjected is inserted in the formula $S = Mc/I$, the resulting value of S is called the "modulus of rupture" of the beam.   It cannot be considered as the unit stress in the outermost fibers of the beam at the moment of failure, because the equation $S = Mc/I$ holds true only when no unit fiber stress in the beam exceeds the proportional limit.   When a beam is stressed to failure, the deformations of the fibers continue throughout the test to be proportional to their distance from the neutral axis (in the ordinary beam the cross-sections of which are symmetrical with respect to the neutral axis).   Since the proportional limit is exceeded in the outer fibers, however, Hooke's law no longer holds true for them, and the stresses in the fibers of the beam are not proportional to their distances from the neutral axis.   The modulus of rupture is greater than the actual stress in the outer fibers and bears no fixed relation to that stress.   The more brittle the material, the more closely the modulus of rupture approaches the true stress.

The modulus of rupture, as determined from beams of similar cross-section, is used in comparing the bending strength of different materials, such as different species of wood.   It is also sometimes used to determine the *probable* breaking load on a beam, and the term is one which is fairly frequently encountered in engineering literature.   The stress distribution that occurs in beams at cross-sections where stresses exceed the proportional limit is discussed in Chapter 19.

GENERAL PROBLEMS

9-17. Select an I-beam to carry a load of 2,500 lb per ft distributed over a span of 20 ft with a maximum bending stress of 18,000 psi.

9-18. Three planks the dimensions of which are 2×8 in. are spiked together to form a beam of the type shown in Fig. 8-14.   The span is 8 ft center to center of supports.   What uniformly distributed load will cause a maximum shearing stress of 120 psi?   What bending stress will this load cause?   *Ans.   W* = 4,480 lb.

9-19. A southern pine beam $11\frac{1}{2}$ in. deep and $9\frac{1}{2}$ in. wide rests on supports 16 ft apart.   What concentrated load at the midpoint will bring the stress up to 1,300 psi? What percentage of this stress is caused by the weight of the beam itself?   What is the maximum longitudinal shearing stress?   *Ans. S_s* = 41 psi.

9-20. Solve Problem 9-19 if the beam is $11\frac{1}{2}$ in. wide and $9\frac{1}{2}$ in. deep.

9-21. Select the lightest steel beam to serve as a cantilever 20 ft long with 4,800 lb at the end.   (S = 18,000 psi.)

9-22. Select the lightest steel beam to carry the loads shown in Fig. 9-12.   (S = 20,000 psi.)

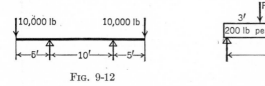

FIG. 9-12   FIG. 9-13

9-23. An 8×10 in. (actual size) beam carries the loads shown in Fig. 9-13. Allowable bending stress is 1,800 psi, and allowable shearing stress is 100 psi.   Calculate the allowable value of *P*.   *Ans.   P* = 2,740 lb.

9-24. It is necessary to support a concentrated load of 8,400 lb at the midpoint of a 20-ft span. Wooden beams of 12-in. nominal depth and of various widths are available. The allowable stress of 1,600 psi must not be exceeded. Determine the total width required, assuming that this required width can be approximated by using one or more of the available beams.

9-25. The wrench shown in Fig. 9-14 is to have the same factor of safety in bending of the arms and torsion of the stem. If the ultimate strength in bending is 70,000 psi and in shearing is 55,000 psi, what must be the diameter of the arms?

$Ans.$ $d = 1.01$ in.

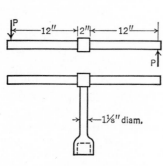

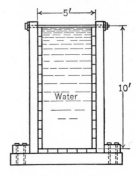

FIG. 9-14   FIG. 9-15

9-26. A temporary water tank is constructed as shown in Fig. 9-15. The vertical beams are in pairs as shown and are 3 ft apart along the length of the tank. Draw shear and bending-moment diagrams, and select a suitable beam of select-grade cypress. Allowable stresses are: bending, 1,200 psi; shearing parallel to grain, 110 psi.

9-27. A steel I-beam having a span of 24 ft carries a total load of 24,000 lb. This load varies uniformly from zero at the supports to a maximum at midspan. Select a suitable steel beam. The allowable stress is 20,000 psi.

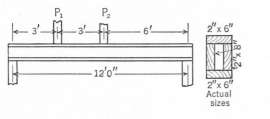

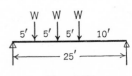

FIG. 9-16   FIG. 9-17

9-28. A beam is made of four spruce planks spiked together as shown in Fig. 9-16. It rests on 6 × 6 in. short posts and carries two loads as shown. What are the maximum shearing and bending stresses when $P_1 = 2,600$ lb and $P_2 = 2,200$ lb? Neglect weight of beam. $Ans.$ $S_s = 90$ psi.

9-29. In Fig. 9-16, $P_1 = 1.2P_2$. Draw shear and bending-moment diagrams, and determine the allowable value of P_1 and of P_2 neglecting the weight of the beam. Allowable stresses are: bending, 1,600 psi; shearing, 110 psi.

9-30. Draw the shear and bending-moment diagrams for the beam shown in

Fig. 9-17, expressing values in terms of the applied loads W. If the beam is an 18 in. 54.7 lb American standard I-beam, in which the fiber stress is not to exceed 18,000 psi, what can the magnitude of the loads W be? Do *not* neglect the weight of the beam itself.

9-31. If, in Fig. 9-17, $W = 12,000$ lb, select the lightest steel beam that will carry the loads and its own weight, with an allowable stress of 18,000 psi.

9-32. Solve Problem 9-30 but let the beam be 14-in. WF 30-lb.

9-33. If the beam shown in Fig. 9-17 is Douglas fir $9\frac{1}{2}$ in. wide and $13\frac{1}{2}$ in. deep, allowable bending stress is 1,800 psi, and allowable shearing stress is 110 psi, calculate the allowable load W. Neglect weight of beam. *Ans.* $W = 3,320$ lb.

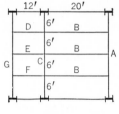

Fig. 9-18

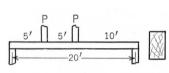

Fig. 9-19

9-34. The diagram shown in Fig. 9-18 shows the arrangement of beams supporting a platform in a factory building. Beams A, C, and G are connected to columns. Beams B, D, E, and F are supported by beams A, C, and G and support a 6-in.-thick concrete floor slab (150 lb per cu ft). The "live load" on the platform is 125 lb per sq ft. Select suitable American standard beams for C, E, and G. Allowable bending stress is 18,000 psi.

9-35. Solve Problem 9-34 but select beams for A, B, and D.

9-36. Solve Problem 9-34 but assume that beam F was omitted in order to leave a "stair well" 12 ft square.

9-37. The beam shown in Fig. 9-19 is 8×12 in. (actual size), allowable bending stress is 1,800 psi, and allowable shearing stress is 110 psi. Calculate the allowable load P. *Ans.* $P = 3,630$ lb.

9-38. In Fig. 9-19, P equals 3,200 lb. Determine the necessary size of a beam to carry these loads plus an allowance of 40 lb per ft for the weight of the beam. Allowable stresses are: bending, 1,600 psi; shearing, 100 psi. Make depth of beam twice the width.

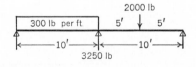

Fig. 9-20

9-39. For the two-span continuous beam shown in Fig. 9-20 the center reaction is 3,250 lb. Draw shear and bending-moment diagrams, locating points of inflection. If the beam is 5.5 in. wide, how deep must it be if the allowable bending stress is 1,600 psi? What will be the maximum shearing stress in the beam selected?
Ans. $h = 5.54$ in.

10

The Deflection of Statically
Determinate Beams

10-1. Reasons for Calculating Beam Deflections. It has already been
mentioned that a beam changes its shape when loads are applied. The
vertical movement of a point on the neutral surface of a horizontal beam
is called the *deflection* of the beam at that point. For several reasons an
engineer should be able to calculate the amount of the deflection of a
beam. Under some circumstances a limitation upon the amount of
deflection determines the size of a beam. For some machine parts and
for the structural supports of some types of machinery the deflections
must not exceed certain very small amounts. For instance, in foundations for turbogenerator units it is sometimes specified that the deflection
of any beam must not exceed 1/2,000 of the length of the beam. Another example is that of floor beams which carry plastered ceilings
underneath. It is generally specified that the deflection of such beams
must not exceed 1/360 of the span in order to avoid cracking the plaster.
Beams which would be strong enough may be found to deflect too much.
The designer must select a beam which will not deflect excessively even
though this beam may be stronger than necessary. In certain other
cases, any reasonable amount of deflection may be permissible, but it
may be important to know how much the beam deflects at some point.

One of the most important reasons for understanding a method of
calculating deflections arises in connection with certain types of indeterminate beams which occur very frequently. Beams are said to be
"indeterminate" (see Fig. 7-4) when the reactions cannot be found by
the equations of equilibrium. In these cases the additional equations
needed are obtained from deflections or slopes of the beam.

This chapter takes up methods by which deflections can be calculated
and applies these methods to cantilever beams and beams on two supports, under ordinary types of loading. Before taking up the actual
calculation of deflections, however, certain fundamental relations
between curvature and bending moment will be considered.

10-2. Curvature and Bending Moment. The line of intersection of
the neutral surface of a beam and a vertical longitudinal plane is called
the *elastic curve of the beam.*

A definite relation exists between the unit stress in the extreme fibers of a given beam and the radius of curvature of the elastic curve.   It is here assumed that the beam is straight when it is unloaded.   In Fig. 10-1, AB is a short part of the elastic curve of a beam which has been bent by loads.   Planes through A and B which were originally parallel (and vertical) now meet at O. A and B are very close together, the length ds being infinitesimal, and it may be assumed without any appreciable error that the bending moments at A and B are equal and also that the radii of curvature OA and OB are equal.   If a plane BG is passed through B parallel to the plane AF, FG is the original length of the extreme fibers, which have increased in length by the amount GG'.   The unit

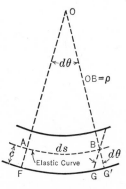

Fig. 10-1

deformation of the extreme fibers is GG'/FG, which equals GG'/AB. If the proportional limit is not exceeded, the unit stress equals the unit deformation multiplied by the modulus of elasticity, or

$$S = (GG'/AB)E$$

If the curvature is slight, so that ρ is large compared to c, and if AB is very small, GBG' and AOB may be considered to be similar triangles. Hence

$$GG'/AB = c/\rho$$

Substituting c/ρ for GG'/AB in the expression for stress,

$$S = \frac{c}{\rho} E \qquad \text{or} \qquad \frac{S}{E} = \frac{c}{\rho} \qquad\qquad (10\text{-}1)$$

That is, the stress in the extreme fibers of a beam is to the modulus of elasticity as the distance to the extreme fibers from the neutral axis is to the radius of curvature.   But $S = Mc/I$.   Equating this expression for S with the expression in equation 10-1 above,

$$Ec/\rho = Mc/I$$

from which

$$M = \frac{EI}{\rho} \qquad\qquad (10\text{-}2)$$

This relation makes it possible to compute the bending moment required to bend a beam to a given radius of curvature or to compute the radius of curvature of the elastic curve at any point in a beam if the bending moment is known. The formula $M = EI/\rho$ indicates that, if the bending moment is constant over part of the length of a beam, the radius of curvature is also constant and the elastic curve is the arc of a circle.

Where the bending moment varies, as it usually does, the curvature is sharper where the bending moment is larger.

PROBLEMS

10-1. A small steel band saw is 0.027 in. thick. The pulleys on which it runs are 10 in. in diameter. What bending stress results in the extreme fibers?

Ans. $S = 81{,}000$ psi.

10-2. If the diameter of steel wire is d in., what is the diameter D of the coil in which it can be wound without causing a stress of more than 50,000 psi?

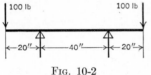

FIG. 10-2

10-3. Solve Problem 10-2 but let the wire be aluminum alloy ($E = 11{,}000{,}000$ psi and the unit stress 30,000 psi).

10-4. A steel bar 0.72 in. square is loaded as shown in Fig. 10-2. Calculate the radius of curvature of the part between the supports.   Ans. $\rho = 28$ ft.

10-5. A stick of oak 3 in. wide and $\frac{1}{2}$ in. thick is bent to a radius of curvature of 62 in. by a bending moment of 670 lb-in. Calculate E.

10-3. Methods of Calculating Deflections in Beams; Assumptions Made. Several methods are available for calculating the deflection of a beam at any point.

In the method first used an equation for the elastic curve of the beam is written. This equation may be solved and the slope and deflection obtained. This method was employed by Leonhard Euler before 1750 and is still in use.

In 1875 Professor Wilhelm Fraenkel of Dresden published a formula based upon the equality between work done by the movement of a load on the beam as the beam deflects and the work of resistance of the fibers of the beam (the product of the stress in the fibers and their change in length). This method has many merits but is not widely used, except for indeterminate structures.

In 1873 Professor Charles E. Greene discovered a method which he called the *area-moment* method. This he taught in his classes at the University of Michigan, and he published it in 1874. Professor Greene was unaware that a somewhat similar method had been published in 1868 by Professor Otto Mohr in Germany.

Both the method based on the equation of the elastic curve of the deflected beam and the area-moment method are used in this chapter. Each method has some advantages.

Assumptions.   In calculating deflections, the following assumptions are commonly made.

1. It is assumed that the stresses caused by bending are below the proportional limit, so that Hooke's law holds.

2. It is assumed that a plane section across the beam remains a plane after the beam is bent.

3. It is assumed that the length of the elastic curve is the same as the length of its horizontal projection.   For the actual beams in ordinary use this assumption is well within the limits of accuracy of ordinary methods of calculation.

4. It is commonly assumed that deflections due to shear are negligible. By the methods of this chapter the deflection computed is that due to bending alone, and the deflection due to shearing stress must be calculated separately if necessary.   Deflections due to shearing stress are generally so much smaller than those due to bending that they may be entirely neglected without appreciable error.   They are discussed in Chapter 19.

BEAM DEFLECTIONS BY THE DOUBLE-INTEGRATION METHOD

10-4. Equation of the Elastic Curve.   In Art. 10-2 there was derived a relationship between the bending moment and the radius of curvature of the elastic curve, expressed by the equation

$$1/\rho = M/EI$$

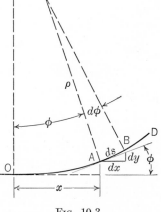

If, in this equation, $1/\rho$ is expressed in terms of x and y, an equation for the elastic curve of the beam results which can be used in calculating slopes and deflections.   An expression for $1/\rho$ in terms of x and y will now be derived.

In Fig. 10-3, OD is part of the elastic curve of a beam originally straight and horizontal.   The origin for the coordinate axes may be chosen at any point and need not be on the curve.   Consider two points A and B, the distance between

them along the curve being ds and the horizontal distance between them being dx.   Let ϕ be the angle between a vertical line and the normal to the curve at A, and let $d\phi$ be the angle subtended by the arc AB.

It will be seen that $ds/\rho = d\phi$, whence $1/\rho = d\phi/ds$.   At any point on the curve where the slope is small, the difference between ds and its horizontal projection dx is extremely small, so that dx may be substituted for ds, giving $1/\rho = d\phi/dx$.

At A the slope of the curve is dy/dx, and it will be seen that $dy/dx = \phi$ in radians if ϕ is a small angle, as it is when a beam has a small deflection. Since $\phi = dy/dx$, it follows that

$$\frac{d\phi}{dx} = \frac{d(dy/dx)}{dx} = \frac{d^2y}{dx^2}$$

which is an expression for the rate of change of the slope with respect to x.

Equating the two values found above for $d\phi/dx$ there results the equation $1/\rho = d^2y/dx^2$, which is not exact but is nearly exact for curves with small slopes.[1]

In Art. 10-2 it was shown that for a bent beam $1/\rho = M/EI$. Equating these values for $1/\rho$,

$$\frac{d^2y}{dx^2} = \frac{M}{EI} \tag{10-3}$$

This equation is commonly called the *general equation of the elastic curve* of a deflected beam. When M for a given beam has been expressed as a function of x (the x axis being parallel to the undeflected beam and a convenient origin having been chosen), the equation represents a definite curve. It is evidently not the common type of equation of this curve, expressing directly the relation between the abscissas x and the ordinates y of points on the curve. Instead, it defines the curve by giving *the curvature* (d^2y/dx^2) at any point in terms of x, the abscissa of the point. To convert the equation into the usual form of expression in x and y, it is necessary to perform two integrations, evaluating the resulting constants and inserting their values in the final equation.

In succeeding articles this general equation of the elastic curve will be applied to several important types of beams and loadings, the integrations will be performed, and the equation of the elastic curve for that particular type of beam and loading will be obtained in terms of x and y. Expressions for the maximum y will also be found.

---

[1] Textbooks on calculus show that the exact value is

$$\frac{1}{\rho} = \frac{d^2y/dx^2}{[1 + (dy/dx)^2]^{\frac{3}{2}}}$$

But if the slope of the curve, dy/dx, is small, it follows that $(dy/dx)^2$ is an extremely small quantity compared with unity and may be neglected in the above equation. Therefore the denominator becomes unity and $1/\rho = d^2y/dx^2$.

10-5. Signs of Quantities in Equations for Elastic Curve. When writing an expression for M in terms of x, the sign given to the expression for M should be consistent with the conventions previously given for the sign of bending moment.

The slope of the curve at a given point dy/dx is positive if the tangent to the curve at that point slopes upward and away from the origin. The quantity d^2y/dx^2 is the rate of change of the slope with respect to x,

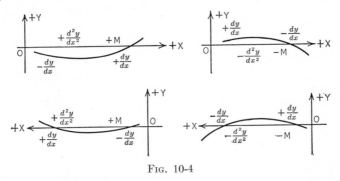

FIG. 10-4

and a plus value for this quantity corresponds to an increasing steepness of a plus slope or a decreasing steepness of a minus slope. Therefore a plus d^2y/dx^2 corresponds to plus bending moment, as will be seen by considering Fig. 10-4.

If, in writing the equation $M/EI = d^2y/dx^2$, the quantity d^2y/dx^2 is always given a plus sign, then the values for the slope dy/dx and for the ordinate y will have the correct signs when the equation is solved.

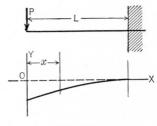

FIG. 10-5

The ordinate y will be the desired deflection only if the x axis is chosen so that it coincides with the original undeflected elastic curve. However, if the x axis is chosen above or below the undeflected elastic curve, the deflection is readily found from the ordinate y.

The positive direction of the y axis will always be considered as upward. The positive direction of the x axis may be taken either to the right or to the left from the origin, as is convenient.

10-6. Cantilever Beam; Concentrated Load at End. The diagrams in Fig. 10-5 show the loaded beam and the approximate shape of the elastic curve. The origin is taken at the free end of the unloaded beam, with the x axis lying in the neutral surface of the undeflected beam.

The value of the bending moment at a point x inches from the origin is $-Px$. Hence

$$d^2y/dx^2 = -Px/EI$$

Integrating,

$$dy/dx = -(Px^2/2EI) + C_1$$

But dy/dx is the slope of the curve, which is seen to be zero when $x = L$. Hence

$$-(PL^2/2EI) + C_1 = 0 \qquad \text{or} \qquad C_1 = PL^2/2EI$$

and

$$dy/dx = -(Px^2/2EI) + (PL^2/2EI)$$

which is an equation giving the slope of the curve at any point in terms of the abscissa x of that point. Integrating,

$$y = -(Px^3/6EI) + (PL^2x/2EI) + C_2$$

It will be seen that $y = 0$ when $x = L$, from which

$$-(PL^3/6EI) + (PL^3/2EI) + C_2 = 0 \qquad \text{or} \qquad C_2 = -PL^3/3EI$$

This, substituted in the above value of y, gives

$$y = -(Px^3/6EI) + (PL^2x/2EI) - (PL^3/3EI)$$

This is the equation of the elastic curve of this beam with reference to the chosen axes. The maximum deflection is the value of y when $x = 0$, or

$$y_{\text{max}} = -PL^3/3EI$$

The minus sign indicates that, with the origin and axes as chosen, the point of maximum deflection is below the x axis. Since E is in pounds per square inch, P must be in pounds and L must be in inches when solving for y, which will then be in inches.

10-7. Significance of the Constants of Integration. The equation

$$dy/dx = -(Px^2/2EI) + C_1$$

in the preceding example expresses the slope of the curve at any point in terms of the abscissa of the point. If the value of x is zero, $dy/dx = C_1$. That is, *the first constant of integration is the value of the slope at the point on the curve where $x = 0$.*

The equation

$$y = -(Px^3/6EI) + (PL^2x/2EI) + C_2$$

gives the value of y in terms of x. If $x = 0$, $y = C_2$, showing that *the second constant of integration is the value of the ordinate of the curve at the point where* $x = 0$.

In order to emphasize the significance of the constants of integration, the axes in the above example were chosen so that neither C_1 nor C_2 would be zero. It is often possible and desirable, however, to choose an origin which makes one or both of these constants zero, thereby simplifying the solution.

In beams where E and I are both constant, as they nearly always are, it is convenient to keep EI in the left-hand member of the equation as a coefficient. When this is done, C_1 is EI times the slope of the curve where $x = 0$; or C_1/EI is the slope of the curve where $x = 0$; and C_2/EI is the ordinate where $x = 0$.

PROBLEMS

10-6. A 4-in. 7.7-lb I-beam is used as a cantilever beam projecting 10 ft. Using formulas derived in Art. 10-6, calculate the deflection at the end and the slope at the midpoint caused by a load of 400 lb at the end.

10-7. Using the data in Problem 10-6, calculate the deflection at the midpoint and the slope at the end.   *Ans.* $y = 0.40$ in.

10-8. Derive expressions for the end slope and end deflection of the cantilever beam of Fig. 10-5, using the double-integration method but taking the origin on the curve of the beam at the fixed end.

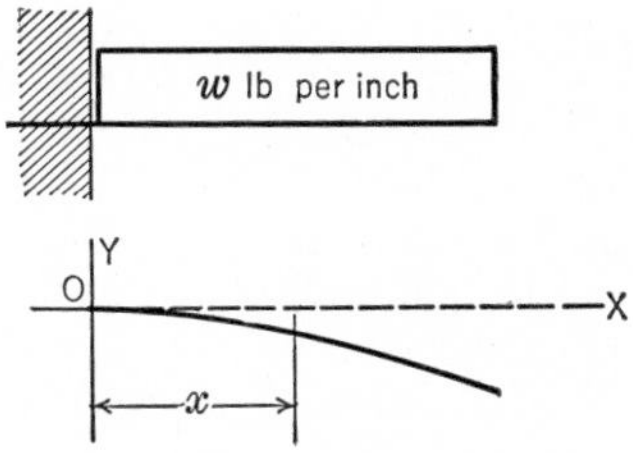

FIG. 10-6

10-8. Cantilever Beam; Uniformly Distributed Load.

The origin will be taken at the fixed end (Fig. 10-6). Then $M_x = -\dfrac{w(L-x)^2}{2}$, and consequently

$$EI\,d^2y/dx^2 = -w(L-x)^2/2 = -(wL^2/2) + wLx - wx^2/2$$

Integrating,

$$EI\,dy/dx = -(wL^2x/2) + (wLx^2/2) - (wx^3/6) + C_1$$

but $dy/dx = 0$ when $x = 0$. Hence $C_1 = 0$, as it must be with the origin as chosen. Integrating again,

$$EIy = -(wL^2x^2/4) + (wLx^3/6) - (wx^4/24) + C_2$$

but $y = 0$ when $x = 0$. Hence $C_2 = 0$, and the equation of this elastic curve referred to the chosen axes is

$$EIy = -(wL^2x^2/4) + (wLx^3/6) - wx^4/24$$

The maximum deflection is the value of y when $x = L$.

$$EIy_{\max} = -(wL^4/4) + (wL^4/6) - (wL^4/24) = -wL^4/8$$

or

$$y_{\max} = -wL^4/8EI$$

If $W = wL$, the total load, then

$$y_{\max} = -WL^3/8EI$$

When $x = L$, $EI\,dy/dx = -wL^3/6$. Hence the end slope of the beam is $\theta = -wL^3/6EI$.

PROBLEMS

10-9. (a) Calculate the deflection of a wooden cantilever beam 4 in. deep, 4 in. wide, and 12 ft long caused by a uniformly distributed load of 30 lb per ft. (b) Calculate the slope at the end. ($E = 1,600,000$ psi.)   *Ans.* (a) $y = 3.94$ in.

10-10. Using the principle of superposition and expressions for slope and deflections previously derived, calculate the deflection at the end of the beam shown in Fig. 10-7, caused by the two given loads. *Hint:* The deflection due to the uniform load is the deflection at the end of the uniform load plus 40 times the slope at the end of the uniform load.

10-11. Using the double-integration method, derive expressions for the end slope and maximum deflection of a cantilever beam due to a moment of T lb-in. applied to the beam at the end. (See Fig. 7-33.)

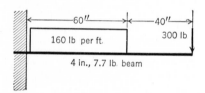

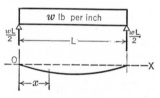

Fig. 10-7   Fig. 10-8

10-9. Beam on Two Supports; Uniformly Loaded. The origin is taken at the left support (Fig. 10-8).

$$M_x = (wLx/2) - (wx^2/2)$$

and consequently

$$EI\,d^2y/dx^2 = (wLx/2) - (wx^2/2)$$

Integrating,

$$EI\,dy/dx = (wLx^2/4) - (wx^3/6) + C_1$$

but $dy/dx = 0$ when $x = L/2$. Therefore

$$C_1 = (wL^3/48) - (wL^3/16) = -wL^3/24$$

Therefore

$$EI\ dy/dx = (wLx^2/4) - (wx^3/6) - (wL^3/24)$$

Integrating,

$$EIy = (wLx^3/12) - (wx^4/24) - (wL^3x/24) + C_2$$

But $y = 0$ when $x = 0$; hence $C_2 = 0$ and

$$EIy = (wLx^3/12) - (wx^4/24) - (wL^3x/24)$$

The maximum deflection is the value of y corresponding to $x = L/2$.

$$EIy = (wL^4/96) - (wL^4/384) - (wL^4/48) = -5wL^4/384$$

Therefore $y_{\max} = -\dfrac{5wL^4}{384EI}$. If the total load is W lb,

$$y_{\max} = -\frac{5WL^3}{384EI}$$

PROBLEMS

10-12. What is the greatest uniformly distributed load that a 10-in. 25.4-lb American standard beam can carry if the deflection is not to exceed that commonly allowed for beams supporting plastered ceilings? The span is 20 ft. What will be the end slope of the beam?

10-13. A wooden beam $5\frac{1}{2}$ in. wide and $11\frac{1}{2}$ in. deep rests on supports 18 ft center to center. It carries a uniform load of W lb. Calculate the value of W to cause a stress of 1,750 psi. What deflection results from this load if $E = 1,600,000$ psi?

$$Ans.\quad y = 0.925\ in.$$

10-14. A beam of length L rests on supports at the ends and carries a concentrated load P at the midpoint. Using the double integration method, derive expressions for $EI\ dy/dx$ and EIy, as is done for the beam with distributed loading in Art. 10-9. Show that $-PL^2/16EI$ is the end slope and $-PL^3/48EI$ is the maximum deflection.

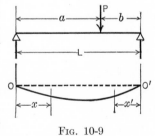

FIG. 10-9

10-10. Beam on Two Supports, with One Non-Central Load.

This entire curve (Fig. 10-9) cannot be expressed by a single equation. The problem can be solved with one origin, but the following solution makes use of two origins, one at each support. Let a in Fig. 10-9 be greater than b, as shown.

BETWEEN LEFT REACTION AND LOAD	BETWEEN RIGHT REACTION AND LOAD

(regard x' as $+$, as shown)

$$M = Pbx/L \qquad\qquad M = Pax'/L$$

Hence, $\quad EI \dfrac{d^2y}{dx^2} = \dfrac{Pbx}{L} \qquad\qquad EI \dfrac{d^2y'}{dx'^2} = \dfrac{Pax'}{L}$

Integrating, $\quad EI \dfrac{dy}{dx} = \dfrac{Pbx^2}{2L} + C_1 \qquad EI \dfrac{dy'}{dx'} = \dfrac{Pax'^2}{2L} + C_2 \quad$ (10-4)

Integrating again,

$$EIy = \dfrac{Pbx^3}{6L} + C_1 x + C_3 \qquad EIy' = \dfrac{Pax'^3}{6L} + C_2 x' + C_4 \ \text{(10-5)}$$

When $x = 0$, $y = 0$, hence $C_3 = 0$. $\quad$ When $x' = 0$, $y' = 0$, hence $C_4 = 0$.

When $x = a$, the deflection of the left segment equals the deflection of the right segment for $x' = b$. Equating these two values of EIy,

$$(Pba^3/6L) + C_1 a = + (Pab^3/6L) + C_2 b \qquad\qquad (10\text{-}6)$$

The slope of the left segment at the load equals the slope of the right segment at the load, but one is upward and the other is downward. Hence the slope dy/dx of left segment for $x = a$ equals minus the slope of the right segment for $x' = b$, whence

$$(Pba^2/2L) + C_1 = - (Pab^2/2L) - C_2 \qquad\qquad (10\text{-}7)$$

Solving equations (10-6) and (10-7) for C_1,

$$C_1 = - (Pab/6L)(L + b)$$

Substituting this value for C_1 in (10-5),

$$EIy = \dfrac{Pbx^3}{6L} - \dfrac{Pabx}{6L}(L + b) = \dfrac{Pbx}{6L}[x^2 - a(L + b)] \quad \text{(10-8)}$$

Substituting the value for C_1 in (10-4),

$$EI \dfrac{dy}{dx} = \dfrac{Pbx^2}{2L} - \dfrac{Pab}{6L}(L + b)$$

The deflection is maximum where $dy/dx = 0$, which will be true when

$$x = \sqrt{\tfrac{1}{3}a\,(L + b)} = \tfrac{1}{3}\sqrt{3a\,(L + b)} \qquad\qquad (10\text{-}9)$$

The maximum deflection is obtained by substituting this value for x in (10-8). Hence

$$y_{\max} = -\frac{Pab\,(L+b)\,\sqrt{3a\,(L+b)}}{27EIL} \tag{10-10}$$

PROBLEMS

10-15. A beam rests on two supports 100 in. apart and carries a load P 20 in. from one reaction. Using equation 10-8 of Art. 10-10, calculate the deflection at the midpoint of the beam and compare it with the maximum deflection. How many inches from the midpoint does the maximum deflection occur? See equation 10-9.

10-16. Referring to equation 10-9 of Art. 10-10, it is apparent that the distance to the point of maximum deflection increases as a increases. Show that the point of maximum deflection in a beam on two supports, without overhang, and carrying a single concentrated load, cannot be more than $0.077L$ from the midpoint.

BEAM DEFLECTIONS BY THE AREA-MOMENT METHOD

10-11. The Area-Moment Method. The principles employed in the area-moment method of determining beam slopes and deflections afford

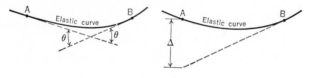

Fig. 10-10

a simple means of calculating the angle θ (in radians) between the tangents to the elastic curve at any two points. They also afford a simple means of calculating the displacement (in a direction perpendicular to the length of the undeflected beam) of any point on the elastic curve of the beam from the tangent to the elastic curve at any other point. These two quantities are illustrated in Fig. 10-10. AB is part of the elastic curve of a beam which was originally straight and horizontal.

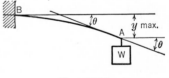

Fig. 10-11

The application of these principles to an actual problem is illustrated in Fig. 10-11. The maximum deflection of the cantilever beam equals the displacement of point A from the tangent to the curve at point B. The slope of the beam at A equals the angle between the tangent at A and the tangent at B.

In the form in which they are stated in Arts. 10-12 and 10-13 the two area-moment propositions apply to beams in which E and I are constant throughout the part of the beam between A and B.

10-12. The First Area-Moment Proposition.

The angle between the tangents to the elastic curve of a beam at any two points A and B equals the area of the part of the bending-moment diagram between A and B, divided by EI.

Proof: AB in Fig. 10-12 is part of the elastic curve of a beam originally straight and horizontal. Radii of curvature are shown at A and B.

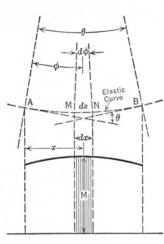

FIG. 10-12

Note that the angle between the radii of curvature at A and B is equal to the angle between the tangents at A and B. MN is any part of the elastic curve of length ds between A and B. The angle $d\phi$ is the angle between the radii of curvature to the curve at M and N. If $d\phi$ is in radians, $\rho\, d\phi = ds$. Hence $1/\rho = d\phi/ds$. But in Art. 10-2 it was shown that $1/\rho = M/EI$. Hence

$$d\phi/ds = M/EI$$

The assumption is made that ds equals dx. This assumption is justified for any ordinary beam where the curvature is very slight. Then

$$d\phi/dx = M/EI \quad \text{or} \quad d\phi = M\, dx/EI$$

$M\, dx$ is the area (shaded in Fig. 10-12) of the part of the bending-moment diagram between M and N. This area is the product of the width dx and the height M.

The angle θ between the radii of curvature at A and B is the sum of all the differential angles $d\phi$ as ϕ varies from zero to θ. Each of these differential angles equals the corresponding differential area $M\, dx$ divided by EI. Hence the sum of all the differential angles equals the sum of all the differential areas divided by EI, or θ equals the area of the bending-moment diagram between A and B, divided by EI.

Mathematically this may be stated thus:

$$\theta = \int_0^\theta d\phi = \int_A^B \frac{M\, dx}{EI} = \frac{A_M}{EI} \qquad (10\text{-}11)$$

in which A_M is the area of the bending-moment diagram between A and B.

The bending-moment diagram is often referred to as the "M diagram."

Example. A 10-in. 25.4-lb I-beam with a span of 15 ft carries a concentrated load of 10,000 lb at the midpoint.   Calculate the angle between the tangents at the center and at the end due to the concentrated load only.

Solution: Figure 10-13a shows the beam and the load.   The elastic curve is evidently symmetrical as shown in (*b*), and the desired angle θ is indicated.   The bending-moment diagram is shown in (*c*).   According to the first area-moment proposition, the area of the shaded part of the *M* diagram divided by *EI* is the value of the angle θ.   Since *E* and *I* are used in inch units, it is also necessary to use inch units for the bending moment and length.

$$\theta = 37,500 \times 12 \times \tfrac{9.0}{2}/(30,000,000 \times 122.1) = 0.00552 \text{ radian}$$

The value of θ in degrees is $0.00552 \times 360/2\pi = 0.32°$

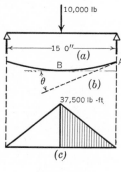

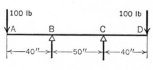

FIG. 10-13   FIG. 10-14

PROBLEMS

10-17. A steel bar $\frac{3}{4}$ in. deep and $1\frac{1}{2}$ in. wide is loaded as shown in Fig. 10-14. Calculate the angle (in radians) between the radii of curvature at *B* and *C* caused by the 100-lb loads.   Give the answer in degrees also.   *Ans.* $\theta = 0.126$ radian.

10-18. With the data of Problem 10-17 calculate the slope (angle with the horizontal) of the elastic curve at *A*.   (Note that because of symmetry the tangent to the elastic curve is horizontal at the midpoint of the beam.)

10-13. The Second Area-Moment Proposition. Let *A* and *B* (Fig. 10-15) be any two points on the elastic curve of a beam originally straight

and horizontal.   Let a line be drawn tangent to the elastic curve at *B*, and let Δ be the vertical distance from *A* to the tangent (Δ is called "the displacement of *A* from the tangent at *B*").

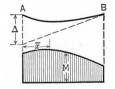

The vertical displacement Δ of point *A* from the tangent to the elastic curve at *B* equals the moment (with respect to *A*) of the area of the part of the bending-moment diagram between *A* and *B*, divided by *EI*.

FIG. 10-15

Proof: *AB* in Fig. 10-16 is part of the elastic curve of a beam originally straight and horizontal. M and N are any two points on the elastic curve, the distance MN being an infinitesimal distance ds. The angle between the tangents to the elastic curve at M and N is $d\phi$. The

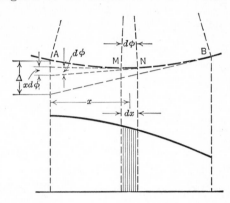

FIG. 10-16

horizontal distance from A to MN is x. If $d\phi$ is in radians, then $x\,d\phi$ is the part of the vertical through A intercepted between these two tangents.[2]

The sum of all such intercepts as x varies from 0 to AB equals Δ; or, expressed as an equation,

$$\Delta = \int_A^B x\,d\phi$$

But from Art. 10-12

$$d\phi = M\,dx/EI$$

But $M\,dx$ is an elementary area (the part of the M diagram with a width dx), and this multiplied by x is the moment of this elementary area with respect to A.

Hence, substituting this value of $d\phi$ in the preceding equation,

$$\Delta = \int_A^B \frac{Mx\,dx}{EI} = \frac{A_M\bar{x}}{EI} \tag{10-12}$$

In which A_M is the area of the bending-moment diagram between A and B and $\bar{x}$ is the distance from the displaced point A to the centroid of A_M.

[2] It should be kept in mind that in the diagram (Fig. 10-16) the distance MN is very greatly exaggerated, being actually infinitesimal. AB, on the other hand, is a finite distance (perhaps several feet). The distance x varies from zero to the distance AB. In any practical case the curvature is very slight, and the tangents at M, N, and B are all very nearly horizontal.

Example 1. Derive expressions for the maximum deflection and the end slope of a cantilever beam with a concentrated load at the end.

Solution: Figure 10-17 shows the loaded beam, the approximate shape of the elastic curve, and the M diagram. The ordinate y_{max} is the displacement of B from the tangent at A and, according to the second area-moment proposition, is equal to the moment, with respect to B, of the area of the M diagram, divided by EI. Thus

$$y_{max} = \frac{(\text{Area of } M \text{ diagram}) \ \bar{x}}{EI} = \frac{\left(-PL \times \dfrac{L}{2}\right) \times \left(\dfrac{2}{3} L\right)}{EI} = -\frac{PL^3}{3EI}$$

The minus sign indicates that the deflection is downward.

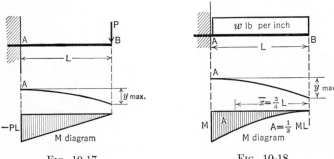

Fig. 10-17   Fig. 10-18

The slope of the curve at B is the angle between the tangents to the curve at A and B and, according to the first area-moment proposition, is the area of the M diagram divided by EI. Thus

$$\theta_B = -\frac{PL \times L/2}{EI} = -\frac{PL^2}{2EI} \text{ radians}$$

Example 2. Derive expressions for the maximum deflection and the end slope of a cantilever beam with a uniform load over the entire beam.

Solution: Figure 10-18 shows the loaded beam, the approximate shape of the elastic curve, and the bending-moment diagram. A tangent to the curve at the fixed end is shown.

It is stated in Appendix A that the parabolic shaded area shown in Fig. 10-18 equals one-third of the base times the altitude and that the centroid is $\frac{3}{4}L$ from the small end. When these values are used,

$$y_{max} = \frac{-(wL^2/2)(L/3)\frac{3}{4}L}{EI} = -\frac{wL^4}{8EI} = -\frac{WL^3}{8EI}$$

where W equals the total load on the beam.

The slope at the end equals the area of the M diagram divided by EI. Hence

$$\theta_B = \frac{-(wL^2/2)(L/3)}{EI} = -\frac{wL^3}{6EI} = -\frac{WL^2}{6EI} \text{ radians}$$

Example 3. Derive expressions for the maximum deflection and the end slope of a beam on two supports with a concentrated load at the midpoint.

Solution: Figure 10-19 shows the loaded beam, the approximate shape of the elastic curve, and the bending-moment diagram. In this problem the tangent at the midpoint is the most convenient tangent to use because it is horizontal. It will be seen in Fig. 10-19 that the maximum deflection, at the midpoint of the beam, equals the displacement of either end from the tangent at the midpoint. Therefore

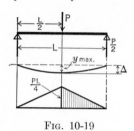

$$\Delta = \frac{(PL/4)(L/4)(\tfrac{2}{3}L/2)}{EI} = \frac{PL^3}{48EI}$$

But $\Delta = -y_{max}$. Therefore

$$y_{max} = -PL^3/48EI$$

The slope at the end,

$$\theta = \frac{(PL/4)(L/4)}{EI} = \frac{PL^2}{16EI} \text{ radians}$$

Fig. 10-19

10-14. Steps in Using the Area-Moment Method. In the solution of *all* problems in deflections by the area-moment method, the following steps are desirable:

(*a*) Sketch, approximately to scale, the beam with loads and dimensions.

(*b*) Draw below this the approximate shape of the elastic curve, exaggerating the deflection. On this drawing indicate the reference tangent used in the application of the area-moment proposition.

(*c*) Draw below this the bending-moment diagram approximately to scale. If this diagram is divided into elementary shapes for easy calculation, indicate these divisions by dotted lines.

(*d*) Perform necessary calculations at one side of these diagrams.

The simplest solution will generally be one based on the use of a *horizontal* tangent to the elastic curve *if the location of its point of tangency is known.* In cantilever beams the tangent at the fixed end is horizontal; in symmetrical beams on two supports the tangent is horizontal at the midpoint of the beam.

In beams that overhang one or both supports the tangent at a support is, in general, not horizontal and should not be so assumed.

As stated in Chapter 7, the curve of the bent beam is concave upward where the bending moment is plus. Consequently, if, in computing the displacement of a point A on a beam, Δ is plus, it means that point A is above the tangent.

Example. A cantilever beam carries two loads as shown in Fig. 10-20. (*a*) Calculate the deflection at C. (*b*) Calculate the deflection at B. $EI = 12,000,000$ lb-in.[2]

Solution: (*a*) The tangent to the curve at A is horizontal and will be used as a reference tangent. This tangent and the approximate shape of the elastic curve are shown in (b). The bending-moment diagram is drawn in two parts in (c). The deflection at C is seen to be also the displacement of C from the tangent at A.

$$y_c = \Delta = \frac{+18{,}000 \times 60 \times 80 - 24{,}000 \times 30 \times 100}{12{,}000{,}000}$$

$$= 7.20 - 6.00 = 1.20 \text{ in.}$$

The plus value indicates that C is above the tangent as assumed.

(b) The deflection of B is the displacement of B from the tangent at A. The plus area between A and B is divided into a rectangle and a triangle as shown by dotted lines.

$$y_b = \frac{+9{,}000 \times 60 \times 30 + 9{,}000 \times 30 \times 40 - 24{,}000 \times 30 \times 40}{12{,}000{,}000}$$

$$= +1.35 + 0.90 - 2.40 = -0.15 \text{ in.}$$

The deflection at B is minus and therefore downward as assumed when sketching the elastic curve.

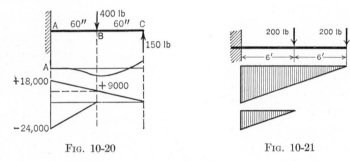

FIG. 10-20   FIG. 10-21

PROBLEMS

10-19. A 4-in. 9.5-lb I-beam is used as a cantilever projecting 12 ft from the fixed end. What deflection at the end is caused by the two loads shown in Fig. 10-21?
Ans. $y = 1.30$ in.

10-20. How many pounds must the load P be to cause zero deflection at the end of the 4-in. 7.7-lb I-beam shown in Fig. 10-22? (*Note:* Draw the bending-moment diagram as two separate triangles, one positive and one negative, as shown.)

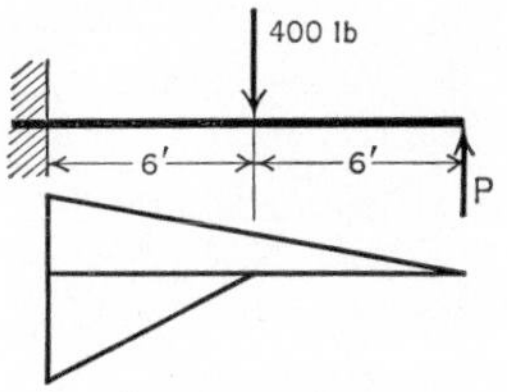

10-21. A cantilever beam of length L carries a load P at the end and another load P at a distance $L/2$ from the end. Show that the deflection at the end caused by these loads is $y = 7PL^3/16EI$. See Fig. 10-21 for a hint concerning the bending-moment diagram.

10-22. Derive an expression for the deflection at the midpoint of the beam of Problem 10-21.

10-23. A cantilever beam of length L carries a load W distributed over a length of $L/2$ from the free end. Derive an expression for the end deflection. Note that the M diagram may be divided into three parts, a parabolic area, a rectangle, and a triangle, as shown in Fig. 10-23.
Ans. $y = -41WL^3/192EI$.

FIG. 10-22

10-24. Derive an expression for the deflection at the midpoint of the beam of Problem 10-23.

10-25. A cantilever beam of length L carries three equal loads P. One is at the end, one $L/3$ from the end, and one $2L/3$ from the end. Derive an expression for the end deflection.   *Ans.* $y = -5PL^3/9EI$.

10-26. Derive an expression for the deflection at a point $L/3$ from the end in the beam of Problem 10-25.

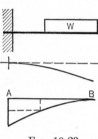

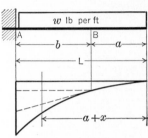

Fɪɢ. 10-23   Fɪɢ. 10-24

10-27. A cantilever beam of length L carries two equal loads P. One is at the end, and one is $2L/3$ from the end. Derive an expression for the end deflection.

10-28. A cantilever beam of length L carries a load W distributed over a length of $L/2$ from the fixed end. Derive an expression for the end deflection.
          Ans. $y = -7WL^3/192EI$.

10-29. It is desired to calculate the deflection at a point B, which is a ft from the end of a cantilever beam carrying a uniformly distributed load of w lb per ft. Show that the part of the M diagram between the fixed end and B may be divided into a rectangle, a triangle, and a parabolic area, as shown in Fig. 10-24. What are the ordinates of each of these areas at the fixed end?

10-15. Symmetrical Beams on Two Supports; Concentrated Loads.

In all symmetrical beams on two supports, carrying symmetrical loads, the tangent to the elastic curve is horizontal at the midpoint. This horizontal tangent may be used as the reference tangent. The maximum deflection, at the midpoint, is found by determining the displacement, from the tangent at the midpoint, of the point on the elastic curve at either support. This procedure is illustrated in the following example, which also illustrates the process of finding the deflection at any other point on the curve.

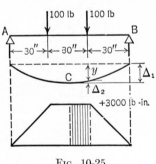

Fɪɢ. 10-25

Example. A steel bar 1 in. square rests on two supports 90 in. apart. (*a*) Calculate the deflection at the midpoint caused by two loads of 100 lb each, 15 in. from the midpoint of the beam. (*b*) Calculate the deflection at one of the loads.

Solution: (*a*) The deflection $y_{\max}$ is wanted. This is equal to Δ_1, Fig. 10-25, the displacement of B from the tangent at the midpoint. This, in turn, is the moment of half the bending-moment diagram with respect to B, divided by EI. For convenience in calculating, this is divided into a triangle and a rectangle.

$$y_{max} = \Delta_1 = \frac{(3,000 \times 15) \times 20 + (3,000 \times 15) \times 37.5}{30,000,000 \times \frac{1}{12}} = 1.035 \text{ in.}$$

(b) The deflection y is wanted. It will be observed that this deflection equals Δ_1 (computed above) minus Δ_2, the displacement of point C on the elastic curve from the tangent at the midpoint. Applying the area-moment principle,

$$\Delta_2 = \frac{(3,000 \times 15) \times 7.5}{30,000,000 \times \frac{1}{12}} = 0.135 \text{ in.}$$

$$y = \Delta_1 - \Delta_2 = 1.035 - 0.135 = 0.900 \text{ in.}$$

In general, the deflection of any point on a symmetrical simple or overhanging beam may be computed as the difference between two displacements. One of these is the displacement of the reaction from the tangent at the center; the other is the displacement of the point at which the deflection is wanted, from the same tangent.

PROBLEMS

10-30. A steel bar 1 in. thick and 3 in. wide rests on supports 120 in. apart and carries two loads of 120 lb 48 in. apart and each 36 in. from the nearer reaction. (*a*) Calculate the maximum deflection caused by these loads. (*b*) Calculate the deflection at one of the loads.

10-31. A beam of length L resting on supports at the ends carries two loads P between the supports, each $L/3$ from the nearer support. Derive an expression for the maximum deflection. *Ans.* $y = 23PL^3/648EI$.

10-32. A small beam in a piece of apparatus rests on supports 12 in. apart and carries a load of 6 lb at the midpoint and two loads of 4 lb each 3 in. from the midpoint. $EI = 1,000$. (*a*) Calculate the deflection at the midpoint. (*b*) Calculate the deflection at 3 in. from the midpoint.

10-33. A small beam rests on supports 24 in. apart and carries a central load of 8 lb and two loads of 6 lb each 6 in. from the midpoint. $EI = 9,000$. (*a*) Calculate the deflection at the midpoint. (*b*) Calculate the deflection at a point 6 in. from the midpoint. *Ans.* (*a*) $y = 0.52$ in.

10-34. A beam of length L carries three loads P, one at the midpoint and one $L/4$ from each reaction. Derive an expression for the maximum deflection.

10-35. Solve Problem 10-34 if the center load is $2P$. *Ans.* $y = -9PL^3/128EI$.

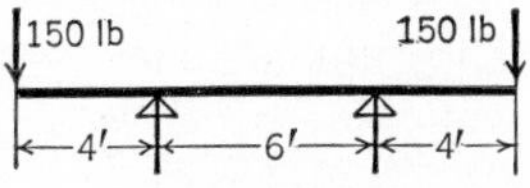

10-36. A beam of rectangular cross-section is supported at the ends and carries a single concentrated load at the midpoint. Derive a formula for the maximum deflection in terms of the maximum bending moment M, the dimensions of the cross-section b and h, and the modulus of elasticity E. *Ans.* $y = ML^2/Ebh^3$.

Fig. 10-26

10-37. The beam shown in Fig. 10-26 is a 2 in. standard steel pipe. Calculate the deflection at the end. *Hint:* Calculate the displacements of end and of reaction from the tangent at midpoint. The difference is the desired deflection.

10-38. A beam rests on two supports the distance between which is L. It overhangs a distance $L/4$ at each end and carries a load P at each overhanging end. Derive an expression for the end deflection. See hint given in Problem 10-37.

$$Ans. \quad y = -7PL^3/192EI.$$

10-16. Bending-Moment Diagrams "by Parts."

Before proceeding further with problems involving beams on two supports, a useful method of drawing bending-moment diagrams will be shown. This method is

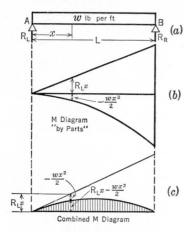

often convenient for concentrated loads and is very useful in many problems of uniformly distributed loading. Consider the beam AB (Fig. 10-27) with a uniform load of w lb per ft. The bending moment at any point distant x from A is

$$M = R_L x - wx^2/2$$

Heretofore in drawing bending-moment diagrams the subtraction has been performed, and the difference of the terms has been plotted (as in the shaded diagram). However, the two terms may be plotted separately as shown in Fig. 10-27b. If ordinates

Fig. 10-27

equal to $R_L x$ are laid off at all points, a triangular positive area results. If ordinates equal to $-wx^2/2$ are laid off at all points, a negative parabolic area results. This is exactly the same parabolic area that is the M diagram for a cantilever beam. The area of this is one-third the height times the length, as has been stated.

Hence the bending-moment diagram may be represented by a triangle and a parabolic area, the areas and centroids of both of which are known. The method illustrated above may be used for any kind of loading and frequently gives bending-moment diagrams much more convenient for the area-moment method.

It is interesting to note that the "combined" bending-moment diagram may be regarded as a triangle from the ordinates of which the negative ordinates of the parabola have been laid off (Fig. 10-27c).

Example. Draw the bending-moment diagram by parts for the beam shown in Fig. 10-28.

Solution: At any point in the left-hand 6 ft the bending moment is due to the left reaction alone and is $M = 400x$. For values of x greater than 6 ft, $M = 400x - 50(x - 6)^2$. The term $400x$ occurs as all or part of the bending moment at every point in the beam. These ordinates vary with x, being zero at the left end and **7,200** lb-ft at the right end.   When plotted, they form a positive triangle.   The negative ordinates $50(x-6)^2$ when plotted form the negative area bounded by the parabolic curve shown.   The maximum ordinate of this area is $-7,200$ lb-ft.

In drawing moment diagrams by parts, it is not necessary to write equations for bending moments as was done above.   The equations were given to show that each term in such an equation is represented by an area.

A moment diagram "by parts" can be started at either end of the beam.   At each concentrated load a triangular area begins, positive for an upward load or reaction and negative for a downward load.   The

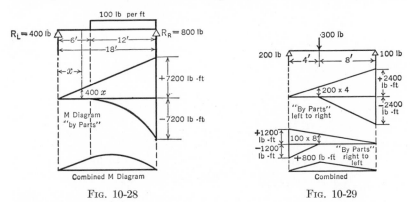

Fig. 10-28   Fig. 10-29

beginning of a uniformly distributed load on the beam marks the beginning of an area in the moment diagram which is bounded by a parabolic curve.   This area is negative for a downward uniform load. If the uniform load ends before the end of the beam is reached, the parabolic boundary line ends at the end of the uniform load.   The area continues with a straight line tangent to the end of the curve.

The advantage of this method of drawing a bending-moment diagram is evident in the foregoing example.   It would be difficult to calculate accurately the area of the "combined" bending-moment diagram, or of part of it.   The distance to the centroid would also be difficult to compute.   The parabola and the triangle of the diagram "by parts," however, are figures of known areas, and the positions of the centroids of these figures are also known.

Because it is important to be able readily to draw bending-moment diagrams by parts, an additional illustration of a simple loading is given in Fig. 10-29.   These examples should be carefully studied and thoroughly understood.

10-17. Symmetrical Beams on Two Supports; Distributed Loads. The bending-moment diagram "by parts" will be found most convenient to use in deflection problems dealing with beams having uniformly distributed loads.

In other respects the method of calculating the deflection at any point is the same as that explained in Art. 10-15 for beams with concentrated loads.

Example 1. Derive an expression for the maximum deflection in a simple beam on two supports with a uniform load over the entire length of the beam.

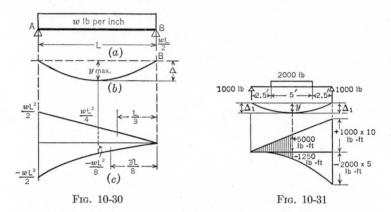

FIG. 10-30   FIG. 10-31

Solution: The loaded beam is shown in Fig. 10-30a and the deflected curve in (b). The tangent at the midpoint of the curve shown in (b) is the reference tangent. The bending-moment diagram by parts is shown in (c).

$$EI\Delta = \frac{wL^2}{4} \times \frac{L}{4} \times \frac{L}{3} - \frac{wL^2}{8} \times \frac{L}{6} \times \frac{3L}{8}$$

$$= wL^4 \left(\frac{1}{48} - \frac{1}{128} \right) = \frac{5wL^4}{384}$$

Since $y = -\Delta$

$$y = -5wL^4/384EI = -5WL^3/384EI$$

in which W is the total load.

Example 2. A 4-in. 7.7-lb American standard I-beam rests on two supports 10 ft apart and carries a load of 2,000 lb uniformly distributed over the middle 5 ft. Calculate the deflection at the midpoint caused by the 2,000-lb load.

Solution: The beam, Fig. 10-31, is symmetrical, and y, the deflection at the midpoint, equals Δ_1, the displacement of either end from the tangent at the midpoint. Only one half the bending-moment diagram is needed. As drawn, the left half (shaded) is more easily used.

$$y = \Delta_1 = \frac{5{,}000 \times 12 \times 30 \times 40 - 1{,}250 \times 12 \times 10 \times 52.5}{30{,}000{,}000 \times 6}$$

$$= \frac{2{,}400 - 262.5}{6{,}000} = 0.356 \text{ in.}$$

PROBLEMS

10-39. Calculate the maximum deflection of the beam shown in Fig. 10-32.

10-40. In Fig. 10-32, $L = 48$ in., $W = 48$ lb, and $EI = 48,000$. Calculate the maximum deflection of the beam.

10-41. In Fig. 10-32, $L = 48$ in., $W = 48$ lb, and $EI = 48,000$. Calculate the deflection at the end of the uniform load.   *Ans.* $y = -1.44$ in.

10-42. Show that the deflection at the midpoint of the beam shown in Fig. 10-33 is zero if P has the value $5W/12$.

10-43. Calculate the value of P that will make the tangents at the supports horizontal in the beam of Fig. 10-33.

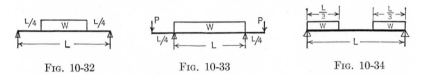

FIG. 10-32   FIG. 10-33   FIG. 10-34

10-44. For the beam in Fig. 10-33, $L = 24$ in., $P = 5$ lb, $W = 48$ lb, and $EI = 7,200$. Calculate the deflection at the midpoint.   *Ans.* $y = -0.90$ in.

10-45. For the beam in Fig. 10-33, $L = 48$ in., $P = 20$ lb, $W = 20$ lb, and $EI = 96,000$. Calculate the deflection at the midpoint.

10-46. Calculate the deflection at the end of the beam of Problem 10-45.

10-47. The beam shown in Fig. 10-34 is a 4-in. 7.7-lb I. $L = 12$ ft, and $W = 2,400$ lb. Calculate the deflection at the midpoint.   *Ans.* $y = -0.768$ in.

10-48. Calculate the deflection of the beam of Problem 10-47 at a point 4 ft from one support.

10-49. The beam in Fig. 10-34 is 36 in. long, $W = 48$ lb, and $EI = 120,000$. Calculate the maximum deflection.

10-50. Calculate the deflection of the beam of Problem 10-49 at a point 12 in. from one support.

10-18. Deflection of Unsymmetrical Simple or Overhanging Beams.

In unsymmetrically loaded simple and overhanging beams the position of the horizontal tangent to the elastic curve of the deflected beam is unknown. Therefore it is generally desirable to take some other tangent as the reference tangent. Usually this will be the tangent at one of the supports. The procedure to be followed in calculating the deflection at any given point in a simple or overhanging beam will be illustrated by a numerical example.

Example. For the beam shown in Fig. 10-35, calculate the deflection at a point 8 ft from the right reaction.

Solution: The approximate elastic curve is sketched in, and below the bending-moment diagram "by parts" is drawn from right to left. The reference tangent used will be the tangent at the right reaction. First calculate Δ_1, the displacement of the left support from the tangent at the right support.

$$\Delta_1 = \frac{700 \times 240 \times 120 \times 80 - 2,000 \times 96 \times 48 \times 32}{1,200,000 \times 256} = 4.29 \text{ in.}$$

By proportion calculate Δ_2. $\Delta_2/\Delta_1 = 8/20$. Therefore $\Delta_2 = 8/20 \times 4.29 = 1.72$ in. Calculate Δ_3, the displacement of a point on the elastic curve from the reference tangent.

$$\Delta_3 = (700 \times 96 \times 48 \times 32)/(1,200,000 \times 256) = 0.336 \text{ in.}$$

$$y = \Delta_2 - \Delta_3 = 1.72 - 0.34 = 1.38 \text{ in.}$$

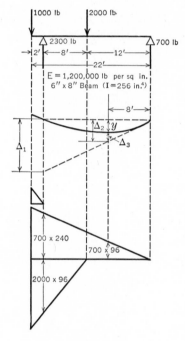

Fig. 10-35

From the foregoing example it can be seen that the deflection at any point in an unsymmetrical beam on two supports is calculated in the following steps:

(*a*) Assume the reference tangent at one reaction, and draw the bending-moment diagram.

(*b*) Calculate Δ_1, the displacement of the other reaction (a point on the elastic curve) from the tangent.

(*c*) Calculate by proportion Δ_2, the distance, at the point where the deflection is wanted, between the original horizontal line of the beam and the reference tangent.

(*d*) Calculate Δ_3, the displacement from the reference tangent of the elastic curve where the deflection is wanted.

(*e*) The deflection y is $\Delta_2 - \Delta_3$ (or in some overhanging beams y is the sum of Δ_2 and Δ_3).

In cases of unsymmetrically loaded beams on two supports, the difficulty of the computation necessary for the solution of a problem frequently depends greatly on whether the moment diagram is drawn from left to right, or vice versa. It should always be drawn in the way which will render the computations as simple as possible. Sometimes it may be desirable, before actually attempting the solution of a problem, to sketch the diagram both ways, and then to determine which is more suitable. No simple rule can be laid down to cover all problems. For a simple beam with a single concentrated or distributed load, however, it will be found desirable to draw the diagram *from* the reaction which is most distant from the load, and to take the tangent at that reaction. With overhanging beams it is sometimes desirable to draw the diagram *from* both ends of the beam *to* one or the other of the reactions.

PROBLEMS

10-51. In the beam of Fig. 10-36, $L = 48$ in., $d = 16$ in., $W = 48$ lb, and $P = 18$ lb. $EI = 96,000$. Calculate the deflection at a point midway between the supports. *Hint:* Take tangent at A and draw M diagram from A toward B.

Ans. $y = 0.288$ in.

10-52. Calculate the deflection at C (Fig. 10-36) of the beam described in Problem 10-51. *Hint:* Take tangent at B. Draw M diagram from A toward B and from C toward B.

10-53. In Fig. 10-37, $L = 12$ in., $P_1 = 4$ lb, $P_2 = 2$ lb, $EI = 1,000$. Calculate the deflection at C.

<table>
<tr><td>Fig. 10-36</td><td>Fig. 10-37</td></tr>
</table>

10-54. Calculate the deflection at D of the beam described in Problem 10-53.

10-55. In Fig. 10-37, $L = 12$ in., $P_1 = 12$ lb, $P_2 = 12$ lb, $EI = 1,200$. Calculate the deflection at C. 　　　　　　　　　　　　　　　　　　 *Ans.* $y = 0.61$ in.

10-56. The beam shown in Fig. 10-37 is a 4-in. 7.7-lb I-beam. $L = 10$ ft, $P_1 = 1,800$ lb, $P_2 = 800$ lb. Calculate the deflection at C.

10-57. A small beam used in laboratory apparatus is 8 ft long. It rests on two supports 72 in. apart and overhangs 24 in. at one end. It supports a uniform load of 2 lb per in. $EI = 720,000$. Calculate the deflection at a point midway between the supports. *Hint:* Take tangent at the end support and start M diagram at that end.

10-58. Calculate the deflection at the overhanging end of the beam of Problem 10-57. *Hint:* Take tangent at the support nearer the overhanging end and draw the M diagram from each end toward the support.

10-59. A small beam for which $EI = 100,000$ is 48 in. long and rests on supports 36 in. apart overhanging 12 in. It carries 180 lb at the overhanging end and 500 lb 24 in. from the overhanging end. Calculate the deflection at the 500-lb load.

Ans. $y = 2.14$ in.

10-60. A beam of length L rests on supports at the ends and carries a uniform load W over one-half. Calculate the deflection at the midpoint.

10-19. Location and Amount of Maximum Deflection, Simple or Overhanging Beams.

The tangent to the elastic curve is horizontal at the point where the deflection is greatest. This fact may be used to determine where the maximum deflection occurs.

In the beam shown in Fig. 10-38 the angle θ between the tangent at the right reaction and the original horizontal line of the beam may be computed from

$$\theta = \Delta_1/L \text{ radians}$$

(It should be kept in mind that this angle in an actual beam is very small. It is greatly exaggerated in the sketch.)

Since the tangent at the point of maximum deflection is horizontal, it also makes the angle θ with the reference tangent at the right reaction.

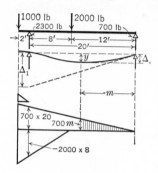

By the first area-moment proposition the area of the shaded part of the bending-moment diagram divided by EI equals θ, the angle between these two tangents. The shaded area therefore equals $EI\theta$. If this area can be expressed in terms of its unknown length m and equated to $EI\theta$, it will be possible to solve for m.

Two examples will illustrate the application of this method.

Fig. 10-38

Example 1. A wooden beam 6 in. wide, 8 in. deep, and 22 ft long is supported and loaded as shown in Fig. 10-38. Calculate the maximum deflection due to the two concentrated loads. Assume $E = 1,200,000$ psi.

Solution:

$$\Delta_1 = \frac{700 \times 20 \times 12 \times 120 \times 80 - 2,000 \times 8 \times 12 \times 48 \times 32}{1,200,000 \times 256} = 4.29 \text{ in.}$$

Also $\theta = \Delta_1/L = 4.29/240 = 0.0179$ radian. But $EI\theta = $ shaded area. Thus $0.0179 \times 1,200,000 \times 256 = 700m^2/2$, whence $m^2 = 15,660$ and $m = 125$ in.

The maximum deflection y is equal in amount to Δ_2, the displacement of the right reaction from the tangent at the point of maximum deflection. But Δ_2 equals the moment of the shaded area with respect to the right reaction, divided by EI.

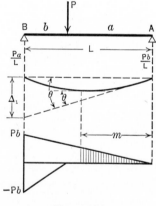

$$y = -\Delta_2 =$$

$$-\frac{700 \times 125 \times \frac{125}{2} \times \frac{2}{3} \times 125}{1,200,000 \times 256} = -1.49 \text{ in.}$$

Example 2. Derive an expression for the maximum deflection in a beam on two supports due to a single concentrated load as shown in Fig. 10-39.

Fig. 10-39

Solution: The bending-moment diagram is drawn by parts beginning at the reaction farthest from the load, and the tangent at the support farthest from the load will be used.

$$EI\Delta_1 = Pb \times \frac{L}{2} \times \frac{L}{3} - Pb \times \frac{b}{2} \times \frac{b}{3} = \frac{Pb}{6}(L^2 - b^2)$$

$$= \frac{Pb}{6}(L - b)(L + b) = \frac{Pab(L + b)}{6}$$

Since θ is a small angle,

$$\theta = \frac{\Delta_1}{L} = \frac{Pab(L+b)}{6EIL}$$

But θ is also the angle between the tangent at the point of maximum deflection and the tangent at the support, and consequently θ equals the shaded area divided by EI.

Hence

$$\theta = \frac{Pbm}{EIL} \times \frac{m}{2} = \frac{Pbm^2}{2EIL}$$

Equating these values of θ,

$$Pbm^2/2EIL = Pab(L+b)/6EIL$$

Whence

$$m = \sqrt{\tfrac{1}{3}a(L+b)} = \tfrac{1}{3}\sqrt{3a(L+b)}$$

Since the tangent at the point of maximum deflection is horizontal, the maximum deflection equals the moment of the shaded area with respect to A, divided by EI.

Hence

$$y_{max} = -\frac{Pbm}{EIL} \times \frac{m}{2} \times \frac{2}{3}m = -\frac{Pbm^3}{3EIL}$$

Substituting the value found above for m,

$$y_{max} = -\frac{Pab(L+b)\sqrt{3a(L+b)}}{27EIL}$$

The steps to be taken in calculating the maximum deflection of an unsymmetrically loaded beam on two supports are:

(a) Assume the tangent at one support as the reference tangent.

(b) Draw the bending-moment diagram in the simplest way.

(c) Calculate Δ_1, the displacement of the other support from the reference tangent.

(d) Compute the angle θ between the reference tangent and the horizontal.

(e) Express the area of the part of the bending-moment diagram between the point of tangency and the point of maximum deflection in terms of the unknown distance m to the point of maximum deflection.

(f) Equate this to $EI\theta$, and solve for m.

(g) Having found m, solve for deflection.

PROBLEMS

10-61. In Fig. 10-40 let $a = 5$ in., $L = 12$ in., $P = 12$ lb, and $EI = 1,200$. Calculate the maximum upward deflection between A and B.

10-62. In Fig. 10-40 let $a = L/3$ and derive an expression for the maximum upward deflection in terms of P, EI, and L. *Ans.* $y = PL^3/27EI\sqrt{3}$.

10-63. In Fig. 10-40 let $a = 4$ ft, $L = 10$ ft, $P = 100$ lb, and $EI = 6,000,000$. Calculate the maximum upward deflection.

10-64. In Fig. 10-41, $a = 12$ in., $L = 72$ in., $P_1 = P_2 = 60$ lb, and $EI = 600,000$. Calculate the maximum deflection.

10-65. In Fig. 10-41, $a = 24$ in., $L = 120$ in., $P_1 = 200$ lb, $P_2 = 100$ lb, and $EI = 12,000,000$. Calculate the maximum deflection.

FIG. 10-40   FIG. 10-41

10-66. A small beam rests on end supports 72 in. center to center and carries a uniformly distributed load of 36 lb covering 24 in. at the end of the beam. Calculate the maximum deflection. $EI = 144,000$.   *Ans.* $y = -0.916$ in.

10-20. Relation between Deflection and Bending Stress. At times it is desirable to know what the maximum deflection of a beam will be when it is loaded, so that the maximum bending stress in it has a known value, or to know what the maximum bending stress in the beam will be when the maximum deflection has a known value. This relationship is obtained for any one of the preceding cases by expressing the load P or W in terms of the maximum stress which it causes, and inserting the quantity in this form into the deflection equation. Thus, for a cantilever beam carrying a concentrated load P at the end, the maximum bending moment is PL lb-in. But $M = SI/c$, from which $P = S_{max}I/cL$. Inserting this value in the equation for the maximum deflection of the beam,

$$y_{max} = \frac{S_{max}(I/cL) \times L^3}{3EI} = \frac{S_{max}L^2}{3Ec}$$

Corresponding relationships can be similarly developed for other types of beams and loadings.

From the above value of y it can be seen that, when the designer selects a beam of given length to carry given loads with a specified allowable stress, the deflection will be inversely proportional to c or, in most cases, inversely proportional to the depth of the beam.

10-21. Errors in Calculated Deflections. The calculation of the true deflection of a beam by the exact equation

$$\frac{M}{EI} = \frac{d^2y/dx^2}{[1 + (dy/dx)^2]^{3/2}}$$

is, in general, very laborious. However, for a beam resting on two supports and bent by equal couples at the supports, as shown in Fig. 10-42, the curve is a circular arc and the middle ordinate can be found

by trigonometry.   As calculated either by the simplified equation for
the elastic curve or by the area-moment method, $y = Mx^2/2EI$, and
both methods give for the maximum deflection $\Delta = ML^2/8EI$.   The
simplifying assumptions make the elastic curve for this case a parabola,
when the curve is, in fact, a circular arc.   How
serious is this error?

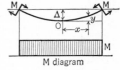

The following tabulations are deflections for
a beam 100 in. (8 ft 4 in.) long, subject to
bending moments such that EI/M (the radius of
curvature) has the values given.   The values
designated as "True Δ" are the calculated middle
ordinates of circular arcs 100 in. long with the given radii of curvature;
the values designated as "Approx. Δ" are calculated by the formula Δ
$= ML^2/8EI$.

M diagram

Fig. 10-42

PERCENTAGE OF ERROR IN DEFLECTION OF A BEAM AS CALCULATED BY
METHODS INVOLVING THE COMMON SIMPLIFICATION

$\rho = EI/M$ (in.)	5,000	1,000	200	100	50
True Δ (in.)	0.250	1.250	6.22	12.24	23.00
Approx. Δ (in.)	0.250	1.250	6.25	12.50	25.00
Error (%)	.....	.....	$\frac{1}{2}$ of 1%	2%	9%
$\dfrac{\text{Approx. }\Delta}{L}$	$\frac{1}{400}$	$\frac{1}{80}$	$\frac{1}{16}$	$\frac{1}{8}$	$\frac{1}{4}$

For the same ratios of calculated deflection to length of beam, but
with different loadings, the percentage errors will be of the *same order* of
magnitude.   For beams used in structures and most machines, Δ/L is
less than 1/400 and consequently the error is entirely negligible.

The errors in computed values of the deflections which result from the
approximate equation can be serious only in relatively slender beams, for
which the ratio of length to depth is large.   Unless the beam is slender,
the stresses accompanying a large deflection will exceed the proportional
limit of the material, and the methods of finding the deflections that
have been discussed do not apply.

In short beams heavily loaded, the deflection due to shearing stresses
(which, as noted in Art. 10-3, is not included in the expressions for
deflection that have been worked out) may be fairly large in comparison
with the deflections due to bending.   This subject is discussed in
Chapter 19.

10-22. Beams with Variable *EI*.   Beams are sometimes used in which
the cross-sections are not the same from end to end.   Two such beams
are shown in Fig. 9-11.   Deflections occurring in such beams can be
calculated by area moments by using the M/EI diagram.   For two

simple cases the M diagrams and the M/EI diagrams are shown in Fig. 10-43 and Fig. 10-44.

Example. Calculate the maximum deflection of the steel beam in Fig. 10-44a and compare with the deflection of a beam of same length and loading but in which $I = 0.5$ in.[4] from end to end.

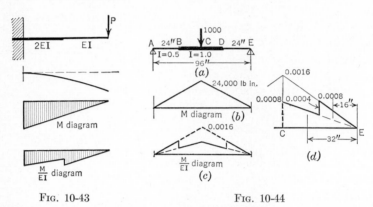

FIG. 10-43   FIG. 10-44

Solution: If I were constant and equal to 0.5 in.[4], the M/EI diagram would be a triangle (Fig. 10-44c) with the maximum ordinate $24,000/(0.5 \times 30,000,000) = 0.0016$. In the beam described the ordinates of the M/EI diagram between B and D are half those of this triangle. The ordinates of the M/EI diagram are shown in Fig. 10-44d. The maximum deflection equals the moment with respect to E of the right half of the M/EI diagram (shown in Fig. 10-44d).

$$y = 0.0008 \times 24 \times 32 + 0.0004 \times 12 \times 16 = 0.616 + 0.076 = 0.692 \text{ in.}$$

If $I = 0.5$ in.[4] for the entire length

$$y = (24,000 \times 24 \times 32)/(30,000,000 \times 0.5) = 1.23 \text{ in.}$$

GENERAL PROBLEMS

10-67. A 4-in. 7.7-lb I-beam is anchored down at one end and rests on a support 10 ft from this end. It projects 4.5 ft beyond the support. A load of 1,000 lb is applied at the overhanging end. Calculate the maximum upward deflection caused by the concentrated load. *Ans.* $y = 0.277$ in.

10-68. A 6×8 in. (actual size) wooden beam ($E = 1,200,000$ psi) rests on supports 20 ft apart. The 8-in. sides are vertical. A uniformly distributed load of 3,600 lb covers 12 ft of the beam at one end. Calculate the deflection at the center caused by this load.

10-69. A 12-in. 35.0-lb American standard beam is used as a cantilever projecting 22 ft. A concentrated load applied 4 ft from the free end causes a maximum bending stress of 20,000 psi. Calculate the deflection at the end of the beam.

10-70. A simple beam L in. long carries a concentrated load of P lb at a distance b from one reaction. (a) Prove that at a point between the load and the other reaction and k in. from the other reaction the deflection is $y = \dfrac{Pbk}{6EIL} (L^2 - b^2 - k^2)$.

(b) A and B are two points on a simple beam. Prove that the deflection of point A caused by a load P applied at B equals the deflection of point B caused by the load P applied at A.

10-71. A floor is to carry a live load of 75 lb per sq ft, and the weight of the floor itself, the joists, and the ceiling below may be taken as 18 lb per sq ft. The floor is carried on 2 × 12 in. (nominal size) joists of southern pine, spaced 16 in. on centers and with a span of 15 ft. For long-continued loading the modulus of elasticity of these joists may be taken as 700,000 psi. (a) Does the maximum deflection of these joists, caused by the live load alone, exceed $\frac{1}{360}$ of the span? (b) Does the stress exceed allowable stress in Table XI?

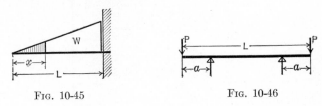

FIG. 10-45   FIG. 10-46

10-72. Derive an expression for the deflection at the end of a cantilever beam carrying a total load of W which varies as shown in Fig. 10-45. (*Hint:* The part of the load on a length x of the beam is Wx^2/L^2.)   *Ans.* $y = WL^3/15EI$.

10-73. Each of two cantilever beams is L in. long and loaded at the end with a load of P lb. One is of circular cross-section, the diameter being D at all sections. The other is circular, the diameter being $D/2$ for the half length nearer the load and D for the other half. How do the deflections compare?

10-74. Prove that the deflection of the end of the beam shown in Fig. 10-46 is $(Pa/6EI)(3aL - 4a^2)$.

FIG. 10-47   FIG. 10-48

10-75. A beam L in. long is bent by a couple of T lb-in. applied at the midpoint, as shown in Fig. 10-47. Calculate the maximum slope of the beam. Calculate the end slope of the beam.

10-76. Prove that the maximum deflection of the beam shown in Fig. 10-48 is $(Pa/6EI)(\frac{3}{4}L^2 - a^2)$.

Note: Problems 10-77 to 10-81 are statically indeterminate. The solutions depend upon the fact that the beams which are in contact deflect equal amounts at the point of contact and each beam exerts the same force on the other at the point of contact. Formulas for deflections given in Appendix C may be used.

10-77. Two wooden cantilever beams, each 6 × 6 in. in cross-section, extend a distance of 8 ft from the face of the wall. One beam is exactly over the other and is 3 in. above it. At the free end a roller is placed between the two beams to keep them 3 in. apart, without exerting any other restraint on them. A load of 600 lb is placed on the upper beam, directly over the roller. (a) Does this cause a reaction of 300 lb on the lower beam? (b) What is the reaction of the roller if, in addition to the 600-lb load on the upper beam, a load of 180 lb is applied to the lower beam at a point 2 ft from the wall?   (Assume $E = 1,200,000$ psi.)

Ans.   (b) $R = 292$ lb.

10-78. A and B (Fig. 10-49) are two similar beams.   A screw-jack C is inserted between the beams and exerts an upward load of P lb upon A and a downward load of P lb upon B.   The strength of each beam is such that a central load of $4P$ causes a stress equal to the proportional limit.   What downward load can be applied to the top of beam A at its midpoint without causing a stress greater than the proportional limit in either beam?

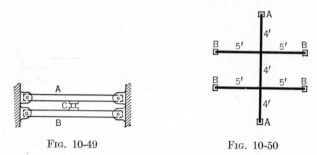

Fig. 10-49   Fig. 10-50

10-79. In Fig. 10-50, A–A is a simply supported beam, and the two beams B–B are simply supported beams which are just in contact with the upper surface of A–A when unloaded.   A load of 1,600 lb is applied to the midpoint of each of the beams B–B.   Calculate the reactions at A and B due to the loads. EI is the same for all three beams.

10-80. A 12-in. 35-lb I-beam projects 15 ft from the face of a wall into which the other end is rigidly fixed.   The free end of the cantilever is just in contact with the midpoint of the top flange of another 12-in. 35-lb I-beam 15 ft long which rests on supports at its end, no force being exerted between the two beams.   A load of 20,000 lb is placed on the cantilever beam 12 ft from the wall.   What reactions does this load cause at the ends of the simple beam?   *Ans.* $R = 6,630$ lb.

10-81. A beam of length L rests on two supports at the ends, and at its midpoint its lower surface is in contact with the top surface of the end of a cantilever beam $L/2$ in length.   If a load of P lb is applied to the upper beam at each quarter-point, calculate the force F exerted by the cantilever beam on the simple beam. E and I are the same for both beams.

11

Restrained Beams

11-1. Introduction. The simple and overhanging beams so far considered have been assumed to rest on supports which offer no *restraint* as the beam deflects, so that the elastic curve is free to assume any slope at the support. Knife-edges and frictionless pins are examples of such supports. Ordinary bearing plates and many riveted connections approximate the condition, and the shears and moments in beams supported on them are customarily calculated on the assumption that there is no restraint at the support.

In this chapter two types of *statically indeterminate beams* will be considered. These are commonly called "beams fixed at one end" and "beams fixed at both ends." A third type, "continuous beams," will be considered in Chapter 17.

Beams that are fixed against rotation at one end or at both ends are not uncommon in modern structures and are of considerable importance.

11-2. Beams with Fixed Ends. In Fig. 11-1 a beam fixed at one end and a beam fixed at both ends are shown. The restraint may actually be furnished by other means than by embedding the end in a wall. The diagrams at the top show the conventional way of representing the beams. Below them are shown the shapes of the elastic curves. The diagrams at the bottom show the beams as free bodies with the external forces and moments which hold the free bodies in equilibrium.

For purposes of analysis the important fact about a fixed end is that the slope of the beam remains zero (the tangent to the elastic curve remains horizontal) at the point of restraint as the beam is loaded. In the conventional representation of the beam, the point of restraint is considered to be at the "face of the wall." Consequently the beam is regarded as extending to the face of the wall (or walls, if the beam is fixed at both ends) and to be in equilibrium under the loads applied to it and the shears and moments that act on it in the plane of the wall as in Fig. 11-1c and f.

The reason for calling these beams "statically indeterminate" can now be understood. Consider the beam which is fixed at one end and supported at the other end. Only two equations of statics exist for the

189

determination of the forces acting on this beam, since there are no horizontal forces. But the free body shows that, in addition to the vertical forces at A and B, the beam is acted on by a moment of unknown amount at A. The two available equations are not sufficient to determine these three unknowns. That is, there are any number of combina-

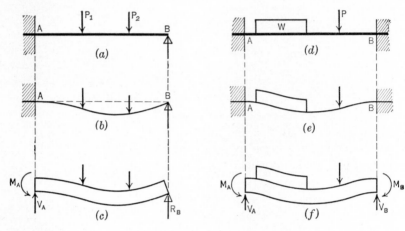

Fig. 11-1

tions of values of M_A, V_A, and R_B which will satisfy the conditions of equilibrium. This can easily be seen if some value for R_B is arbitrarily assumed. Whatever this assumed value of R_B, use of $\Sigma M = 0$ and $\Sigma V = 0$ will establish values of M_A and of V_A consistent with it. Therefore some condition in addition to the two given by the equations of statics is required to establish which one of the possible sets of values is the correct one for the beam in question. Usually this additional condition is that the deflection of B is zero.

When a beam is fixed at *both* ends, there are *two* reaction elements in addition to those required for equilibrium, Fig. 11-1f. *Two* equations in addition to those of statics are needed unless the beam is symmetrically loaded.

In the design or investigation of statically indeterminate beams the first step is to find the values of the moments and forces that act on the beam at the supports. After these have been found, bending moments and shears and deflections at points along the length of the beam can be determined by principles given in previous chapters.

Succeeding articles will outline methods of determining the external moments and forces on restrained beams, and the deflections caused by certain loadings. First the area-moment method will be used, and, after that, the double-integration method. Finally the method of superposition will be applied to beams fixed at one end. For beams fixed at both ends super-position is less advantageous.

AREA-MOMENT METHOD

11-3. Beam Fixed at One End; Concentrated Load at Midpoint. The beam and loading are shown in Fig. 11-2a, and the approxi-mate shape of the elastic curve is shown in b. The bending-moment diagram is drawn in two parts as shown in c, the ordinates of the upper triangle representing the moments due to the unknown re-action R.

If the support at B is on the level of the horizontal tangent at A, the displacement of B from the tangent at A is zero. Therefore the moment, with respect to B,

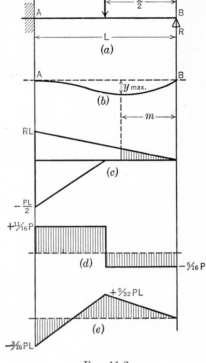

Fig. 11-2

of the bending-moment diagram, divided by EI, is zero. Hence

$$\frac{RL \times \dfrac{L}{2} \times \dfrac{2}{3}L - \dfrac{PL}{2} \times \dfrac{L}{4} \times \dfrac{5}{6}L}{EI} = 0$$

Solving for R, $R = \frac{5}{16}P$

After the value of the reaction is known, it is treated as an upward load in calculating shears and bending moments, which are found by the methods previously explained. It is generally convenient to use the segment which does not include the fixed end in calculating shears and bending moments. At the load, $M = 5PL/32$. At the fixed end, $M_A = 5PL/16 - PL/2 = -3PL/16$.

The shear diagram and the combined bending-moment diagram are shown in d and e. At the point of maximum deflection the tangent to the elastic curve is horizontal and therefore parallel to the tangent at A. From this fact it follows that the area of the bending-moment diagram between the point of maximum deflection and A, the fixed end, is zero.

This fact may be used to determine the location of the point where the deflection is maximum. The total plus area in the M diagram is $\frac{5}{16}PL \times L/2 = \frac{5}{32}PL^2$.

The total minus area is $PL/2 \times L/4 = \frac{1}{8}PL^2$.

Let m be the number of inches from B to the point of maximum deflection; then

$$\tfrac{5}{32}PL^2 - \tfrac{1}{8}PL^2 - \tfrac{5}{16}Pm \times m/2 = 0$$

from which $m^2 = L^2/5$ and $m = 0.447L$

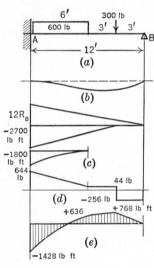

(a)

(b)

(c)

(d)

(e)

Fig. 11-3

The maximum deflection equals the displacement of B from the horizontal tangent. Hence

$$EI\Delta = (5P/16)(0.447L)(0.447L/2) \times$$
$$(2 \times 0.447L/3)$$

and

$$y_{max} = -0.00931PL^3/EI$$

11-4. Beam Fixed at One End; Any Loading. The value of the reaction on a beam fixed at one end with any loading may be found by the procedure used in Art. 11-3. The bending-moment diagram is drawn "by parts," working toward the fixed end. One of the parts is the triangular area due to the unknown R.

Example. A small beam is fixed at one end and loaded and supported as shown in Fig. 11-3. Calculate the value of the reaction. Draw shear and bending-moment diagrams.

Solution: The bending-moment diagram is drawn as shown. Since the deflection at the reaction is zero, the moment of the M diagram with respect to B is zero. Hence

$$12R \times 6 \times 8 - 2{,}700 \times 4.5 \times 9 - 1{,}800 \times 2 \times 10.5 = 0$$

Whence

$$R = (109{,}350 + 37{,}800)/576 = 190 + 66 = 256 \text{ lb}$$

Note that 190 lb of the reaction is caused by the uniform load, and 66 lb by the concentrated load.

The shear at $A = 900 - 256 = 644$ lb. Bending moments are calculated by summing up moments of the loads on the segment on which the reaction acts. Thus $M_A = 12 \times 256 - 9 \times 300 - 600 \times 3 = -1{,}428$ lb-ft.

With R_B, V_A, and M_A known, the shear and combined bending-moment diagrams can be drawn. They are shown at (d) and (e). As with simple beams, it is evident that "dangerous sections" occur at points where the shear line passes through zero. The combined bending-moment diagram shows a point of zero bending moment between the fixed end and the load. Between this point and the fixed end the bending moment is negative, and the beam is bent concave down; between this point and the other end of the beam the beam is concave up.

In examples like this one, where the deflection of the support is zero from the tangent at the fixed end, the amount of the reaction at the support is independent of E and I, provided that EI is a constant throughout the length of the beam. This means that the reaction will be the same for a beam of any cross-section and material carrying this load, provided, of course, that the proportional limits of the material is not exceeded. In such cases the equation may be written in foot units instead of inch units, which simplifies the arithmetic slightly.

PROBLEMS

In each of the following problems calculate the reaction R and draw the shear diagram and the combined bending-moment diagram.

11-1. Figure 11-4, $P_1 = P_2 = 800$ lb.   *Ans.* $R_R = 443$ lb.

11-2. Figure 11-4, $P_1 = 2,000$ lb, $P_2 = 3,000$ lb.

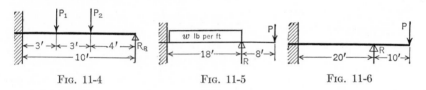

FIG. 11-4   FIG. 11-5   FIG. 11-6

11-3. Figure 11-5, $w = 500$, $P = 1,500$ lb.

11-4. Figure 11-5, $w = 1,000$, $P = 2,000$ lb.   *Ans.* $R_B = 10,100$ lb.

11-5. Figure 11-6, $P = 12,000$ lb. Select lightest WF beam to carry this loading. Allowable stress 18,000 psi.

11-6. Figure 11-6, $P = 15,000$ lb. Select lightest WF beam to carry this loading. Allowable stress 20,000 psi.

11-7. Beam of length L fixed at one end and supported at other end with load P placed $0.4L$ from the reaction.   *Ans.* $R_B = 0.432P$.

11-8. Beam of length L fixed at one end and supported at other end with uniform load. Refer to Fig. 11-16 for answers to this problem.

11-9. A beam of length L ft, fixed at one end and supported at the other end, is loaded with a uniform load of w lb per ft over the half of the beam nearer the fixed end. Calculate the end reaction, and draw shear and bending-moment diagrams. Calculate the distance from the support to the point of contraflexure.

11-10. In Fig. 11-5, $w = 1,000$. Calculate the load P that will make the tangent at R horizontal.   *Ans.* $P = 3,360$ lb.

11-11. Solve Problem 11-9 but let the load cover the half of the beam nearer the support.

11-5. Support Not on Level of Tangent at Fixed End.

If a beam fixed at one end is supported at some point and the support is pushed up above the line of the tangent at the fixed end, the amount of this reaction increases.   If the support settles below the level of the tangent, the amount of the reaction decreases.   The reaction becomes zero when

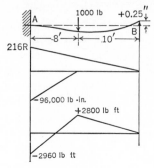

the support is lowered until the beam carries the loads as a cantilever, if it is able to do so.

The method of solving for the amount of the reaction in such problems is much the same as where the support remains on the "level." E and I must be known (or assumed), since they do not go out of the equation as they do when the support is at the same level as the fixed end.

Fig. 11-7

Example.   A 5-in. 10-lb I-beam is fixed at one end and loaded as shown in Fig. 11-7.   The other end is supported, and the support is jacked up 0.25 in. above the tangent.   Calculate the amount of the reaction.

Solution:

$$0.25 = \frac{216R \times 108 \times 144 - 96{,}000 \times 48 \times 184}{30{,}000{,}000 \times 12.1}$$

$$90{,}750{,}000 + 848{,}000{,}000 = 216R \times 108 \times 144$$

$$R = 253 + 27 = 280 \text{ lb}$$

In following through this solution it will be observed that 27 lb of this reaction is due to the fact that the support is elevated.   For each additional $\frac{1}{4}$ in. of upward displacement the reaction will increase by 27 lb; and, if the support is lowered, there will be a decrease of 27 lb for each $\frac{1}{4}$ in.

PROBLEM

11-12. Solve the example above if the support is lowered 0.70 in. below the tangent. Draw combined M diagram.   By what amount does the lowering of the support increase the maximum stress in the beam?

11-6. Beams Fixed at Both Ends.

As was pointed out in Art. 11-1, in a beam fixed at both ends there are an unknown moment and an unknown shear at each support (Fig. 11-8).   The determination of these four unknown quantities requires four equations. $\Sigma M = 0$ and $\Sigma V = 0$ furnish two of these equations.   In the general case of unsymmetrical loading, the other two equations are provided by the area-

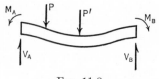

Fig. 11-8

moment propositions, the conditions of restraint that are present being utilized.

In order to understand the drawing of the bending-moment diagram, consider a section at a distance x from the A end of the beam shown in

Fig. 11-8. On the left-hand segment there are the unknown upward force V_A, the downward loads, and also the unknown end moment M_A, assumed positive, which must be included with the moments of the forces. Therefore the bending moment at a distance x from the A end is

$$M_x = M_A + V_A x - \text{Moments of intervening loads}$$

In drawing a bending-moment diagram for the beam, it is convenient to plot these terms separately, as shown in Fig. 11-9a. The moment

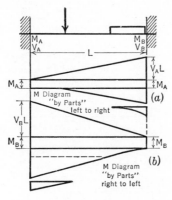

FIG. 11-9

M_A is the same for all values of x and appears as a rectangle in the bending-moment diagram. The term $V_A x$ results in a triangle, since the moment of V_A increases as x increases. The moment of each intervening load results in a triangle if the load is concentrated, and in a parabolic area if the load is uniformly distributed.

If more convenient, the distance x may be measured from the B end of the beam. In this case the moment equation is

$$M_x = M_B + V_B x - \text{Moments of intervening loads}$$

With x measured from the B end of the beam, the bending-moment diagram is as shown in Fig. 11-9b.

11-7. Beams Fixed at Both Ends; Symmetrical Loading. Because of the symmetry of loading, V_A and V_B each equals one-half the sum of the loads. Since V_A is known, only one equation based on the conditions of restraint is necessary. The simplest equation is based on the fact that in a symmetrical beam the tangent at the midpoint is horizontal and therefore parallel to the tangent at either fixed end.

Example. Calculate the shear and bending moment at the left end of the beam in Fig. 11-10 caused by the concentrated loads. Draw shear and combined bending-moment diagrams.

Solution: Since the beam is symmetrical, $V_A = 1,000$ lb. Since the tangent at the midpoint is parallel to the tangent at the left end, the area of the M diagram between these two points is zero. Therefore

$$10,000 \times 5 + 10M_A - 4,000 \times 2 = 0$$

$$M_A = 800 - 5,000 = -4,200 \text{ lb-ft}$$

$$M_6 = M_A + 6V_A = -4,200 + 6,000 = +1,800 \text{ lb-ft}$$

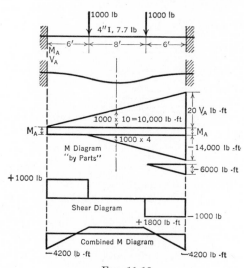

Fig. 11-10

PROBLEMS

11-13. Calculate the deflection at the midpoint of the beam in the preceding example. Calculate the deflection at a load.

11-14. Calculate the end moments, the moment at the midpoint, and the maximum deflection of the beam shown in Fig. 11-11. Draw shear diagram and combined bending-moment diagram.   *Ans.* $M_A = -11WL/96$.

11-15. The beam shown in Fig. 11-11 is a 5-in. 10-lb American standard beam, L is 12 ft, and W is 6,000 lb. Calculate the maximum bending stress caused by the load W. Draw shear and bending-moment diagrams.

11-16. A small beam in a machine is shown in Fig. 11-11. $L = 72$ in., $W = 144$ lb, and $EI = 6,000,000$. Calculate bending moments, and draw shear diagram and combined bending-moment diagram. Calculate maximum deflection.

11-17. Select the lightest WF beam to carry the loads shown in Fig. 11-12 if P_1 is 12,000 lb, P_2 is 14,000 lb, and the allowable stress is 20,000 psi. Draw shear diagram and combined bending-moment diagram. Neglect weight of beam. $L = 30$ ft.

11-18. In Fig. 11-12, $L = 96$ in., $P_1 = 60$ lb, $P_2 = 80$ lb, and $EI = 10,000,000$. Calculate bending moments, and draw shear and combined bending-moment diagrams. Calculate deflection at midpoint.   *Ans.* $M_A = -170$ lb-ft.

11-19. A beam L in. long, fixed at both ends, carries a concentrated load of P lb at the midpoint. Using the area-moment method, calculate the bending moments at the ends and at the midpoint, and the maximum deflection, in terms of E and I. Compare these with the corresponding values for a simple beam loaded in the same way.

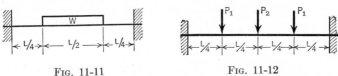

FIG. 11-11   FIG. 11-12

11-20. A beam L in. long, fixed at both ends, carries a load of W lb uniformly distributed over its entire length. Using the area-moment method, calculate the bending moments at the ends and at the midpoint, and the maximum deflection, in terms of E and I. Compare these with the corresponding values for a simple beam loaded in the same way.   *Ans.* $y = -WL^3/384EI$.

11-8. Beams Fixed at Both Ends; Unsymmetrical Loading.

In this case two unknown quantities must be solved for by equations based on the conditions of restraint. The method of drawing the bending-moment diagram which has been shown makes it most convenient to solve for the bending moment and shear at one end. There are three conditions of restraint, and the two which result in the simplest equations should be chosen. Those available are:

1. The tangent at one end is parallel to the tangent at the other end.

2. The displacement of the right end from the tangent at the left end equals zero.

3. The displacement of the left end from the tangent at the right end equals zero.

Example 1. The beam used in the Example of Art. 11-7, with one of the loads omitted, will be considered. This is shown in Fig. 11-13. Solve for the shear and moment at each end, and draw a combined M diagram.

Solution: The equation based on the first condition of the three listed is:

$$20V_B \times 10 + 20M_B - 6{,}000 \times 3 = 0$$
$$10V_B + M_B = 900 \tag{1}$$

The equation based on the third condition listed is:

$$20V_B \times 10 \times \tfrac{2.0}{3} + 20M_B \times 10 - 6{,}000 \times 3 \times 2 = 0$$
$$\tfrac{2.0}{3}V_B + M_B = 180 \tag{2}$$

Subtracting equation 2 from equation 1,

$$\tfrac{1.0}{3}V_B = 720$$
$$V_B = 216 \text{ lb}$$

Therefore, since $\Sigma V = 0$, $V_A = 1{,}000 - 216 = 784$ lb, and with these values the shear diagram can be drawn.

The positive value found for V_B indicates that V_B causes positive bending moment as assumed in the first equation. It is therefore an upward force on the right-hand end of the segment, and, according to the usual shear convention, this is negative shear, and it is so shown in the shear diagram.

Also from equation 1

$$M_B = 900 - 10V_B = 900 - 2,160 = -1,260 \text{ lb-ft}$$

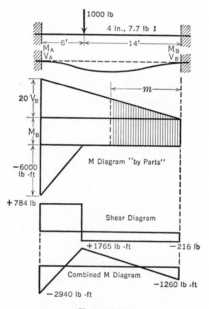

Fig. 11-13

As shown on the bending-moment diagram "by parts,"

$$M_A = 20V_B + M_B - 6,000$$

Therefore $M_A = 4,320 - 1,260 - 6,000 = -2,940$ lb-ft.

At the load the bending moment equals

$$M_6 = M_B + 14V_B = -1,260 + 14 \times 216 = +1,765 \text{ lb-ft}$$

With these values the combined bending-moment diagram can be drawn.

Example 2. Find the location and amount of the maximum deflection of the beam in Example 1.

Solution: The position of the maximum deflection is found more easily in this example than for a simple beam. The maximum deflection occurs where the tangent is horizontal. Between this point and either support the area of the M diagram equals zero. Representing the unknown distance to the right support by m, the area is

$$(216m \times m/2) - 1,260m = 0$$

$$m = (1,260 \times 2)/216 = 11.67 \text{ ft or } 140 \text{ in.}$$

The maximum deflection equals the statical moment of this part of the area, with respect to one end, divided by EI. Taking the statical moment of this area about the right-hand end, the deflection is

$$y = \frac{140 \times 216 \times 70 \times \frac{2}{3} \times 140 - 1{,}260 \times 12 \times 140 \times 70}{30{,}000{,}000 \times 6.0} = 0.275 \text{ in.}$$

PROBLEMS

11-21. A 4-in. 7.7-lb I-beam is fixed at both ends, the fixed points being 18 ft apart. A load of 2,600 lb is applied 6 ft from one end. Calculate the shear and bending moment at each end and the deflection at the midpoint caused by the 2,600-lb load.   *Ans.* $y = 0.560$ in.

11-22. A steel beam has a span of 24 ft, clear, and is fixed at both ends. A load of 6,000 lb is uniformly distributed over the left half of the beam. Neglecting weight of beam, draw shear and bending-moment diagrams, indicating values at significant points, including maximum bending moment. Select the lightest steel I-beam that can be used with a stress of not more than 18,000 psi. Calculate the deflection at the center.

11-23. In Fig. 11-14, $L = 72$ in., and $P = 20$ lb. Calculate bending moments, and draw shear diagram and combined bending-moment diagram. Calculate the deflection at the midpoint if $EI = 100{,}000$.

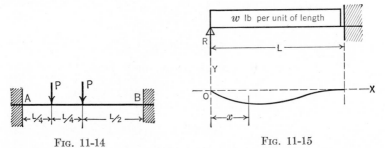

Fig. 11-14	Fig. 11-15

11-24. In Fig. 11-14, $L = 120$ in., $P = 80$ lb. Calculate shears and bending moments, and draw shear diagram and combined bending-moment diagram. Calculate the deflection at the midpoint. $EI = 6{,}000{,}000$.   *Ans.* $y = 0.180$ in.

11-25. A beam of length L, fixed at both ends, has a single load P at a distance $L/3$ from one end. Calculate the end shears and end moments, and draw shear diagram and combined bending-moment diagram.

11-26. Solve Problem 11-25 if the beam carries two loads P at distances from one end of $0.3L$ and $0.6L$, respectively.

DOUBLE-INTEGRATION METHOD

11-9. Beam Fixed at One End; Double Integration. The solution of beams fixed at one end by double integration will be illustrated by the solution of a beam with uniform loading.

To find the amount of the reaction, R (Fig. 11-15), the equation of the elastic curve may be utilized, employing the condition specified in

Art. 11-12 that the deflection at the supported end is zero.   After R has been found, the conditions of equilibrium are sufficient to permit determination of shears and moments throughout the length of the beam, and the equation of the elastic curve can be used to determine the maximum deflection.

If the origin is chosen at the unrestrained end, the value of M at a distance x from the origin is

$$M_x = Rx - wx^2/2$$

The equation for the elastic curve is therefore

$$EI\, d^2y/dx^2 = Rx - wx^2/2$$

Integrating, $EI\, dy/dx = (Rx^2/2) - (wx^3/6) + C_1$

When $x = L$, $dy/dx = 0$; therefore $C_1 = -RL^2/2 + wL^3/6$, and

$$EI\frac{dy}{dx} = \frac{Rx^2}{2} - \frac{wx^3}{6} - \frac{RL^2}{2} + \frac{wL^3}{6} \tag{1}$$

Integrating again,

$$EIy = \frac{Rx^3}{6} - \frac{wx^4}{24} - \frac{RL^2x}{2} + \frac{wL^3x}{6} + C_2$$

But $y = 0$ when $x = 0$; hence $C_2 = 0$, and

$$EIy = \frac{Rx^3}{6} - \frac{wx^4}{24} - \frac{RL^2x}{2} + \frac{wL^3x}{6} \tag{2}$$

But also, $y = 0$ when $x = L$; hence

$$\frac{RL^3}{6} - \frac{wL^4}{24} - \frac{RL^3}{2} + \frac{wL^4}{6} = 0$$

Solving for R,

$$R = \tfrac{3}{8}wL = \tfrac{3}{8}W$$

The bending moment at the fixed end is

$$M = \frac{3}{8}wL^2 - \frac{wL^2}{2} = -\frac{wL^2}{8}$$

The shear and bending-moment diagrams are shown in Fig. 11-16.   The maximum $+$ bending moment occurs where the shear changes sign, which is $\tfrac{3}{8}L$ from the support.

At this point $M = \dfrac{3}{8}wL \times \dfrac{3}{8}L - \dfrac{\frac{9}{64}wL^2}{2} = \dfrac{9}{128}wL^2.$

To find the location and amount of the maximum deflection of this beam, the value $R = \frac{3}{8}wL$ is substituted in equation 1. Then

$$EI\frac{dy}{dx} = \frac{3}{16}wLx^2 - \frac{wx^3}{6} - \frac{3}{16}wL^3 + \frac{wL^3}{6} \qquad (3)$$

But, since the slope of the elastic curve is zero at the point of maximum

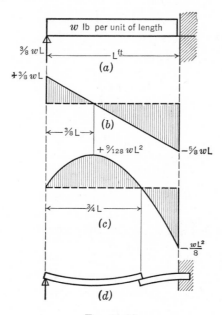

FIG. 11-16

deflection, the abscissa of this point can be found by equating the right-hand member of equation 3 to zero. Hence

$$\tfrac{3}{16}wLx^2 - (wx^3/6) - \tfrac{1}{48}wL^3 = 0$$

One of the roots of this equation is $x = 0.4215L$, which is the distance from the supported end of the beam to the point of maximum deflection. Substituting $\frac{3}{8}wL$ for R in equation 2,

$$EIy = \frac{wLx^3}{16} - \frac{wx^4}{24} - \frac{3}{16}wL^3x + \frac{wL^3x}{6} = -\frac{wL^3x}{48} + \frac{wLx^3}{16} - \frac{wx^4}{24}$$

The value of y for $x = 0.4215L$ is the maximum deflection, which is

$$y_{max} = wL^4/185EI = WL^3/185EI \qquad (11\text{-}1)$$

The same slopes, deflections, and stresses would result in the two beams shown in Fig. 11-16d.

PROBLEMS

11-27. A 4-in. 7.7-lb I-beam is fixed at one end and supported at the other end, the distance between the fixed point and the support being 12 ft. Calculate the maximum bending stress caused by a load of 2,800 lb uniformly distributed.

Ans. $S = 16,800$ psi.

11-28. A beam fixed at one end and simply supported at the other end is 22 ft long and carries a load of 1,000 lb per ft. Select a suitable steel beam. $S = 18,000$ psi.

11-29. Compare the weights of two steel beams of square cross-section, each to carry a uniform load of 2,000 lb with a span of 10 ft and with a unit stress of 20,000 psi, one beam being simply supported at the ends, and the other being fixed at one end and supported at the other.

11-30. A beam 36 ft long on three supports, with two equal spans, carries a uniform load of 4,000 lb on each span. The beam weighs 60 lb per ft. Calculate the maximum bending moment and the amount of the center reaction. (*Hint:* Bending moments and end reactions in each span of a symmetrical continuous beam on three supports are the same as those of a beam fixed at one end and simply supported at the other end. Why?)

FIG. 11-17

11-31. A beam of length L, fixed at end A and supported at end B, has no load, but a couple of T lb-in. is applied at B as shown in Fig. 11-17. By the double-integration method, solve for the vertical reaction at B. Draw shear and bending-moment diagrams. (*Hint:* The bending moment at a distance x from B equals $R_B x - T$.)

Ans. $R = 3T/2L$.

11-10. Beam Fixed at Both Ends; Uniform Load.

In this case there are four unknowns acting on the beam: M_A, M_B, V_A, and V_B (Fig. 11-18). These are two more than the available conditions of static equilibrium. Because of the symmetry of the restraints and the loading, however, $V_A = V_B = wL/2$ and $M_A = M_B$. The equation of the elastic curve can be used to establish the value of M_A. After this has been done, shears and moments can be determined throughout the length of the beam.

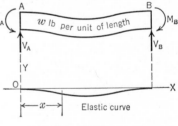

FIG. 11-18

To write an expression for the bending moment at a distance x from the A end, consider the left-hand segment of length x. On this is the upward force V_A, the downward load wx, and also the unknown moment M_A, which must be included with the moments of the forces. Hence

$$M_x = M_A + \frac{wLx}{2} - \frac{wx^2}{2}$$

Hence,

$$EI \frac{d^2y}{dx^2} = M_A + \frac{wLx}{2} - \frac{wx^2}{2}$$

Integrating,

$$EI\frac{dy}{dx} = M_A x + \frac{wLx^2}{4} - \frac{wx^3}{6} + C_1$$

But $dy/dx = 0$ when $x = 0$.   Therefore $C_1 = 0$.

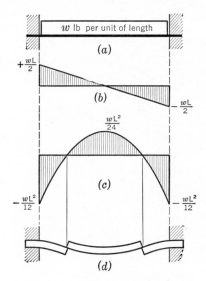

w lb per unit of length

(a)

$+\frac{wL}{2}$

(b)

$-\frac{wL}{2}$

$\frac{wL^2}{24}$

(c)

$-\frac{wL^2}{12}$ $-\frac{wL^2}{12}$

(d)

Fig. 11-19

Also, because of symmetry $dy/dx = 0$ when $x = L/2$.   Hence
$$\frac{M_A L}{2} + \frac{wL^3}{16} - \frac{wL^3}{48} = 0,\ \text{and}$$

$$M_A = -\frac{wL^2}{8} + \frac{wL^2}{24} = -\frac{wL^2}{12} = -\frac{WL}{12} \qquad (11\text{-}2)$$

At the midspan,

$$M = -(wL^2/12) + (wL/2)(L/2) - (wL/2)(L/4)$$

Hence $$M = +wL^2/24 = +WL/24$$

The shear and bending-moment diagrams are as shown in Fig. 11-19b and c.   Substituting the value of M_A in the equation for the slope,

$$EI\frac{dy}{dx} = -\frac{wL^2 x}{12} + \frac{wLx^2}{4} - \frac{wx^3}{6}$$

and integrating,

$$EIy = -\frac{wL^2 x^2}{24} + \frac{wLx^3}{12} - \frac{wx^4}{24} + C_2$$

But $y = 0$ when $x = 0$. Therefore $C_2 = 0$. At center

$$y_{\max} = -\frac{wL^4}{384EI} = -\frac{WL^3}{384EI} \qquad (11\text{-}3)$$

The same slopes, deflections, and stresses would result in the three beams shown in Fig. 11-19d.

PROBLEM

11-32. A beam L in. long and fixed at both ends carries a single concentrated load P at the midpoint. Calculate the bending moments at the ends and at the midpoint, and draw shear and bending-moment diagrams. Find the deflection at the midpoint in terms of E and I. *Ans.* End $M = -PL/8$; $y_{\max} = -PL^3/192EI$.

11-11. Beam Fixed at One End ; Superposition. This article discusses and illustrates the solution of beams fixed at one end by a method based on the "principle of superposition," which affords a simple solution making use of known deflection values for cantilever beams that have been found by area moments or double integration.

As applied to problems of this type, the principle of superposition may be stated thus: The deflection at any point in a beam fixed at one end is the algebraic sum of two deflections: (1) the deflection at that point in a cantilever beam with the same given loads, and (2) the deflection at that point in the same cantilever beam caused by the reaction. If the deflection at the reaction of a beam fixed at one end is zero, the reason is that the reaction has such a value that it produces an upward deflection at the reaction equal to the downward deflection at the same point of the unsupported cantilever due to the given loads. This fact may be expressed as an equation, the solution of which yields a value for R.

In Chapter 10 it was shown that the deflection at the end of a cantilever beam with a concentrated load P at the end is $PL^3/3EI$. In a cantilever beam with any given loading let the deflection at point B due to the loading be y_B, and let the distance to B from the fixed end be L. Then, for a beam fixed at one end and having a support at B and this same loading, the principle of superposition as stated above may be expressed by the following equation:

$$RL^3/3EI - y_B = 0$$

In this equation an expression for y_B in terms of the loads is substituted, and then the equation is solved for R.

Example. A beam of length L, fixed at one end and supported at the other end, as shown in Fig. 11-20a, carries a load P at the midpoint of the beam. (*a*) Calculate the reaction. (*b*) Draw shear and bending-moment diagrams for the beam.

Solution: (*a*) In Table XIII, case 3, the expression for the end deflection of a cantilever beam with a load at the midpoint is $5PL^3/48EI$.   Inserting this value for y_B in the equation given above,

$$RL^3/3EI - 5PL^3/48EI = 0$$

whence

$$R = \tfrac{5}{16}P$$

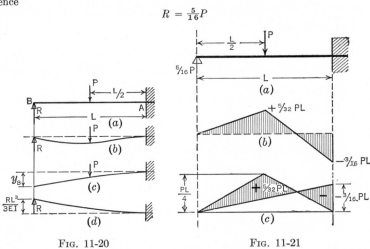

Fig. 11-20   Fig. 11-21

A further application of the principle of superposition indicates that the bending moment at any given point in a beam fixed at one end is the algebraic sum of the bending moment at that point in a beam on two supports (without restraint) and the bending moment at that point due to the end moment M_A.   The bending-moment diagram therefore may be obtained by drawing the bending-moment diagram for a simple beam on two supports and superposing on this diagram the negative triangular area constituting the bending-moment diagram for a simple beam on two supports with a negative moment M_A at one support.   This combination is shown in Fig. 11-21*c*.

PROBLEMS

11-33. Using the value for deflection given in case 3, Table XIII, derive an expression for the reaction in a beam fixed at one end and loaded with a single concentrated load.   If $a = 0.6L$, draw shear and bending-moment diagrams.

11-34. Using the value for deflection given in case 7, Table XIII, derive an expression for the end reaction in a beam fixed at one end with a triangular load. Draw shear and bending-moment diagrams.   *Ans.* $R = W/5$.

11-12. Beam with Fixed Ends Considered as Simple Beam with End Moments.   It is sometimes convenient to think of a restrained beam as a beam simply supported at the ends and acted on not only by a load, or a system of loads, *but also by moments applied to the beam at its ends.*

If these moments are of the proper amounts, they will rotate the ends of the beam until the tangents to the elastic curve are horizontal at those points. In this case the beam meets all the conditions of a beam "fixed at both ends." A restrained beam, then, is simply a beam supported at the ends and acted on by both a system of loads and a system of end moments so adjusted to the loads that the tangents to the elastic curve are horizontal at the ends of the beam.

It follows from this proposition that the bending-moment diagram for a restrained beam may be shown in two parts: (1) the bending-moment diagram for a simple beam carrying the given loads, and (2) the bending-moment diagram for the beam without loads but acted on by the end moments.

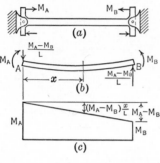

Fig. 11-22

Since the drawing of bending-moment diagrams for simple beams has already been discussed at length, it remains to consider the diagram which represents the bending moments caused in a beam by end moments.

In Fig. 11-22a is shown a beam supported at the ends and with end moments M_A and M_B acting in directions corresponding to plus bending moment. In b is shown the beam as a body in equilibrium with the forces exerted by the supports. These reactions will act in the directions shown if M_A is greater than M_B. At a distance x from A the bending moment is

$$M_x = M_A - \frac{M_A - M_B}{L} x = M_A - (M_A - M_B) \frac{x}{L}$$

If $x = L$, the value of M_x becomes M_B. Therefore, as shown in Fig. 11-22c, the bending-moment diagram due to end moments is a trapezoid with end ordinates of M_A and M_B. If there is an end moment at only one end, the bending-moment diagram is a triangle.

As an example of considering a beam with fixed ends as a simply supported beam with end moments, take the beam shown in Fig. 11-23a. The bending-moment diagram, drawn in two parts, is shown in b. Above the axis is the plus bending-moment diagram for a simple beam with this loading, and below the axis is the negative bending-moment diagram due to the negative end moments. From symmetry M_A and M_B are equal.

The solution for the value of M_A is very simple. Since the tangents at the ends are horizontal, the total area of the M diagram is zero.

Hence

$$(PL/4)(L/2) + M_A L = 0$$

from which

$$M_A = - PL/8$$

The combined bending-moment diagram shown in Fig. 11-23c may be obtained by rotating the negative area about its upper edge. The overlapping plus and minus areas can-
cel. It will thus be seen that the bending-moment diagram for any beam with fixed ends may be drawn by starting with the bending-moment diagram for a simple beam with the same loading and drawing across this diagram a straight line with end ordi-nates of M_A and M_B, respectively. This straight line is then the zero axis.

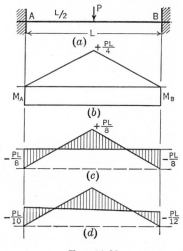

Fig. 11-23

There are many beams with ends not perfectly fixed; in other words, the tangents at the ends are not ex-actly horizontal. Rotation of the right-hand end in a clockwise direc-tion tends to increase the minus bending moment at the right end and decrease the minus bending moment at the left end, as is easily seen if the effect of this rotation on the curvature at the ends of the beam is visualized. The bending-moment diagram for such a beam may be drawn by starting with the bending-moment diagram for a beam on two supports having the same loading and drawing across this a straight line having end ordinates equal to the minus end moments, respectively. As an example Fig. 11-23d shows the bend-ing-moment diagram for the beam shown in Fig. 11-23a but with the end restraints slightly "relaxed."

PROBLEMS

The solution of Problems 11-35 to 11-38 is to be based on bending-moment diagrams drawn in two parts, as suggested in the second paragraph of Art. 11-12. The area-moment propositions are to be used.

11-35. Show that, for a beam fixed at both ends, with any symmetrical loading, the end moment equals $-A/L$, where A is the area of the moment diagram for a simple beam with the same span and loading.

11-36. Show that, for a beam fixed at one end and supported at the other end with any system of loads symmetrical about the midpoint, the bending moment at the fixed end equals $-\frac{3}{2}A/L$, in which A is the area of the moment diagram of a simple beam with the same span and loading.

11-37. Calculate the bending moment at the fixed end of the beam shown in Fig. 11-2.

11-38. Calculate the bending moments at the ends of the beam shown in Fig. 11-13.

GENERAL PROBLEMS

11-39. For a beam fixed at one end and carrying a single concentrated load not at the midpoint (Fig. 11-24) show that $R = (Pb^2/2L^3)(a + 2L)$.

11-40. Using the value of R of Problem 11-39, draw shear and bending-moment diagrams for a beam in which $a = L/4$.

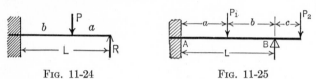

FIG. 11-24　　　　　　FIG. 11-25

11-41. In Fig. 11-24, $L = 72$ in., $a = 24$ in., $P = 100$ lb, and $EI = 600,000\cdot$ Calculate R. Draw shear diagram and combined M diagram. Calculate the deflection at the load.

11-42. In Fig. 11-25 let $L = 120$ in., $a = 60$ in., $c = 30$ in., $P_1 = 600$ lb, $P_2 = 400$ lb. Calculate the reaction, and draw shear diagram and combined bending-moment diagram. Calculate the end deflection. $EI = 60,000,000$.

Ans. $R = 738$ lb.

11-43. In Fig. 11-25 let $L = 24$ ft, $a = 15$ ft, and $c = 6$ ft. $P_1 = 3$ kips, $P_2 = 2$ kips. Calculate the reaction, and draw shear diagram and combined bending-moment diagram.

11-44. In Fig. 11-25 let $P_1 = P_2 = P$, let $a = L/2$, and $c = L/2$. Derive an expression for R.

11-45. A beam L ft long is fixed at one end and supported at the other end. A load of w lb per ft is uniformly distributed over the half of the beam nearest the support. Calculate the amount of the reaction.

FIG. 11-26　　　　　　FIG. 11-27

11-46. The principle of superposition shows that, in a beam fixed at one end and supported at the other end, if the end support is raised (or lowered) Δ in., the change in reaction equals the force required to produce an end deflection of Δ in. in a cantilever beam of the same length and stiffness. Show that, for such a beam uniformly loaded, if the end reaction is raised or lowered, $R = \frac{3}{8}wL \pm 3EI\Delta/L^3$. Discuss the change in the bending-moment diagram due to raising or lowering the end reaction.

11-47. Calculate the reaction R_B for the small beam shown in Fig. 11-26. Draw shear diagram and combined bending-moment diagram.

11-48. The beam shown in Fig. 11-27 is a 4-in. 9.5-lb I-beam. Calculate the maximum deflection caused by the concentrated loads. $P = 1,500$ lb.

Ans. $y = 0.415$ in.

11-49. A beam L ft long is fixed at both ends. A load of w lb per ft extends from the midpoint to one fixed end. Calculate the bending moments and shears at the fixed ends. Draw shear and bending-moment diagrams.

11-50. A beam fixed at both ends carries three equal loads P, one at a distance $L/4$ from each end and one at the midpoint. Calculate end shears and the moments, and draw shear and bending-moment diagrams. Calculate maximum deflection.

11-51. A beam of length L fixed at end A and supported at end B carries a triangular load W as shown in Fig. 11-28. Draw the shape of the elastic curve, and calculate the value of R_B and the slope at B. Draw shear and bending-moment diagrams. (See Appendix A for properties of M diagram.)

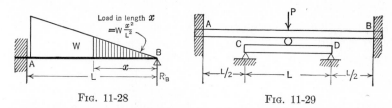

FIG. 11-28   FIG. 11-29

11-52. The beam AB, Fig. 11-29, is fixed at both ends, and the beam CD is of the same material and cross-section but simply supported at the ends. At the midpoint of both beams is a roller which is just in contact with both beams before the load is applied. Calculate the reactions at C and D caused by the load P.

Ans. $R_c = P/3.$

11-53. Solve Problem 11-52 but let EI of AB be twice the EI of CD.

11-54. A beam AB of length L, fixed at both ends, carries no load, but the B end settles a small distance Δ relative to the A end. Neither end rotates (tangents remain horizontal at both ends). Calculate M_A in terms of Δ, L, and EI. Draw shear and combined bending-moment diagrams.

<h1 style="text-align:center">12</h1>

Direct Stress Combined with Bending

12-1. Tension or Compression Member with Transverse Load.
There are many members subject to forces causing tensile or compressive
stress on which there are also transverse forces causing bending stresses.

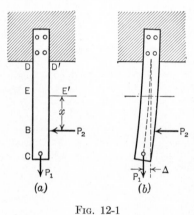

FIG. 12-1

As a simple example consider a
short vertical tension member (Fig.
12-1). This carries an axial load P_1
and a transverse load P_2. Between
B and C the only stress on a cross-
section is the tensile stress due to P_1.
Above B this tensile stress exists,
but there are also the stresses caused
by P_2, which are the same as in a
cantilever beam. The resultant stress
at any point in any cross-section E–E'
above B is the algebraic sum of the
tensile stress caused by P_1 and the
bending tension or compression
caused by P_2.

This statement is slightly inexact. Load P_2 bends the member BD,
and because of this bending the load P_1 has a small moment arm with
respect to an axis through the centroid of any cross-section between B
and D. There is thus a moment caused by P_1 which is subtracted from
the moment caused by P_2. If P_1 were a compression load, its moment
would be added to the moment caused by P_2.

The deflection Δ is very much exaggerated in Fig. 12-1b. If BD is
short, this deflection is exceedingly small so that $P_1\Delta$ is entirely negligible compared with P_2x. For the present, only problems in which the
length of the member is relatively small will be considered. In such
cases the bending stresses caused by axial loads may be neglected without appreciable error.

In general, the stress at any point in a cross-section of a member subject to direct stress and bending may be expressed thus:

$$S = \pm \frac{P}{A} \pm \frac{Mc}{I} \tag{12-1}$$

In both terms of the right-hand member the + sign is commonly used to designate tensile stress, and the − sign compressive stress.

Example 1. In Fig. 12-1a, CD is a steel bar 1 in. by 4 in. BD is 30 in., P_1 is 10,000 lb, and P_2 is 1,000 lb. Calculate the stress at both edges of the bar at D and also for a section between B and C.

Solution: The stress due to $P_1 = 10,000/4 = 2,500$ psi at any point of any cross-section far enough above C so that the stress can be assumed to be uniformly distributed. Below B there is no bending stress due to P_2, and the stress is only the 2,500 psi tension. At D there is bending stress caused by P_2. This is

$$S = \frac{Mc}{I} = \frac{1,000 \times 30 \times 2}{(1 \times 4^3)/12} = 11,250 \text{ psi}$$

This is tension on the right-hand edge. At D the stress is $2,500 - 11,250 = -8,750$ psi compression. At D' the stress is $2,500 + 11,250 = 13,750$ psi tension.

Example 2. Find the maximum compressive stress in the member AB shown in Fig. 12-2.

Solution: By the principles of statics, the tension in BC is $(12,000 \times 2.0)/2.4 = 10,000$ lb. If this is resolved into horizontal and vertical components, it is seen that the force acting at B may be considered to consist of an axial compressive force of 8,000 lb and a vertical force of 6,000 lb. AB then is a beam subjected to a concentrated force of 12,000 lb at its midpoint and to an axial compressive force of 8,000 lb. The maximum bending moment occurs over the load and is equal to $6,000 \times 24 = 144,000$ lb-in. For this beam $I/c = 14.2$ in.^{3} Therefore the

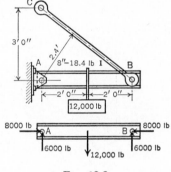

Fig. 12-2

maximum bending stress is $144,000/14.2 = 10,140$ psi. In addition to this bending stress there is axial compressive stress $P/A = 8,000/5.34$ sq in. $= 1,500$ psi. Therefore the maximum compressive stress in the beam is 11,640 psi at the top of the beam, directly above the load.

PROBLEMS

12-1. What are the maximum tensile and compressive unit stresses in the vertical member of Fig. 12-3 at a section 1 ft, 8 in. above the pulley? The weight of the member itself may be neglected. (*Hint:* Resolve the pulley reaction into its horizontal and vertical components.) *Ans.* $S_t = 1,750$ psi.

12-2. Solve Example 2 above if the load is 15,000 lb and its distance from A is 2.6 ft.

12-3. A 6 × 12-in. timber beam (Fig. 12-4), 10 ft long, carries a load of 5,000 lb at its midpoint, a uniformly distributed load of 1,200 lb (not shown), and is subjected to an axial pull of 10,000 lb. What are the maximum tensile and compressive stresses in the beam? *Ans.* $S_t = 1,305$ psi.

12-4. The beam AC in Fig. 12-5 is a 4-in. 7.7-lb I-beam. The load P is 1,200 lb. Calculate the maximum stress in the beam caused by the load P.

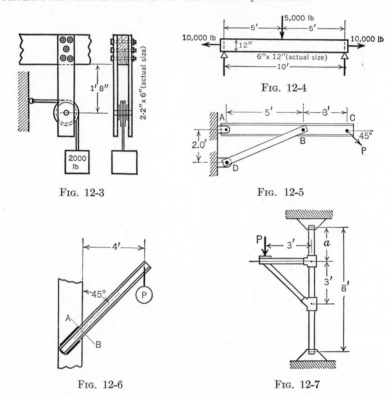

FIG. 12-4

FIG. 12-3

FIG. 12-5

FIG. 12-6

FIG. 12-7

12-5. Solve Problem 12-4 if the strut BD is made a tension member by moving the hinge D to a point 2 ft above A.

12-6. A 5-in. 9.0-lb channel is used to support a large water pipe, as shown in Fig. 12-6, the lower end being welded to part of the steel framing of a building. If the maximum compressive stress on section AB is not to exceed 12,000 psi, what is the maximum load P? (Assume that the load is so applied that it does not cause twisting of the channel.) *Ans.* $P = 860$ lb.

12-7. A post is to support a bracket, as shown in Fig. 12-7. The post is supported by loosely fitting sockets, top and bottom. The dimension a may have any value from 1 ft to 4 ft. With the dimension a such that the greatest stress in the post results, determine the value of the load P if the post is 4-in. standard steel pipe and the stress is not to exceed 10,000 psi.

12-8. Solve Problem 12-6 if the channel is inclined 30° with the vertical, all other data being the same.

12-9. Solve Problem 12-7 if the pipe is a $3\frac{1}{2}$-in. standard pipe.

Ans. $P = 1,270$ lb.

12-2. Unit Stresses Caused by Eccentric Load on a Prism.   The short prism shown in Fig. 12-8a rests on a rigid surface and supports a rigid plate to which loads are applied.   The resultant of these loads, shown in Fig. 12-8b as the load P, is not axial but is parallel to the axis of the prism, at a distance of e in. The distance e is called the eccentricity of the load.   Only problems in which the resultant load lies on one axis of symmetry of the cross-section will be considered in this article.

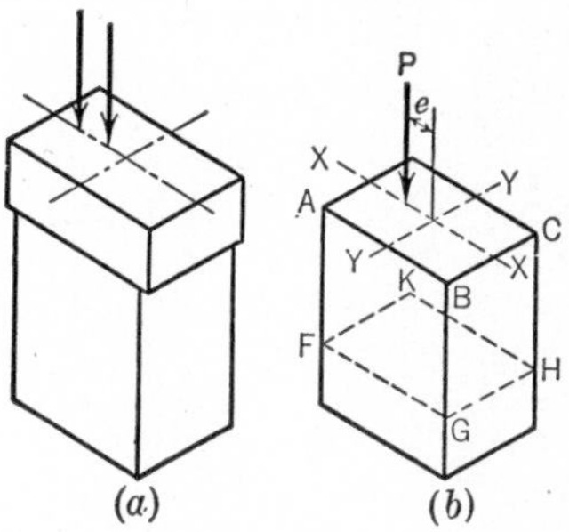

Consider as a body in equilibrium the part of the prism above the

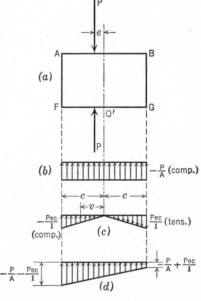

FIG. 12-8

FIG. 12-9

plane $FGHK$ which represents any transverse plane.   For simplicity the side view of this part of the prism is shown in Fig. 12-9 and will be referred to in the following discussion.

Since the body is in equilibrium, the resultant of all the forces on the horizontal plane through FG must be a force equal and opposite to and collinear with the load P.   In stressing the prism, this eccentric resultant force has two effects: a direct compressive effect and a bending effect. It is convenient to evaluate these effects separately.   This is done by noting that the eccentric force P is the resultant of an equal axial force P and a couple, or moment, Pe.   The stress on FG can therefore be treated as the result of this axial load and this moment.   The axial force P causes a uniformly distributed compressive stress P/A.   The moment Pe produces bending forces that vary from zero at the neutral axis of the cross-section to maximum values at the edges F and G.   The intensity of the bending stress at a distance c from the neutral axis is, of course, given by $S = Mc/I$ or Pec/I, since the bending moment is Pe. The total stress intensity at any distance v from the neutral axis is $- P/A \pm Pev/I$, in which, as heretofore in this chapter, the minus sign is used to indicate compressive stress.

Although derived for a prism of rectangular cross-section, this formula holds good for a prism of any cross-section provided that it has an axis of symmetry and that the resultant of the loads lies on this axis.

Example. In Fig. 12-8b the length of FG is 12 in. and the length of GH is 8 in. Calculate the stresses at the ends of the cross-section if a load of 24,000 lb is applied 3 in. from the axis Y–Y.

Solution: The stresses may both be represented by the equation $S = - (P/A) \pm Mc/I$. Substituting the values in the problem,

$$S = \frac{-24,000}{96} \pm \frac{24,000 \times 3 \times 6}{1,152} = -250 \pm 375 = +125 \text{ psi and}$$
$$-625 \text{ psi}$$

There is compressive stress along the edge FK, as was to be expected.   It may seem remarkable that a compressive load has caused tensile stresses along the edge GH, as the solution shows.

PROBLEMS

12-10. A short piece of 24-in. 120-lb I-beam is used as a strut.   An axial load of 360,000 lb is applied on the end.   An additional parallel load P is to be applied so that its resultant acts on the end of the beam at the intersection of axis 2–2 with the face of one flange.   What is the greatest value that P can have without causing the compressive stress to exceed 18,000 psi?

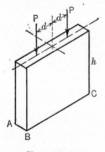

Fig. 12-10   Fig. 12-11

12-11. A short wooden block is shown in Fig. 12-10.   Dimension AB is 2 in., BC is 12 in., and h is 10 in.   It rests on a concrete foundation and carries two symmetrically placed loads P of 15,600 lb each.   Distance d is 3 in.   (a) Calculate the compressive unit stress.   (b) Later one of the loads is removed.   Calculate the maximum unit stress caused by the remaining load, and compare it with the unit stress caused by two loads.   *Ans.* (b) $S_c = 1,625$ psi.

12-12. Calculate the distance d for the block described in Problem 12-11 such that if one of the loads is removed the maximum unit stress on a horizontal cross-section will be the same as the unit stress on the cross-section due to both loads.

12-13. A short 2×12 in. (actual size) plank, shown in Fig. 12-11, carries an axial load which causes a compressive stress of 1,400 psi. If a 1-in.-diameter hole is bored through the plank, the center of the hole being 3 in. from the axis of the plank, how much is the maximum compressive stress increased?

12-3. Maximum Eccentricity for No Tensile Stress.   In the example of Art. 12-2 for some eccentricity less than 3 in. there would be no tensile stress in the prism.   The case of zero stress at one edge is of some importance, and the greatest eccentricity which will not cause tensile stresses will now be found.

When the stress at one edge is zero, $P/A = Mc/I$. If, in Fig. 12-8, FG equals h and GH equals b, this equation becomes

$$\frac{P}{bh} = \frac{Pe \times h/2}{bh^3/12}$$

from which $e = h/6$.

If the eccentricity exceeds $h/6$, the stress Mc/I becomes greater than P/A and the stress along GH is tensile.

If the prism is a solid piece of elastic material which can resist tensile stresses as well as compressive stresses, this condition is not objectionable. If, on the other hand, the prism is made up of a pile of separate blocks, the tensile stress cannot exist between the separate blocks.   In fact, the blocks will separate from each other at each surface of contact for a short distance from the face $BCHG$ of the prism.   On a masonry post or "pier," a load whose eccentricity exceeds $h/6$ will cause tensile stresses in some part of the pier and will tend to cause the joints to open. This tendency is objectionable.   Hence it is an old and accepted rule that in

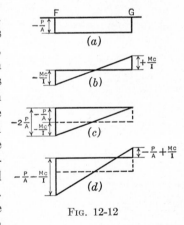

Fig. 12-12

masonry structures the resultant pressure should fall within the "middle third" if the cross-section is a rectangle.

The stress distribution in a rectangular pier loaded with the maximum eccentricity for no tensile stress is shown in Fig. 12-12a, b, and c.

Figure 12-12a is a diagram representing the constant term $-P/A$. The minus sign is used for compressive stress, which is plotted below the line FG.   The bending stress is shown in (b).   In (c) the bending stress diagram is superimposed on the direct stress diagram.

Figure 12-12d is a diagram representing a more general case in which e is greater than $h/6$ and the tensile stress $+Mc/I$ exceeds the compressive stress $-P/A$. The resulting tensile stresses are represented by the ordinates of the area above the base line.

PROBLEMS

12-14. In a solid masonry pier of circular cross-section, what eccentricity of the load will cause zero stress at the side away from the load?

12-15. A brick pier is 6 ft square and 10 ft high. The masonry weighs 110 lb per cu ft. The pier carries a load of 36,000 lb. How far from the center of the top of the pier, on a line parallel to the sides, may the resultant of the 36,000-lb load be placed without causing tension at the base of the pier?   *Ans.* $e = 25.2$ in.

12-16. With the load placed as found in Problem 12-15, what maximum tensile and compressive stresses occur on a horizontal section 7 ft below the top of the pier?

12-17. Solve Problem 12-15, making the load 180,000 lb instead of 36,000 lb.

12-4. Eccentric Loads on Machine Parts. Numerous examples of bending combined with tension or compression occur in machine frames and other parts of machines and in tools of various sorts. In many of these the eccentricity is very large, the resultant external forces being entirely outside the cross-sections where the combined stresses occur. In such cases the bending stresses predominate, and the part subjected to the combined stress is more in the nature of a beam with some loads causing direct stress. The previous examples were regarded as tension or compression members which were subject to some bending. In both cases the stresses on a cross-section are found in the same way.

Example.   The cast-iron frame of a small press is shaped as shown in Fig. 12-13. Calculate the loads P that would cause stresses on the cross-section A–A not exceeding these values: tension, 3,000 psi; compression, 15,000 psi.

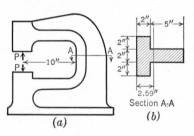

Section A-A

(b)

(a)

Fig. 12-13

Solution: The eccentricity of the load is the distance from its line of action to the axis through the centroid of the cross-section A–A. It is therefore necessary to determine the position of the centroid and, in order to compute bending stresses, the moment of inertia with respect to the axis through the centroid. By the methods explained in Appendices A and B, the distance from the left edge to the centroid is found to be 2.59 in., and the moment of inertia of the cross-section for the centroidal axis is found to be 91.6 in.[4] The *tensile* stress due to bending will be maximum on the "fibers" nearest the load P. The maximum *compressive* stress due to bending will occur at the opposite edge. The bending moment is $12.59P$ lb-in. The equation $S = P/A \pm Mc/I$ is used to determine P for each case. For tensile stress,

$$3,000 = +\frac{P}{22} + \frac{12.59P \times 2.59}{91.6} = 0.045P + 0.356P = 0.401P$$

$$P = 3,000/0.401 = 7,480 \text{ lb}$$

A greater load than 7,480 lb would cause the resultant tensile stress to exceed the allowable.

For compressive stress,

$$-15,000 = +\frac{P}{22} - \frac{12.59P \times 4.41}{91.6} = +0.045P - 0.606P = -0.561P$$

$$P = 15,000/0.561 = 26,700 \text{ lb}$$

Hence the maximum allowable value of the force P is 7,480 lb.

PROBLEMS

12-18. Find the maximum load P that the cast-iron frame shown in Fig. 12-14 can carry without exceeding allowable stresses of 3,000 psi tension, and 15,000 psi compression   *Ans.* $P = 2,360$ lb.

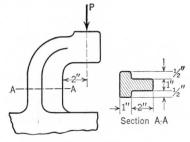

Section A-A

Fig. 12-14

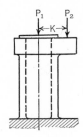

Fig. 12-15

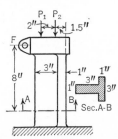

Sec. A-B

Fig. 12-16

12-19. If the shape of the frame in Fig. 12-13 is changed so that the 10-in. distance to the load becomes 7 in., calculate the allowable load P. Allowable stresses in the cast iron are: tension, 3,000 psi; compression, 15,000 psi.

12-20. The machine part shown in Fig. 12-15 supports an axial load P_1 of 10,000 lb and an eccentric load P_2 of 6,000 lb. The upright post is a hollow cylinder 3 in. in outside diameter and 2 in. in inside diameter. Calculate the maximum value of K if the allowable compressive stress is 18,000 psi.

12-21. Solve Problem 12-20 but let $P_1 = P_2 = 8,000$ lb.   *Ans.* $K = 3.70$ in.

12-22. The casting shown in Fig. 12-16 is used in a machine. Calculate the amount and direction of the horizontal force F such that the stress at B in the post will be 12,000 psi compression. $P_1 = 15,000$ lb, $P_2 = 45,000$ lb.

12-23. Solve Problem 12-22 but find the amount and direction of F that will cause a tensile stress of 3,000 psi at A.

12-24. The forging ABC in Fig. 12-17 supports a vertical load P of 2,000 lb. Calculate stresses at E and F. The cross-section EF is rectangular. The vertical dimension is 3 in. and the horizontal dimension 1 in.

Ans. At E, $S = 4,800$ psi.

12-25. Solve Problem 12-24 but let P be 3,000 lb horizontally to the left.

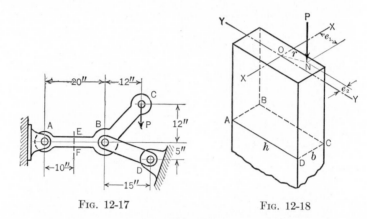

Fig. 12-17   Fig. 12-18

12-5. Eccentric Load Not on Principal Axis. Consider a prism the cross-section of which has principal axes of inertia X–X and Y–Y (Fig. 12-18). By the principles of mechanics it may be shown that the load P at N is equivalent to a load P at O plus a couple Pr. It may also be shown that the couple Pr in the plane ON in the figure may be resolved into two component couples Pe_1 and Pe_2 in the planes of the principal axes, respectively. The stress at any point of the cross-section $ABCD$ is the sum of (1) the stresses due to load P at O, (2) the stress due to the moment Pe_1 with respect to axis X–X, and (3) the stress due to the moment Pe_2 with respect to axis Y–Y.

Hence, $S = -P/A \pm Pe_1 y_1/I_x \pm Pe_2 x_1/I_y$, in which x_1 and y_1 are the coordinates of the point where the stress is computed.

For the rectangular cross-section $ABCD$ of Fig. 12-18 the limits of the position of P in order that no tensile stress shall exist will now be found. The stress at A will be zero when

$$\frac{P}{bh} = \frac{Pe_1 h/2}{bh^3/12} + \frac{Pe_2 b/2}{hb^3/12}$$

Whence $\dfrac{e_1}{h/6} + \dfrac{e_2}{b/6} = 1$. This is the equation of a straight line with intercepts of $h/6$ on the Y axis and $b/6$ on the X axis. It therefore follows that there will be no tensile stress anywhere within an eccentrically loaded rectangular prism if the resultant load is compressive and if the resultant acts within the diamond-shaped area the length and width of which are $b/3$ and $h/3$ (Fig. 12-19). This area is called the "kern" of the cross-section. A kern exists for any cross-section, and its shape depends upon the shape of the cross-section.

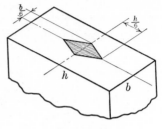

Fig. 12-19

12-6. Line of Zero Stress. If a prism carries a load the resultant of which does not come within the kern, the stresses at some points of a cross-section will be compressive and those at other points will be tensile. There must therefore be some line lying within the cross-section at every point along which the combined bending and direct stress is zero. This is called the "line of zero stress" of the cross-section.

The stresses at various points on the cross-section of the prism are proportional to the distances of those points from the line of zero stress.

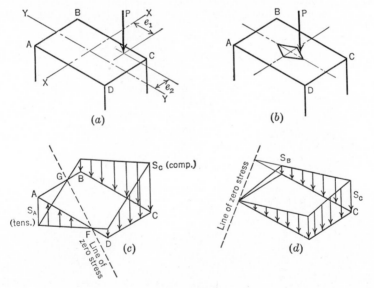

Fig. 12-20

If this fact is used, the position of the line of zero stress is easily determined. For instance, if, in Fig. 12-20a, S_b and S_c are calculated and laid off to scale, the point of zero stress on BC (or BC extended) is readily calculated or located graphically. Two such points of zero stress locate the line of zero stress.

If the resultant load acts at one of the boundary lines of the kern, as in Fig. 12-20b, the line of zero stress passes through the opposite corner of the prism. There is only one kind of stress in the prism, but the value of this stress decreases to zero at the corner (or along the edge of the cross-section, if the load acts through the point at which one of the principal axes cuts the kern).

Example. In Fig. 12-20a the post is 6 in. by 10 in., $e_1 = 2.5$ in., $e_2 = 2$ in., $P = 10,000$ lb. P is the resultant of a load applied to the end of the post by a rigid plate or cap. Calculate the stresses at each corner of a cross-section, and locate the line of zero stress.

Solution:

$$S = -\frac{P}{A} \pm \frac{M_1 c_1}{I_1} \pm \frac{M_2 c_2}{I_2} = -\frac{10,000}{60} \pm \frac{25,000}{6 \times 100/6} \pm \frac{20,000}{10 \times 36/6}$$

The stress at each corner is the algebraic sum of these three stresses. At the four corners the stresses are as given below (all stresses are in pounds per square inch).

S_A	S_B	S_C	S_D
+250	+250	−250	−250
+333	−333	−333	+333
−167	−167	−167	−167
+416	−250	−750	− 84

The distance from A along AD to the neutral axis is

$$AF = 10\,\frac{416}{416 + 84} = 8.33 \text{ in.}$$

Also

$$AG = 6\,\frac{416}{416 + 250} = 3.75 \text{ in.}$$

PROBLEMS

12-26. A 6×8 in. (actual size) post carries a load of 14,000 lb, the resultant of which is on a diagonal at a distance of 3 in. (measured on the diagonal) from the center. Calculate the stresses at each corner of a cross-section, and locate the line of zero stress.

12-27. An 8×10 in. (actual size) post carries a load of 16,000 lb, the resultant of which is 2 in. from one 8-in. edge and 3 in. from one 10-in. edge. What is the least additional axial load that will prevent tensile stress at any point in a cross-section of the post?   *Ans.* $P = 24,800$ lb.

GENERAL PROBLEMS

12-28. A hollow rectangular pier is 20×16 in. in outside dimensions and has walls 4 in. thick. The resultant of a 30,000-lb load acts on the axis through the center parallel to the 20-in. sides, at a distance of 3 in. from the center. What are the maximum and minimum compressive stresses in the pier?

Ans. Maximum $S_c = 229$ psi.

12-29. A piece of 3-in. standard pipe is bent into the form shown in Fig. 12-21. The lower end is rigidly embedded in the foundation. What is the greatest load P that can be suspended from the end of the gooseneck, if the allowable compressive stress at A is 6,000 psi?

12-30. A wall of a tank is to be built of masonry weighing 150 lb per cu ft. The water is to be 6 ft deep. (*a*) If the wall is 8 ft high and of uniform thickness, how thick must it be to avoid tension at the base of the wall? (*b*) If 3 ft thick, how high must it be to avoid tension at the base? *Ans.* (*b*) $h = 10$ ft.

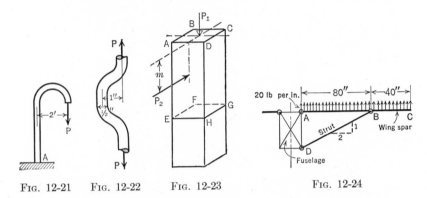

FIG. 12-21   FIG. 12-22   FIG. 12-23   FIG. 12-24

12-31. A $\frac{1}{2}$-in.-diameter rod is bent as shown in Fig. 12-22. What is the allowable load P that can be applied, if the tensile unit stress is not to exceed 16,000 psi? How does this load compare with the allowable load on a straight rod?

12-32. A short post 6×8 in. in cross-section is shown in Fig. 12-23. An axial load P_1 of 4,200 lb is applied to the upper end, and a horizontal load P_2 of 400 lb is applied to one 6-in. side of the post, $m = 10$ in. At what distance below the top of the post will there be zero stress along one edge of the cross-section?

12-33. A short wooden post is shown in Fig. 12-23. $AB = 6$ in., and $AD = 8$ in. The axial load P_1 is 4,400 lb. The horizontal force P_2 is 300 lb, and $m = 12$ in. (*a*) At what distance below P_2 will there be zero stress at one edge of the cross-section? (*b*) What will be the stress at the opposite edge? *Ans.* (*b*) $S = 183.4$ psi.

12-34. A rectangular brick pier is shown in Fig. 12-23. $AB = 4$ ft and $AD = 6$ ft. The axial load P_1 is 12,000 lb. The horizontal load P_2 is 4,000 lb. The brick masonry weighs 110 lb per cu ft. Section $EFGH$ is 8 ft below the top of the pier. Calculate the distance m such that there will be zero stress at one edge of section $EFGH$. What will be the stress on the opposite edge?

12-35. The wing spar in a small airplane is shown in Fig. 12-24. It is hinged at A and held in position by the member BD. The spar is an aluminum-alloy I-beam of which the depth is 3.00 in., the cross-sectional area is 1.64 sq in., and the section modulus is 1.70 in.³ For the loading shown determine the maximum tensile stress and the maximum compressive stress in the wing spar. *Ans.* $S_c = 11,600$ psi.

12-36. Calculate the unit stress at A and the unit stress at B in the forging shown in Fig. 12-25 due to the two loads shown.

12-37. Brackets in a factory are built as shown in Fig. 12-26. The brackets support a continuous beam at D and a long, heavy conduit hung at E. Loads P_1

and P_2 are both 3,200 lb. The member AD is made of two 3-in., 5-lb channels. Calculate the stresses at F and at G both 10 in. from A. $Ans. S = 13,300$ psi at G.

12-38. Solve Problem 12-37 but let $P_1 = 3,000$ lb and $P_2 = 3,600$ lb.

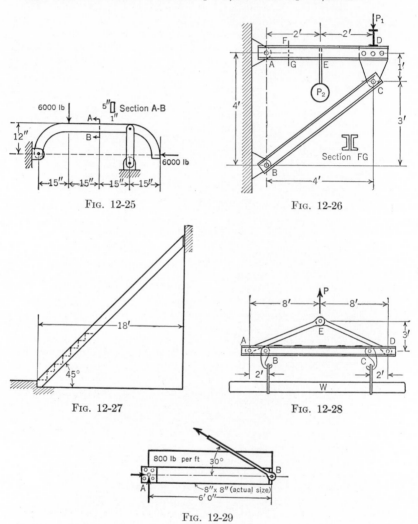

FIG. 12-25

FIG. 12-26

FIG. 12-27

FIG. 12-28

FIG. 12-29

12-39. Stairs in a factory are supported by two 10-in., 15.3-lb channels resting against smooth vertical bearing plates at the top, as shown in Fig. 12-27. The maximum total dead load plus live load on the two channels, including their own weight, is 9,200 lb, uniformly distributed. Calculate the maximum and minimum stresses in one channel at a section at its midpoint.

12-40. The arrangement shown in Fig. 12-28 is used for hoisting heavy bodies (concrete piles or precast wall slabs) that require support at two points when being lifted.   Member AD is made of two 6-in. 10.5-lb channels.   Calculate the allowable load W if the unit stress in the channels is not to exceed 10,000 psi on any cross-section between B and C.   The center of gravity of W is directly below E.

12-41. Solve Problem 12-40 but increase vertical distance from AD to E from 3 ft to 4 ft.

12-42. Find the maximum tensile and compressive stresses in the beam AB, Fig. 12-29.   Neglect the weight of the beam itself.   *Ans.*   Max S_c = 571 psi.

12-43. In Fig. 12-25 change the 6,000-lb horizontal load to 10,000 lb, and calculate the stresses at A and B.

13

Columns with Axial Loads

13-1. Introduction. In Chapter 12 a relatively short prism under an eccentric compressive load was considered, and it was shown that the maximum stress produced has two components: (1) a uniformly distributed stress P/A due to direct compression, and (2) a stress Pec/I due to bending.

In this chapter it will be shown that a sufficiently slender prism will bend under a compressive load even if the load is intended to be axial. This bending results in a considerable eccentricity of the load with respect to some cross-section. Because of the bending stresses resulting from the eccentricity the allowable load on the end of a slender prism is less than the allowable load on a short prism with the same cross-section. A compression member so slender that the allowable axial end load must be reduced because of the bending stresses is called a column.

Generally speaking, any compression member with an unsupported length more than eight to ten times its least transverse dimension is considered to be a column. For ratios less than this, the effect of lateral deflection due to bending of the member may usually be disregarded in stress or load computations. As the ratio increases above this range, however, the deflection of the member under load is of greater and greater importance.

Because of differences in their behavior, columns may be divided into two classes, "slender" and "intermediate."[1] The action of slender columns will be discussed first, and in the light of that discussion the distinction between slender and intermediate columns will be made clear.

In this chapter the behavior of columns with axial loads and the methods used in their design will be considered. Chapter 14 will deal with columns with eccentric loads.

IDEAL COLUMNS UNDER AXIAL LOADS

13-2. Round-Ended Ideal Slender Columns. Small imperfections in material and fabrication and unavoidable accidental eccentricities of

---

[1] Using this terminology, compression members will be divided into *short compression blocks, intermediate columns,* and *slender columns.*

loading (of indeterminate amount) greatly affect the behavior of actual columns under load.   For this reason, in approaching the study of actual columns, it is desirable first to develop the theory of column action under simpler and more definite conditions.   Therefore the theoretical analysis of slender columns will assume a perfectly straight, homogeneous slender bar of round cross-section, having its ends held against any lateral movement but perfectly free to rotate.   Such a bar as this, with ends in this condition, may be called a round-ended ideal column.   The loading on this ideal column will be assumed perfectly axial.

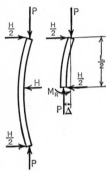

FIG. 13-1

The maximum axial load which can be applied to an ideal slender column depends not upon the strength (yield point) of the material but upon its stiffness (modulus of elasticity).

For an understanding of this fact, it is necessary to consider the relation which exists in a bent mem-ber between the deflection of the member and the resisting moment which accompanies the deflec-tion.   It was shown in Chapter 8 that the resisting moment in a beam is proportional to the stress in the extreme fibers.   It follows from the theory of beam deflection given in Chapter 10 that at the midpoint of a symmetrically loaded simple beam the stress in the extreme fibers is proportional to the deflection.   Therefore it follows that, as such a beam is bent, *the resisting moment is proportional to the deflection.*   This proposition is also true if the bent member is a slender column.

Keeping this relation in mind, suppose that axial loads P are placed on the ends of an ideal column (Fig. 13-1).   Let a small lateral deflection Δ then be caused by a lateral force H, applied at the midpoint of the column.   For any value of Δ, the bending moment at the midpoint is $P\Delta + \frac{1}{2}H \times \frac{1}{2}L$.   If the top half of the column is considered a body in equilibrium, the resisting moment equals the bending moment, or

$$M_R = P\Delta + \tfrac{1}{4}HL$$

Now let P be increased while H is simultaneously decreased in such a way that the deflection remains the same.   Then, when H becomes zero, P has such a value, P', that $P'\Delta = M_R$.   The column will now hold this deflection without any side thrust.   This is true for any value of Δ that does not cause stresses above the proportional limit.   (Since M_R varies as Δ, P' is a constant in the equation $P'\Delta = M_R$, whatever the value of Δ.)   If P is made greater than P', however, $P\Delta$ is greater than the resisting moment for every value of Δ, and the column rapidly deflects until it fails.   On the contrary, if P is less than P', $P\Delta$ is always less than the resisting moment, and the column will straighten itself when the deflecting side force is removed.   The load which is just sufficient to hold the column in a bent condition is called the *critical load* for the column.   The critical load may also be defined as the greatest load that the column will support.

13-3. Euler's Formula for Slender Columns.   The equation which gives the value of the critical load in terms of the dimensions of the column and the modulus of elasticity of the material was first derived by Leonhard Euler, a Swiss mathematician, in 1757 and is known as Euler's formula for slender columns.

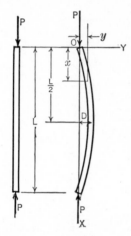

The column shown in Fig. 13-2 is an ideal slender column with both ends fixed against lateral movement but perfectly free to rotate as the column deflects.   The load P applied to the upper end is the critical load for the column. Now let the column be given the deflection D, sufficiently small so that the difference in length of the curve and its vertical projection is negligible.

Because P is the critical load it will just maintain this small deflection as was explained in the preceding article.   A larger load would cause the column to collapse, and a smaller load would permit the column to straighten itself.   The equations written below cannot be written for any other value of P.   The value of this critical load will now be determined.   The shape of the elastic curve will also be found.

Fig. 13-2

Let the origin be taken at the upper end of the column, and let the X axis extend in the direction of the length of the column, which is consistent with the direction of axes assumed in the discussion of the elastic curve of a beam.   The equation of the elastic curve of a slightly bent member is $EI\, d^2y/dx^2 = M$.   In this case the magnitude of M is Py. Also the sign of the moment is opposite to that of the curvature.   Therefore

$$EI\frac{d^2y}{dx^2} = -Py \qquad (1)$$

As was shown in Art. 10-4, $\dfrac{d^2y}{dx^2}$ is the rate of change of the slope $\dfrac{dy}{dx}$

with respect to x.   Equation (1) can be written

$$EI\ \frac{d\left(\dfrac{dy}{dx}\right)}{dx} = -Py$$

To integrate this expression, multiply both sides of the equation by $2\,dy$.   Then

$$EI\left(2\frac{dy}{dx}\,d\,\frac{dy}{dx}\right) = -2Py\,dy$$

Both members of this equation are in the form $2u\,du$.   Integrating,

$$EI\left(\frac{dy}{dx}\right)^2 = -Py^2 + C_1$$

To evaluate C_1, note that, when dy/dx is $0, y = D$.   Therefore $C_1 = PD^2$, whence

$$\left(\frac{dy}{dx}\right)^2 = \frac{P}{EI}\,(D^2 - y^2)$$

Taking the square root, $\dfrac{dy}{dx} = \left(\dfrac{P}{EI}\right)^{\frac{1}{2}}(D^2 - y^2)^{\frac{1}{2}}$ (2)

Equation 2 can be rewritten

$$\frac{dy}{\sqrt{D^2 - y^2}} = \left(\frac{P}{EI}\right)^{\frac{1}{2}}dx$$

Whence, integrating again,

$$\sin^{-1}\frac{y}{D} = \left(\frac{P}{EI}\right)^{\frac{1}{2}}x + C_2$$

To evaluate C_2, note that, when $x = 0$, $y = 0$;   therefore $C_2 = 0$.   Whence

$$\sin^{-1}\frac{y}{D} = \left(\frac{P}{EI}\right)^{\frac{1}{2}}x, \quad \text{or} \quad y = D\sin\left(\frac{P}{EI}\right)^{\frac{1}{2}}x \qquad (3)$$

This is the equation, in terms of the maximum deflection D, of the curve in which the column is maintained by the critical load P.   The column is evidently bent into a sine curve.

As was pointed out in Art. 13–2, the maximum deflection D under the critical load does not have a single value but may theoretically range from a very small value up to the deflection at which the maximum stress equals the yield point (when collapse will occur). However, equation 3 is valid for only small values of D since it is based on the approximate equation for the elastic curve. Columns with large deflections have no practical use.

The usefulness of equation 3 is not in showing the shape of the elastic curve of the column, but in permitting a determination of the value of the critical load P. To determine this value in terms other than the unknown deflection D note that, when $x = L/2$, $y = D$. Then

$$\sin\left(\frac{P}{EI}\right)^{\frac{1}{2}}\frac{L}{2} = 1, \qquad \text{whence} \qquad \left(\frac{P}{EI}\right)^{\frac{1}{2}}\frac{L}{2} = \frac{\pi}{2}$$

or $P = \dfrac{\pi^2 EI}{L^2}$, for the value of the critical load.[2]

PROBLEMS

13-1. To determine the modulus of elasticity of a certain brass, a bar of the material $54\frac{1}{2}$ in. long and with a diameter of 0.318 in. (mean of four measurements) was tested as a slender column. The bar was placed vertically on a platform scale, and load was gradually applied until the critical load was reached. With the ends of the bar supported on small hemispheres to allow freedom of rotation, the maximum scale reading was 29.5 lb. The weight of the bar was 1.2 lb, so that the maximum load on the mid cross-section was 28.9 lb. (a) Compute the modulus of elasticity. (b) For a check on the foregoing determination the bar was supported horizontally on rollers 52 in. apart. A load of 2 lb applied at the midlength of the bar caused a deflection of 0.66 in. (mean of four measurements). Compute the value of E, and compare it with the value found in part (a).

13-2. Calculate the value of the greatest axial load that can be applied to the end of a steel bar $\frac{1}{2}$ in. square and 42 in. long. What percentage of this load can be supported by a steel bar $\frac{1}{2}$ in. square and 54 in. long?   *Ans.* $P = 875$ lb.

13-3. Calculate the value of the greatest axial load that can be applied to the end of a round bar of aluminum alloy $\frac{1}{2}$ in. in diameter and 40 in. long. What percentage of this load can be supported by a bar of the same stock 50 in. long? Take E as 10,300,000 psi.

13-4. Graphical Representation of Euler's Formula. Euler's formula is commonly written in a slightly different form. The moment of inertia I equals Ar^2, where A is the area of the cross-section of the column and r is its *radius of gyration*[3] with respect to the centroidal axis.

[2] The equation $\sin (P/EI)^{\frac{1}{2}} L/2 = 1$ leads to the value of $\pi/2$ for $(P/EI)^{\frac{1}{2}} L/2$, as given above, or to $3\pi/2$, $5\pi/2$, etc. The correspondingly larger values of P are those required to bend the column into several nodes instead of into the single curve shown in Fig. 13-2. All such values of P will be larger than the value corresponding to $\pi/2$, which is therefore the only important value from an engineering standpoint.

[3] The *radius of gyration of an area* is a concept devised to make it possible to substitute Ar^2 for I in column formulas. This can be done if $r = \sqrt{I/A}$. The radius of gyration of an area has no physical meaning.

If this substitution is made and terms are rearranged Euler's formula for a round-ended column becomes

$$\frac{P}{A} = \frac{\pi^2 E}{(L/r)^2} \tag{13-1}$$

This expression gives the *average* stress over the cross-section of the column when the critical load is being carried. This average stress under the critical load is often called the *critical stress* for the column. The ratio L/r is called the *slenderness ratio* of the column. These are terms commonly used in column discussions.

With the equation in the above form, if E is known and if various values of L/r are assumed, the corresponding values of P/A can be computed. The simultaneous values of P/A and L/r can be plotted as the ordinates and the abscissas, respectively, of an Euler curve.

Figure 13-3 shows an Euler curve for round-ended columns of high-strength steel. The curve pictures very clearly the way in which the load-carrying capacity of columns decreases as their slenderness increases. A round column having a length equal to 20 diameters would have an L/r of 80, since the radius of gyration of a circle is one-fourth the diameter. Such a column, if round-ended, would have

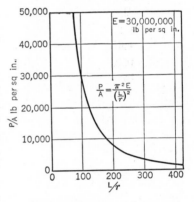

FIG. 13-3. Euler curve for round-ended steel columns.

a critical stress of 44,300 psi. A column having a length equal to 100 diameters ($L/r = 400$), however, would have a critical stress of only 1,770 psi (one-twenty-fifth as much).

It should be noted that Euler's formula tells nothing about the *maximum* unit stress in a column carrying its critical load. The maximum stress depends on the deflection of the column. At a load just under the critical load, the maximum stress equals the average stress; but at the critical load, the maximum stress may be anything between the average stress and the yield point of the column material. It should be noted, too, that the only property of the column material which enters into Euler's formula is E, which measures its stiffness. This mathematical analysis therefore confirms the reasoning of Art. 13-2, which led to the conclusion that the maximum load on a slender column is determined by the stiffness of the column material and not by its strength.

13-5. Limitations of Euler's Formula. As a mathematical expression, Euler's equation may be represented by a curve extending indefinitely both horizontally and vertically. As an expression applicable to columns of any given material, however, it holds good only for values of P/A within the proportional limit of the material to which it is applied, since the derivation of the formula is based on the proportionality of unit stress and unit strain. From Fig. 13-3, then, it can be seen that for steel having a proportional limit of 33,000 psi Euler's formula applies to any axially loaded, round-ended column having a slenderness ratio of 95 or over. For stronger steel having a proportional limit of 40,000 psi, the formula applies to all columns with slenderness ratios greater than 86.

There is no correspondence between the elastic strength and the elastic stiffness of different materials, and therefore each material has its particular value of L/r below which Euler's formula is inapplicable. The greater the strength in relation to the stiffness, the lower this value of L/r will be, that is, the greater the range of slendernesses over which Euler's formula will be valid. The following table shows for a number of common materials, having elastic strengths and stiffnesses as given, the values of L/r below which Euler's formula will not apply.

ROUND-ENDED SLENDER COLUMNS

Material	Proportional Limit	Modulus of Elasticity	Least Value of L/r for Application of Euler's Formula
Nickel steel	50,000	30,000,000	77
Silicon steel	40,000	30,000,000	86
Carbon steel	28,000	30,000,000	103
Aluminum alloy 17S-T	37,000	10,300,000	52
Southern pine	7,000	1,600,000	47
Cypress	5,000	1,200,000	49

PROBLEMS

13-4. Plot Euler curves for nickel steel and for aluminum alloy 17S-T for all values of P/A less than the given proportional limit and for values of L/r up to 300. Scales: 1 in. = 8,000 psi; 1 in. = L/r of 100. Plot both curves on same axes.

13-5. Plot Euler curves for southern pine and cypress for all values of P/A less than the given proportional limits and for values of L/r up to 300. Scales: 1 in. = 2,000 psi; 1 in. = L/r of 100. Plot both curves on same axes.

13-6. Round rods of aluminum alloy 1.6 in. in diameter and 20, 48, 96 in. long are used as axially loaded columns. For the columns to which Euler's formula applies calculate the greatest load each column will carry.

Ans. For 96-in. rod, $P = 3,550$ lb.

13-7. Solve Problem 13-6 if the rods are made of carbon steel with a proportional limit of 28,000 psi.

13-6. Slender Columns Having Other End Conditions. Up to this point all discussion of columns has been based on the supposition of complete freedom of rotation of the ends of the column; the columns have been "round-ended." The ends of a column, however, may be wholly fixed, so that, as the column bends under load, the tangents to the elastic curve at the ends of the unsupported length of the column retain their original direction. Such a column is said to have "fixed ends" (Fig. 13-4*b*). When a column with fixed ends bends, it can be shown that the inflection points are at the quarter-points of the un-

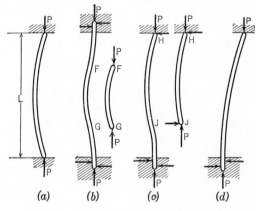

Fig. 13-4

supported length of the column. Since the points of contraflexure are points of zero bending moment, however, they are points equivalent to the ends of a round-ended column. Therefore the *middle half* of the unsupported length of a column with fixed ends can be considered equivalent to a round-ended column. If the unsupported length of the column be called L, then the load-carrying capacity will be the same as that of a round-ended column with a length of $L/2$. If $L/2$ is substituted for L in the Euler equation for a round-ended column, it will be found that a *slender* column with fixed ends will support a load four times as great as the load that the same column will support if round-ended.

Most of the columns used in actual engineering practice have end conditions intermediate between round and fixed ends. That is, the column bends in reversed curvature, but the inflection points are nearer to the ends than to the midsection of the column. Any such column can be analyzed by the formulas for a round-ended column if the distance between inflection points is known or can be assumed satisfactorily. For example, if the distance between inflection points is 0.80 of the unsupported length L, then $0.80L$ is inserted in the formula for a round-ended column to make the formula apply to the column in question.

Columns may also have one end wholly fixed and the other end wholly free to move laterally as well as to rotate (Fig. 13-4d), or one end may be wholly fixed and the other end be fixed against lateral movement but wholly free to rotate (Fig. 13-4c). If we consider column d, it is evident that the whole unsupported length is equivalent to half the length of a round-ended column. Therefore, if the free length of column a be called L, column d can be analyzed by means of the formulas for round-ended columns, provided $2L$ is substituted for L in the column formula. It can be shown that the inflection point in column c is at very nearly $0.7L$ from the "round" end of the column. Therefore the formulas for round-ended columns can be applied to this case by substitution of $0.7L$ for L.

In Art. 13-5 the limitations of Euler's formula as applied to round-ended columns were discussed. As an example, it was stated that for columns made of steel having a proportional limit of 33,000 psi, Euler's formula applies to round-ended columns having a slenderness ratio of 95 or more. Figure 13-4b shows that for *fixed-ended* columns of such steel, Euler's formula applies if the L/r of the middle half is 95 or more, or if the L/r of the entire column is 190 or more. For columns made of steel with a proportional limit of 40,000 psi, Euler's formula applies to round-ended columns having an L/r of 86 or more and to columns fixed at both ends having an L/r of 172 or more.

PROBLEMS

13-8. For steel columns with end conditions such as are shown in Fig. 13-4a, b, c, and d, determine the lower limits of L/r for the application of Euler's formula if the proportional limit is 45,000 psi.

13-9. Solve Problem 13-8 if columns are of an aluminum alloy with a proportional limit of 45,000 psi and $E = 10,300,000$ psi.

13-7. "Slender" Columns, "Intermediate" Columns, and "Short Compression Blocks." The discussion of columns up to this point has been limited to columns that are "slender." But what is a slender column?

The best definition is that it is a column that fails through lack of stiffness, by elastic instability, a column the ultimate load on which is reached while the average stress is still within the proportional limit of the column material. It is, therefore, any column for which Euler's formula is valid. Referring to the table in Art. 13-5, it is seen that any round-ended column of nickel steel of the grade there given can be considered a slender column if its L/r is greater than 77.   Any round-ended column of the aluminum alloy 17S-T can be considered slender if its L/r is greater than 52.

A column with so small a value of L/r that the average stress on the cross-section reaches the proportional limit of the material before the critical stress is reached is called an "intermediate" column.   A still shorter compression member for which L/r is so small as to make the effect of lateral deflection negligible may be called a "short compression block."

The maximum axial load which a short compression block can carry is determined solely by the *strength* of the material.   Such a block may be considered to have failed when the average stress on its cross-section has reached the compression yield point of the material.   As noted in Art. 13-2, the maximum load which a *slender* column can carry is determined by the *stiffness* of the material.   But what determines the strength of an intermediate column?   This is a very important question, since most of the columns entering into engineering practice have slenderness ratios that place them in the intermediate column class.

13-8. The Load-Carrying Capacity of Intermediate Columns.   The analysis of intermediate columns is much more complex than that of slender columns.   The material composing a slender column is stressed below the proportional limit right up to the maximum load which the column can carry—the critical load.   Long before the ultimate load on an intermediate column is reached, however, stresses throughout the column may have exceeded the proportional limit of the material. Therefore there is a great deal of inelastic action while an intermediate column is being loaded to failure.   Whereas Euler's analysis of a slender column dates back almost two centuries, it is only within the last few decades that the problem of the intermediate column has been successfully attacked by Considère, Engesser, von Kármán, and others.   The intermediate column is not susceptible of as complete and exact an analysis as the slender column.   Nevertheless the behavior of an ideal intermediate column is quite well understood.   An analysis explaining the action of columns of intermediate slenderness is called the "double-modulus" or "reduced-modulus" theory.[4]

As applied to steel with a yield point at 33,000 psi and a typical stress-strain curve, the double-modulus equation gives relations between P/A and L/r as shown in Fig. 13-5.   These values close the gap between the Euler curve and the straight horizontal line representing the yield-point

[4] See F. B. Seely and J. O. Smith, *Advanced Mechanics of Materials*, John Wiley & Sons, 2nd ed., 1952; also F. R. Shanley, "Applied Column Theory," *Trans. A.S.C.E.*, Vol. 115, 1950, p. 698.

stress, which is the limiting stress for load-carrying capacity in short compression blocks.

Because of its complexity the double-modulus theory is not a useful design tool. Column design is based on the use of empirical formulas

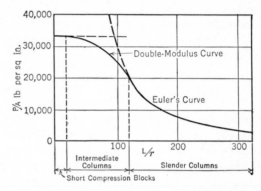

FIG. 13-5. Average stress causing failure of round-ended structural steel columns.

that agree reasonably well with theory and with tests.   Such formulas will be discussed later.

13-9. End Conditions in Intermediate Columns.   In a previous article it was stated that fixing the ends of a *slender* column will quadruple the

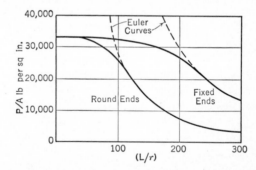

FIG. 13-6. P/A causing failure in columns of same steel but with different end conditions.

ultimate load or will quadruple the strength of the column, as distinct from the column material.   Fixing the ends increases the strength of the column by increasing the stiffness of the column.   Since the stiffness of the column has comparatively little effect on very short columns, which fail largely by crushing of the column material rather than by bending or lateral deflection, the end conditions of columns of inter- mediate slenderness are of less importance.

Figure 13-6 shows the ultimate loads, as given by the double-modulus

Euler curves, on series of ideal columns with round ends and fixed ends, respectively. On short compression blocks, the end condition is absolutely without importance, since the blocks fail entirely by crushing. As the slenderness increases and with it the importance of bending, the influence of end conditions becomes greater and greater. When L/r equals about 240, and both the round-ended and the fixed-ended columns have become slender columns, the load-carrying capacity of the fixed-ended column is four times that of the round-ended.

THE DESIGN AND INVESTIGATION OF COLUMNS

13-10. Design. To design a column of a given length to support a given load generally means to select a suitable shape for the cross-section and to determine the required area of the cross-section so that the column will support the load with approximately the same factor of safety as that with which the other parts of the structure support their loads. The curve shown in Fig. 13-5 makes it clear that in designing columns of a given material for a given use the average stress on the cross-section cannot have one specified value, as it does, for instance, in tension members or in beams of a given material for a given use. Instead the allowable average stress decreases with the slenderness or L/r of the column.

It has been seen that shafting and beams are readily designed by the use of formulas derived in considering the theory of torsion and bending. Imperfections and uncertainties of actual columns, however, result in behavior that is less in accord with theory; moreover, the complex formulas representing column theory are very difficult to apply.

Consequently, in practice, the design of a column is based on the use of an empirical column formula, which expresses a relationship between P/A and L/r, so that the designer can determine the value of P/A that the specification allows for any value of L/r.

Before giving further consideration to column formulas and their use, some of the differences between the ideal columns so far considered and the actual columns used in structures will be discussed.

13-11. Structural Steel Columns. The ideal column assumed in the discussion of column theory was a perfectly straight prismatical bar, with ends so arranged that the amount of restraint offered to rotation was definitely known, and with perfectly axial loads.

This perfection of material, fabrication, and loading is impossible to attain in practice. Specifications of the American Institute of Steel Construction, for example, permit an initial bend of $1/1,000$ of the length. This means that a column 25 ft long may have a crookedness of almost $\frac{1}{3}$ in. Most columns fall well within the specification, but crookedness must be considered in design, since enough may be present to affect materially the stresses in the loaded column.

Another uncertain condition in structural columns is the amount of restraint at the ends. In a building frame each of the floor systems provides restraint against lateral movement, so that the unsupported length L of the column is usually taken as the distance from center to center of beam connections for successive stories. However, although the floors may be considered to prevent any lateral movement of the

Fig. 13-7. Pin-ended column and fixed-ended column. Both columns are in railroad viaducts.

column axis, they do not wholly prevent its rotation. The end condition is intermediate between complete fixation and complete freedom to rotate.[5] The same situation exists in trusses, whether riveted or pinned. In a riveted truss, deformation of the truss as a whole permits some rotation of the joints. On the other hand, in a pinned truss, friction between the pin and the column offers a considerable amount of restraint, so that the condition is not comparable to that of a round-ended column. Figure 13-7 shows a column with a "pinned" end and a column with the end at least quite largely "fixed."

A third uncertainty in structural columns is eccentricity of load. In loading a column, the load is, of course, not applied directly to the axis of the column. The load may be applied through plates covering the ends of the column or through pins or through rivets. When a

[5] For columns of the proportions ordinarily used in practice, the rotation of the ends of a round-ended column as it is gradually loaded to nearly the buckling load is very small, often only 20 or 30 minutes of arc.

column is said to be "axially loaded," it is meant that the line of action of the resultant of the loads is *intended* to coincide with the axis of the unbent column.   It is reasonable to believe, however, that this condition is rarely attained.

Any initial eccentricity of load on a column will reduce the load at which the column fails, and on the other hand any restraint at the ends of the column will increase the ultimate load as compared with the ultimate load on a column with no restraint whatever at the ends.   For these reasons and because of imperfections the ultimate loads on actual columns tested to failure rarely agree exactly with the ultimate loads determined by analysis.   It follows that the design of columns is a less exact procedure than the design of beams.

13-12. Cross-Sections of Actual Columns.   For simplicity the ideal column previously considered was round.   Solid round columns are rarely encountered in structures, however, because of the small radius of gyration of a circle and because of the difficulty of connecting beams and other members to round columns.   Economy of fabrication,

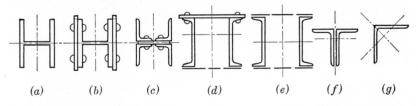

(a)   (b)   (c)   (d)   (e)   (f)   (g)

Fig. 13-8.   Some common cross-sections of structural columns.

simplicity of connections, and other considerations have led to the adoption of many different column cross-sections.   Some of those which are extensively used are shown in Fig. 13-8.

a. The H-column rolled out of a single piece of material, widely used, especially in buildings but also in bridges.

b. The H-column with cover plates riveted to the flanges to provide a larger cross-section.

c. The "built-up" H-column, made by riveting together a "web" plate and four angles.   This section may also have cover plates added.

d. The plate and channel column, frequently used in bridge chords. The open side is generally "latticed" with diagonal flat steel bars to stiffen the lower flanges of the channels.   (This latticing is not considered a part of the column cross-section.)

e. The channel column latticed on both sides.   (See Fig. 13-9 for side view.)   This type of column is often used for truss diagonals and verticals.

f. Two angles, back to back, either in contact or separated by the thickness of a plate, often used in roof trusses.

g. A single angle, sometimes used for columns carrying small loads.

Still other types of cross-section are used, compression members in large bridge trusses often being very elaborate. A *hollow* round section makes a very effective column. Until the in-

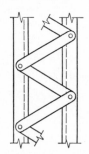

troduction of welded connections round columns were difficult to attach to other members, but steel tubing and pipe are now coming into more general use for columns and are extensively used in airplanes.

Fig. 13-9. Latticed column.

13-13. Least Radius of Gyration. Any area which does not have the same value of I with respect to every centroidal axis will have one centroidal axis with respect to which the moment of inertia is greater than for any other. Perpendicular to this will be the centroidal axis for which the moment of inertia is least. These axes are called the *principal axes* of the cross-section, and the moments of inertia with respect to these axes are called the principal moments of inertia of the cross-section. If an area has an axis of symmetry, that axis is one of the principal axes. In the cross-sections shown in Fig. 13-8 the principal axes are parallel to the sides of the cross-sections except for the single angle in which the principal axes are inclined as shown.

A column under a nominally axial load will bend about that axis for which the moment of inertia is least. That is, it will bend in the direction of the *least radius of gyration* of the cross-section, as may be demonstrated with a slender bar of rectangular cross-section, such as a yardstick. Consequently the *least* radius of gyration is the radius of gyration to be used in figuring the slenderness ratio of a column.

Example 1. A 12-in. WF 65-lb section is used as a column with a length of 16 ft. Find its slenderness ratio.

Solution: From Table III, the least r of this section (with respect to axis Y–Y) is 3.02 in. Therefore the slenderness ratio is $(16 \times 12)/3.02 = 63.6$.

Example 2. Find the slenderness ratio of a single $4 \times 4 \times \frac{3}{8}$ in. angle if used as a column with a length of 6 ft 2 in.

Solution: For this column, $L = 74$ in., and the least radius of gyration is that with respect to the axis Z–Z and is 0.79 in. (Table V). Therefore $L/r = 74/0.79 = 93.7$.

PROBLEMS

13-10. A column is made by riveting a 1×16 in. plate to each flange of a 14-in. WF 34-lb beam. What is the slenderness ratio if the column is 22 ft long?

Ans. $L/r = 64.5$.

13-11. A $5 \times 5 \times \frac{7}{8}$ in. angle has almost exactly the same cross-sectional area as two $5 \times 3\frac{1}{2} \times \frac{1}{2}$ in. angles. For any given length, compare the slenderness ratio of a column consisting of a single $5 \times 5 \times \frac{7}{8}$ in. angle with that of a column made by riveting two $5 \times 3\frac{1}{2} \times \frac{1}{2}$ in. angles "back to back," (a) if the 5-in. legs are riveted together, (b) if the $3\frac{1}{2}$-in. legs are riveted together.

13-12. A 5-in. 14.75-lb I-beam has almost exactly the same cross-sectional area as a 5-in. standard steel pipe. Find the ratio of the slenderness ratios of columns having the respective cross-sections and equal lengths.

13-13. A column is made of one $16 \times \frac{1}{2}$ in. plate and two 10-in. 20-lb channels, arranged as shown in Fig. 13-8d. The length of the columns is 14 ft 8 in. The distance back to back of channels is 10 in. Find the slenderness ratio.

$$Ans. \quad L/r = 46.$$

13-14. Column Formulas for Structural Steel Columns.

A column formula is an equation expressing the relationship between any slenderness ratio and the corresponding allowable P/A permitted by the specification of which the formula is a part. Three types of column formulas have been widely used for the design of structural steel columns. In the order in which they came into use, they are (1) Rankine formulas, (2) straight-line formulas, and (3) parabolic formulas. These types of formulas will be discussed in later articles.

In selecting a column to carry a given load P with a given unsupported length L, the designer uses the formula to determine the allowable P/A corresponding to the L/r of the column he is considering. Generally after two or three trials he finds the lightest column that will support the load and for which P/A is not more than the formula allows. The procedure followed in doing this will be illustrated in a later article.

A widely used column formula that will serve to illustrate the use of such formulas in design is that of the American Institute of Steel Construction. The A.I.S.C. formula is plotted in Fig. 13-10. Above this curve is curve B, the ordinates of which are theoretical values of P/A causing failure of ideal, structural steel, round-ended columns. This curve was discussed in Art. 13-9. Ordinates of curve B are approximately twice as large as corresponding ordinates of curve A. This means that round-ended columns of structural steel complying with the A.I.S.C. specifications would have factors of safety of approximately 2. However, curve C gives values of P/A at failure of columns with ends partly fixed. These values are more typical of structural steel columns as used in buildings where considerable fixity of ends always exists. Compared with this curve it will be seen that columns complying with the A.I.S.C. specifications and with ends partly fixed have factors of safety between 2 and 3 except for columns with very small values of L/r. A column designed by any of the typical column formulas for structural steel columns if used where its ends are well fixed against rotation will have a higher factor of safety than it will have if used where its ends are only slightly fixed. The purpose of a column formula is to make certain that columns designed by its use will have adequate factors of safety and at the same time be reasonably economical.

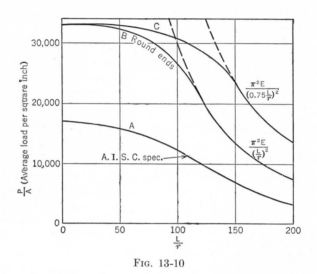

FIG. 13-10

13-15. Use of a Column Formula. To illustrate the procedure followed in selecting a column of given length to carry a given load, the parabolic formula of the American Institute of Steel Construction will be used. The procedure is the same when other column formulas are used. In this article discussion will be limited to columns having slenderness ratios (L/r) not more than 120. This includes nearly all the columns used in ordinary steel-frame buildings.

The A.I.S.C. specifications state that, for columns with L/r not exceeding 120, the value of P/A must not exceed $17,000 - 0.485(L/r)^2$. This formula is commonly written

$$P/A = 17,000 - 0.485(L/r)^2$$

in which P/A is the *allowable* P/A. The actual P/A is often less than the value given by the formula but must never be more.

The procedure to determine the allowable load on a given column is given in the following example.

Example 1. A 12-in. WF 65-lb beam is used as a column 20 ft long. What load is permitted by the A.I.S.C. specifications?

Solution: In the table of wide-flange beams, Appendix C, the area of a 12-in. WF 65-lb beam is given as 19.11 sq in. and the least radius of gyration is 3.02 in. For this column the slenderness ratio is $20 \times 12/3.02 = 79.5$. The allowable load per square inch of cross-section is

$$P/A = 17,000 - 0.485 \times 79.5^2$$
$$= 17,000 - 3,065 = 13,935 \text{ psi}$$

Hence the allowable load $P = 13,935 \times 19.11 = 266,000$ lb.

"Designing" a column usually means determining a suitable cross-section for a column of specified length to carry a given load in accordance with some design formula. This is a more difficult problem than investigation. Neither A nor L/r can be known in advance. Moreover, there is no fixed relationship between A and r for column sections such as are ordinarily used, whether the sections be rolled or "built-up." Therefore there are too many unknowns for a direct solution, and a process of selection and trial is necessary.

When selecting a column to comply with the A.I.S.C. specifications, it is convenient to remember that the maximum P/A permitted by the specifications is 17,000 psi and that when the slenderness ratio is 120 the P/A given by the formula is 10,000 psi. If, therefore, the load is divided by 13,500 or 14,000 a rough indication of the required area is obtained.

Example 2.   Select the lightest wide-flange beam to support a load of 380,000 lb and to comply with the A.I.S.C. specifications of 1949, the column length being 28 ft.

Solution: A rough indication of the required area is $380,000/14,000 = 27.1$ sq in. Referring to Table III, sections with about this area are the 12-in. WF 92-lb (area $=$ 27.06 sq in.) and the 14-in. WF 95-lb (area $= 27.94$ sq in.).   Of these the latter has the larger least r ($r_y = 3.71$ in.) and would therefore be the more efficient column section.   Investigating this section, $L/r = 336/3.71 = 90.6$, which, inserted in the column formula, gives $P/A = 13,020$ psi.   This column will therefore carry a load of $P = 27.94 \times 13,020 = 364,000$ lb.   Since this is less than the required load, a larger section must be found.

Try the 14-in. WF 103-lb beam, which has an area of 30.26 sq in. and an r of 3.72 in.   For this column $L/r = 336/3.72 = 90.2$, and the formula gives $P/A = 13,060$ psi.   The allowable load for this column is therefore $P = 30.26 \times 13,060 = 394,000$ lb.   Hence this column will more than meet the requirements.

The 12-in. WF 99-lb beam ($A = 29.09$ sq in.) is slightly lighter than the 14-in. WF 103-lb beam and might be considered.   For this column $L/r = 336/3.09 = 108.5$.   The formula gives for this slenderness ratio $P/A = 11,280$, and the allowable value of $P = 29.09 \times 11,280 = 328,000$ lb.   Hence this column does not meet the requirements.

Therefore use the 14-in. WF 103-lb beam.

If the calculations are arranged as shown on the next page, the successive steps will be readily performed, and all important values will be recorded compactly.   If the need arises, they can be readily followed, a very desirable feature in all engineering calculations.

Column. $P = 380,000$ lb, $L = 28$ ft $= 336$ in., A.I.S.C. specifications.

Try	Area	Min. r	L/r	P/A	P
1. 14-in. WF 95-lb	27.94	3.71	90.6	13,020	364,000 (small)
2. 14-in. WF 103-lb	30.26	3.72	90.2	13,060	394,000 (large)
3. 12-in. WF 99-lb	29.09	3.09	108.5	11,280	328,000 (small)

Use 14-in. WF 103.

PROBLEMS

13-14. Following the procedure outlined in this article, find the axial load permitted on each of the following steel sections by the A.I.S.C. specifications:

Column Section	Length
(a) 14-in. WF 426-lb	30 ft 0 in
(b) 14-in. WF 150-lb	16 ft 0 in.
(c) $6 \times 6 \times \frac{1}{2}$ in. angle	10 ft 0 in.

Ans.   (b) $P = 700,000$ lb.

13-15. Following the procedure outlined in this article, find the axial load permitted on each of the following steel sections by the A.I.S.C. specifications:

Column Section	Length
(a) 14-in. WF 74-lb	24 ft 0 in.
(b) 12-in. WF 72-lb	14 ft 0 in.
(c) $5 \times 5 \times \frac{5}{8}$ in. angle	9 ft 0 in.

Ans.   (c) $P = 65,200$ lb.

Following the procedure outlined in this article, select the lightest wide-flange beam to serve as a column and to comply with the A.I.S.C. specifications for each of the loads and lengths listed below:

13-16. $P = 340,000$ lb, $L = 26$ ft.   **13-23.** $P = 300,000$ lb, $L = 18$ ft.

13-17. $P = 780,000$ lb, $L = 32$ ft.   **13-24.** $P = 270,000$ lb, $L = 24$ ft.

13-18. $P = 500,000$ lb, $L = 30$ ft.   **13-25.** $P = 100,000$ lb, $L = 14$ ft.

13-19. $P = 500,000$ lb, $L = 14$ ft.   **13-26.** $P = 180,000$ lb, $L = 12$ ft.

13-20. $P = 250,000$ lb, $L = 22$ ft.   **13-27.** $P = 530,000$ lb, $L = 31$ ft.

13-21. $P = 420,000$ lb, $L = 34$ ft.   **13-28.** $P = 690,000$ lb, $L = 28$ ft.

13-22. $P = 600,000$ lb, $L = 34$ ft.   **13-29.** $P = 360,000$ lb, $L = 36$ ft.

13-30. Select the lightest equal-leg angle to serve as a column and to comply with the A.I.S.C. specifications if $P = 63,000$ lb and $L = 9$ ft 0 in.

13-31. Solve Problem 13-30 if $P = 70,000$ lb and $L = 11$ ft 0 in.

13-16. Rankine Column Formulas.

The purpose and method of use of a column formula have been illustrated by considering the parabolic-type formula in the specifications for structural steel of the American Institute of Steel Construction.   In this and the following articles a brief discussion of the three common types of column formulas will be given.   When wrought-iron columns and, later, structural steel columns came into use, Euler's was the only theoretical analysis of column action that had been achieved.   For the design of intermediate columns to which Euler's formula was inapplicable, various semi-rational or frankly empirical formulas were used.

Rankine's formula was perfected between 1856 and 1860 by a Scottish engineer, Rankine, from an earlier formula derived by another Scotchman, Gordon.   For this reason it is sometimes called the Rankine-Gordon formula.

Rankine's formula is derived as follows: Let S be the allowable stress in a column at the point of maximum stress.   Let P be the nominally axial load which causes this allowable stress, and let D be the maximum deflection which the column has under the load P.   Then

$$S = P/A + PDc/I = P/A + PDc/Ar^2$$

where r is the least radius of gyration.   From this

$$S = \frac{P}{A}\left(1 + \frac{Dc}{r^2}\right) \quad \text{or} \quad \frac{P}{A} = \frac{S}{1 + Dc/r^2}$$

So far this is correct and rational but not usable, becaue D is not known and cannot be determined.   It is assumed in the derivation of the Rankine formula that D will vary as L^2/c in columns made of a given material and all loaded to the same maximum stress.   This assumption is not exact, but it is reasonably near the truth.   If this assumption is admitted, then $D = qL^2/c$, where q is the constant relating D and L^2/c.   If this value is substituted for D in the equation above, it becomes

$$\frac{P}{A} = \frac{S}{1 + q(L/r)^2}$$

which is Rankine's formula.

Rankine's formula has been used with many different values of S and q, depending on the material, the end conditions, and the purpose of the column.   One formula of the Rankine type which has been very widely used in the design of columns in the frames of buildings was first given in the 1923 Specifications (for buildings) of the American Institute of Steel Construction.   The steel specified for this use was of such strength that 18,000 psi was taken as the basic stress in tension and compression.   Therefore this value was used for S in the formula.   The value of 1/18,000 was given to q, the formula therefore becoming

$$\frac{P}{A} = \frac{18,000}{1 + (1/18,000)\,(L/r)^2}$$

In this formula the right-hand member gives the *allowable* value for

P/A. The actual value of P/A may be less and often is less because the area of the actual cross-section chosen is often slightly greater than is required.

In addition to stipulating that the allowable P/A must not exceed the value given by the above formula, the specifications state that P/A

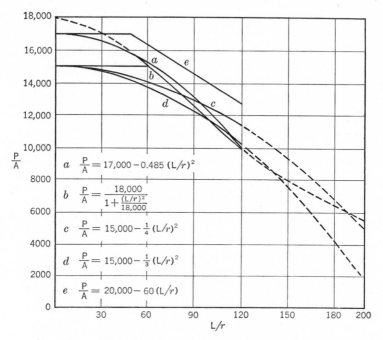

Fig. 13-11.   Five column formulas for structural steel columns.

must not exceed 15,000 psi, even though the above formula gives greater values for low values of L/r.   There is also a clause limiting values of L/r to 120, the purpose of which is to avoid too slender columns and thus to insure substantial construction.

The use of the "flat" stress of 15,000 psi (for all slenderness ratios to and including 60) is based on column tests.   Such tests have indicated that, for all slenderness ratios up to the neighborhood of 60, slenderness of the column has no pronounced effect on the value of P/A at which failure occurs.

The above Rankine formula makes no provision for variation in end conditions, and this has been true of most of the other Rankine-type formulas commonly used.   The value given q in this formula implies a condition between round and fixed ends such as exists in typical columns of steel building frames.

The above Rankine formula has been incorporated in many building codes. It was in the New York City building code for many years until 1949, when the New York City code was amended by substituting the A.I.S.C. specifications for structural steel columns. The Rankine formula given above is now part of the A.I.S.C. specifications for columns having slenderness ratios over 120 as is explained in Art. 13-19. Several column formulas, including this Rankine formula, are plotted in Fig. 13-11.

PROBLEMS

The problems of Art. 13-15 may be assigned to be solved using the above formula.

13-17. Straight-Line Formulas. Rankine's formula came into wide use during the years following its publication. During these same years, however, the experimental testing of columns was greatly extended. As a mass of data on actual column tests accumulated, it was observed that, for the lower slenderness ratios particularly, these test results when plotted did not lie along any *line* but covered a wide band. From this fact T. H. Johnson in 1884 drew the conclusion that, in the then-existing state of column theory (at that time neither the secant analysis nor the double-modulus analysis was known), the values of P/A at failure of columns of varying slenderness ratios could be represented by a graph consisting of Euler's curve for large slenderness ratios and a *straight line* tangent to Euler's curve for smaller ratios, as well as by any more complex curve. The general equation of such a straight line is $P/A = S_y - q(L/r)$, in which S_y is the yield-point stress.

The particular formulas which Johnson proposed did not come into wide use, but other straight-line formulas were widely adopted and extensively used as design formulas.

An example is the straight-line formula for columns of rolled carbon steel in the specifications for the design of the George Washington bridge. For rolled carbon steel the allowable P/A was given by

$$P/A = 20{,}000 - 60L/r$$

with a maximum of 17,000 psi (for columns with L/r of 50 or less). This formula is somewhat less conservative than the A.I.S.C. parabolic formula.

Other straight-line formulas will be given in later articles.

PROBLEMS

The problems of Art. 13-15 may be assigned to be solved using the above formula.

13-18. Parabolic Formulas. In 1882 Professor J. B. Johnson proposed a parabolic column formula in the form $P/A = S_y - q\,(L/r)^2$, in which

P is the load at failure, S_y is the yield point, and the value of q is such as to make the parabola tangent to the Euler curve. The curve representing this formula fitted the plotted results of the available tests on columns as well as any curve could. Parabolic column formulas did not come into wide use until it was realized that they can be made to agree very closely with values given by the secant formula which will be derived in Chapter 14. The secant formula is a theoretically correct formula for columns with *eccentric* loads but, when written with a suitable assumed small eccentricity, is now believed by many persons to represent better than any other formula the relationship between P/A and L/r for columns with *nominally axial* loads within the limits of L/r used in structures. Because the secant formula is complicated and very inconvenient to use in design, the parabolic formulas giving substantially the same results are used.

The specifications of the American Institute of Steel Construction have included a parabolic column formula since 1936

$$P/A = 17{,}000 - 0.485L^2/r^2$$

for columns with L/r not more than 120. This formula and the other stipulations concerning columns that are part of the A.I.S.C. specifications (see Art. 13-19) are incorporated in the building codes of many cities.

The following parabolic formulas occur in the specifications for steel railway bridges of the American Railway Engineering Association:

$$P/A = 15{,}000 - \tfrac{1}{4}(L/r)^2 \text{ for riveted ends}$$

$$P/A = 15{,}000 - \tfrac{1}{3}(L/r)^2 \text{ for pinned ends}$$

This specification states that L/r for main columns shall not exceed 100.

The use of the larger coefficient of $(L/r)^2$ for pinned ends is based on the correct assumption that riveted ends offer somewhat more restraint than pinned ends. Both the above formulas give about the same values of P/A for low values of L/r, which is consistent with the fact that end conditions have little effect on the load-carrying capacity of short columns. Formulas of the straight-line type or Rankine type can also be modified for different end conditions by using different coefficients of L/r or $(L/r)^2$.

13-19. Structural Steel Columns with L/r More Than 120. For many years most specifications for structural steel for buildings and bridges have prohibited the use of columns with slenderness ratios greater than 120 except for "braces and secondary columns." The purpose of the restriction is to insure substantial structures that are not only strong but also free from excessive vibration and deflection. Actually Euler's formula shows that for structural steel columns somewhat fixed at the ends the value of P/A at failure is in the neighborhood of 15,000 psi when L/r is 200.

The American Institute of Steel Construction now permits main columns with slenderness ratios up to 200. The A.I.S.C. column formulas for columns with L/r more than 120 are given below.

For bracing and other secondary members the allowable P/A is given by the Rankine formula

$$\frac{P}{A} = \frac{18,000}{1 + (L/r)^2/18,000}$$

In regard to main compression members the specifications state, "The slenderness of a main compression member may exceed 120, but not 200, provided that it is not ordinarily subject to shock or vibratory loads." For such columns the allowable P/A is given by the formula

$$\frac{P}{A} = \frac{18,000}{1 + (L/r)^2/18,000}\left(1.6 - \frac{L}{200r}\right)$$

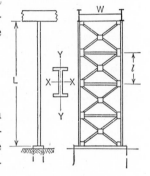

Fig. 13-12. Columns braced in one direction.

13-20. Columns with Intermediate Braces in One Plane. An I-beam is generally uneconomical for use as a column because of the very small radius of gyration. In some structures, however, it is possible to support a column in one plane at one or more points between the ends of the column as shown in Fig. 13-12. In this way the slenderness ratio in the direction of the smaller radius of gyration is l/r_y, which may be made as low as the slenderness ratio L/r_x in the direction of the larger radius of gyration. Where so used, I-beams and other shapes with a small radius of gyration in one direction are economical columns.

PROBLEMS

13-32. Each of the two columns shown in Fig. 13-12 is a 21 WF 62-lb. $L = 48$ ft. (a) With the bracing as shown, calculate the load W that the two columns will support. Use $P/A = 15,000 - \frac{1}{3}(L/r)^2$. (b) If the bracing is changed so as to brace the column at four intermediate points, calculate the allowable load.

Ans. (a) $W = 462,000$ lb.

13-33. A 16 WF 88-lb beam is used as a column 55 ft long. At how many intermediate points must it be braced in one plane to enable it to carry the greatest possible load?   Calculate the load permitted when so braced by the specification $P/A = 15,000 - \frac{1}{3}(L/r)^2$.

13-34. Solve Problem 13-32 if each column is a 21 WF 82-lb.

13-35. Solve Problem 13-33 if the column is a 15-in. 42.9-lb I.

13-21. Euler's Formula Applied to Design.
The general form of Euler's equation for the critical load P_c is $\dfrac{P_c}{A} = \dfrac{\pi^2 E}{(kL/r)^2}$. Here kL represents the length of the column between inflection points, the value of k being 1 for a column without end restraint, 0.5 for a column with fully fixed ends, etc. (Art. 13-6).   To convert this equation into a design formula giving the average allowable stress P/A, the right-hand side of the equation is divided by any desired factor of safety f.   The formula then becomes $\dfrac{P}{A} = \dfrac{\pi^2 E}{f(kL/r)^2}$.   This formula is not applicable to columns of the slendernesses commonly used in building frames and roof and bridge trusses.   It has been employed considerably in airplane design, particularly with high-strength steels and with wood and aluminum alloys.   For all these materials it is applicable to lower ratios of L/r than for structural steel.   In such use k is taken as unity except in very rigid frames, where it may be taken as $\frac{7}{8}$ or, in exceptional cases, $\frac{3}{4}$.

PROBLEMS

13-36. Part of a mechanism for opening and closing a ventilating transom is to be a round brass bar ($E = 14,000,000$ psi) 30 in. long.   The maximum force that can act on the ends of the bar is to be taken as 50 lb.   At its end the bar is to be supported on lubricated pins; it is to be treated as a round-ended column.   A factor of safety of 2 is considered sufficient.   What is the required bar diameter?

13-37. For a derrick mast 24 ft long it is proposed to use a standard steel pipe.   The maximum load which the mast is designed to withstand is 8 tons.   The factor of safety is to be 3.   Connections at the ends of the mast are such that loads may be assumed axial.   Consider the mast to be a round-ended column, and determine whether a 4-in. or a 5-in. pipe should be used.

13-38. If a 10 × 10 in. (nominal size) Douglas fir stick ($E = 1,600,000$ psi) is substituted for the steel pipe of Problem 13-37, what will the factor of safety become?

13-22. Formulas for Columns of Other Metals.
The curve representing a column formula for columns of a given material generally becomes tangent to Euler's curve (with a factor of safety) for columns of the same material.   A formula for high-strength steel columns gives higher values of P/A for small values of L/r than a formula for carbon steel.   The Euler curve, however, is the same for both.   It follows that the coefficients of L/r or $(L/r)^2$ in straight-line formulas and parabolic formulas for high-strength steel are larger than in similar formulas for structural

steel.   In Rankine formulas q is larger for high-strength steel than for structural steel.

Similarly for aluminum-alloy columns the curve representing a column formula would slope downward more rapidly than the curve of a column formula for steel having the same yield point.   This is because E for aluminum is only about one-third the value of E for steel.

High-Strength Steel Columns.   Typical formulas for high-strength steel are given below and, if compared with formulas for structural steel already given, show that q has been increased as well as S.

The specifications for the George Washington bridge included these formulas for high-strength steel columns.

Silicon steel: $P/A = 27,000 - 80L/r$ with maximum of 23,000

Nickel steel: $P/A = 33,000 - 100L/r$ with maximum of 28,000

American Railway Engineering Association (1952) formula for silicon steel with yield point of 45,000 psi (for values of L/r not greater than 130):

$$P/A = 20,000 - 0.46(L/r)^2 \text{ for riveted ends}$$
$$P/A = 20,000 - 0.61(L/r)^2 \text{ for pinned ends}$$

Aluminum-Alloy Columns.   Because of low weight in comparison with strength, columns made of certain aluminum alloys are widely used, particularly in the frames of aircraft and in movable cranes. There are many different aluminum alloys with widely varying characteristics, and the processes of fabrication, such as tempering and cold-working, also greatly affect the properties of the different alloys.   Two "strong" alloys are 17S (aluminum alloyed with copper, manganese, and magnesium) and 27S (aluminum alloyed with copper, manganese, and silicon).   When heat-treated and properly aged to bring out their best qualities, these alloys are designated as 17S-T and 27S-T.

The manufacturer states that typical yield strengths[6] in both tension and compression for these alloys are 37,000 psi for 17S-T and 50,000 psi for 27S-T.   The modulus of elasticity of aluminum alloys is taken at 10,300,000 psi.   In column formulas for aluminum alloys as now generally given, P is the load causing failure of the column.   In using one of these formulas, the designer divides it by a suitable factor of safety and then follows the procedure that has already been illustrated.

---

[6] Unlike mild steel, the aluminum alloys do not have a definite yield point at which there is an increase in deformation with no increase in load.   Their yield strength is arbitrarily set at the stress at which the stress-strain curve shows a departure of 0.002 in. per in. from the initial modulus line produced. See *Alcoa Structural Handbook*, published by the Aluminum Company of America.

Typical of the formulas given in the *Alcoa Structural Handbook* is that for 17S-T.   For values of KL/r less than 83

$$P/A = 43,800 - 350KL/r$$

and for values of KL/r more than 83

$$P/A = 102,000,000/(KL/r)^2$$

For columns with both ends perfectly fixed $K = 0.5$, and for columns with both ends hinged $K = 1.0$.   The second one of these formulas is an Euler formula which applies to all the aluminum alloys, regardless of their strength properties.   This is consistent with the fact that E is the same for all the alloys.

The two formulas may be represented graphically by a straight-line and an Euler curve which are practically tangent at $KL/r = 83$.

Cast-Iron Columns.   Cast-iron columns were extensively used in the nineteenth century but are no longer used in large and important structures, largely because of the likelihood of defects in the castings and because of the brittleness of the material, both of which make the column unreliable.   Cast-iron columns in building work are nearly always circular in cross-section and hollow, though occasionally hollow and square.

The Building Code Committee of the National Bureau of Standards recommends

$$P/A = 9,000 - 40L/r$$

with a maximum L/r of 90.   The 1951 New York City Building Code uses the same equation but limits the maximum slenderness ratio to 70.

PROBLEMS

13-39. Calculate the load permitted on a 14-in. WF 87-lb beam used as a column 30 ft long by each of the formulas for high-strength steel given in this article.

13-40. In a riveted aluminum-alloy truss one member consists of two $4 \times 3 \times \frac{1}{4}$ in. angles placed as shown in Fig. 13-13. The length of the column is 6 ft 6 in., and the distance between inflection points may be considered to be $\frac{3}{4}$ of the length.   What load is allowed on the column by the formulas of this article if the factor of safety is 3?

13-41. What load would be allowed by the New York City Building Code on a cast-iron column 7 ft long with an outside diameter of 5 in. and an inside diameter of 4 in.?   *Ans.* $P = 48,800$ lb.

Fig. 13-13

13-42. A tube of aluminum alloy 17S-T is 2.00 in. in outside diameter and has walls $\frac{1}{4}$ in. thick.   It is to be used as a column with hinged ends and is to have a factor of safety of 2.2.   Calculate the allowable load (*a*) if the length is 43 in.; (*b*) if the length is 72 in.   *Ans.*   (*a*) $P = 12,300$ lb.

13-43. Solve Problem 13-42 if the outside diameter is 2.25 in.

13-23. Wooden Columns.   Timber columns nearly always have solid rectangular cross-sections.   It is customary to specify allowable average stresses in terms of L/d instead of L/r (d is the least dimension of the cross-section).

A formula which has been extensively used for the design of wood columns is $P/A = C - 20L/d$, where C is the allowable compressive unit stress on the end of a short block. L/d must not exceed 40. Values of C given for the following woods are:

Southern pine and Douglas fir	1,300
Red and white oak	1,000
Spruce	800

The Forest Products Laboratory of the Department of Agriculture has proposed a column formula for wood columns which is based on a large number of tests.   The formula is

$$P/A = S[1 - \tfrac{1}{3}(L/Kd)^4]$$

In this formula S is the "safe unit compressive stress parallel to the grain" and K is the value of L/d at which the curve representing the above formula becomes tangent to an Euler curve (with a factor of safety).   The value of K is given by the formula $K = 0.64\sqrt{E/S}$.

Typical values of S and E are tabulated for a few common woods. Values of K corresponding to these values of S and E are also given. The values of S are for grades of lumber commonly procurable, used under shelter in continuously dry conditions.   They are based on recommendations of the National Lumber Manufacturers Association,[7] 1952.

	S	K	E
Douglas fir (coast)	1,300	22.4	1,600,000
Hemlock (western) No. 1	1,075	23.1	1,400,000
Oak (commercial red and white)	1,050	24.2	1,500,000
Pine (southern longleaf) structural	1,300	22.4	1,600,000
Spruce (eastern) structural	900	23.4	1,200,000

If L/d is 11 or less, the allowable stress S may be used without reduction.

If L/d exceeds the number given for K, the column is a "long column," and the above formula does not apply; Euler's formula should be used instead.   With a factor of safety of 3, and in terms of d instead of the least radius of gyration, the Euler formula for a round-ended column is

$$P/A = 0.274E/(L/d)^2$$

[7] *National Design Specifications for Stress Grade Lumber and Its Fastenings,* Washington, D.C.

and this is specified. The Forest Products Laboratory formulas have been included in many specifications.

PROBLEMS

13-44. Plot the Forest Products Laboratory formula for southern longleaf pine, from $L/d = 0$ to $L/d = 40$. Scales: 1 in. = 200 psi; 1 in. = $8L/d$.

13-45. A column of Douglas fir is $7\frac{1}{2} \times 7\frac{1}{2}$ in. and 10 ft long. (a) Calculate the allowable load, using the formula of the Forest Products Laboratory. (b) Find the load if the column is 17 ft long.

13-46. Solve Problem 13-45 but let the column be $9\frac{1}{2} \times 9\frac{1}{2}$ in.

13-47. Solve Problem 13-45, using the straight-line formula of this article.

13-48. What size of Douglas fir timber would you purchase for use as a column 18 ft long to carry a load of 90,000 lb? Use the straight-line formula given in this article.   *Ans.* Use 10 × 12 in.

13-49. Determine the required size if the timber is spruce in Problem 13-48.

13-50. A column 12 ft long is to be made of a piece of 3 × 4 in. Douglas fir lumber (actual size). (a) Find the allowable load as specified by the Forest Products Laboratory if the column is unbraced throughout its length. (b) If the column is to be braced at its midpoint, find the allowable load.

GENERAL PROBLEMS

13-51. A built-up H-section is formed of a $14 \times \frac{3}{8}$ in. web and four $6 \times 6 \times \frac{1}{2}$ in. angles. Depth of the column, back to back of angles, is $14\frac{1}{2}$ in. If the length is 20 ft, what nominally axial load is allowed by the A.I.S.C. specifications?

13-52. Solve Problem 13-51 if the angles are $6 \times 4 \times \frac{1}{2}$ in. with 4-in. legs in contact with the web plate.

13-53. If two $14 \times \frac{3}{4}$ in. cover plates are added to the column section of Problem 13-51, what is the allowable load?

13-54. A light derrick mast 40 ft long is made of four steel angles $4 \times 4 \times \frac{3}{8}$ in., forming a square as shown in Fig. 13-14. The angles are latticed together so that they act together as a column. What central load is permitted on this column by the formula $P/A = 15,000 - \frac{1}{3}(L/r)^2$? Is this a suitable column formula to use? (The lattice bars are assumed not to carry any of the load.)

13-55. Solve Problem 13-54 if the length is 44 ft and the angles are $3\frac{1}{2} \times 3\frac{1}{2} \times \frac{3}{8}$ in.

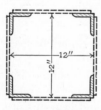

Fig. 13-14   Fig. 13-15

13-56. Four $4 \times 4 \times \frac{3}{8}$ in. angles are riveted back to back as shown in Fig. 13-15 to form a column 12 ft 6 in. long. What load is permitted on it by the A.I.S.C. parabolic formula?   *Ans.* P = 150,600 lb.

13-57. Solve Problem 13-56 if the angles are $3 \times 3 \times \frac{5}{16}$ in.

13-58. A sand bin which weighs 100 tons when full is to be supported by four square timber columns 20 ft long. What size of southern pine timbers should be bought to comply with the straight-line formula of Art. 13-23?

Ans. Use 10 × 10 in.

13-59. What load does the Forest Products Laboratory formula allow on a column $9\frac{1}{2}$ in. square and 20 ft long of Douglas fir?

13-60. Columns in a welded bridge in Europe are made of two steel beams and a web plate as shown in Fig. 13-16. In some of the columns the beams are equivalent

FIG. 13-16   FIG. 13-17

to 24-in. WF 84-lb, and the plate thickness is about $\frac{3}{4}$ in. The distance h is 18.0 in. If the length of the column is 46.0 ft, calculate the axial load permitted by the formula $P/A = 15,000 - \frac{1}{4}(L/r)^2$.

13-61. Solve Problem 13-60 if the beams are 24 WF 100-lb.

13-62. Solve Problem 13-60 if $h = 16$ in., $L = 44$ ft, and beams are 21-in. WF 82-lb.

13-63. A steel column 25 ft long is made of a 12-in. 35-lb I-beam and two 12-in. 20.7-lb channels, as shown in Fig. 13-17. Calculate the allowable axial load, using $P/A = 15,000 - \frac{1}{4}(L/r)^2$.   *Ans.* $P = 292,000$ lb.

13-64. Solve Problem 13-63 if $L = 22$ ft and channels are 10 in. 20 lb.

13-65. A warehouse, 60 ft wide and 140 ft long, is to be built. The floor is supported by columns spaced 12 ft center to center north and south and spaced 14 ft center to center east and west. The floor weighs 30 lb per sq ft and is designed for a live load of 75 lb per sq ft. Columns are 12 ft long. Each column also carries an assumed roof and snow load of 8,400 lb. What size southern pine columns would you order for this job? (Use a straight-line formula.)

13-66. A column is made of a 14 WF 34-lb beam with a 14 × $\frac{1}{2}$ in. cover plate attached to each flange as in Fig. 13-8b. Calculate the allowable load using A.I.S.C. specifications if the length is 25 ft.

13-67. Solve Problem 13-66 if the cover plates are each 14 × $\frac{3}{4}$ in.

13-68. Many modern water tanks are supported on tubular columns. A 500,000-gal tank at Fresno, California, is supported by 10 tubular columns and a central riser. When full, it weighs approximately 2,260 tons, and the columns support 80 per cent of the load. Each column is 65 ft long with an outside diameter of 38 in. and thickness of $\frac{5}{16}$ in. The design was based on the formula $P/A = 16,000 - 70L/r$. Calculate the load permitted by this formula on one column. How does this compare with the actual load? (The r for a thin tube is approximately 0.707 times the radius of the tube.)

13-69. A square sand bin with a total weight of 360,000 lb is supported by a column at each corner. Length of column is 11 ft 6 in. Select the lightest steel equal-leg angle to serve as a column. Use $P/A = 15,000 - \frac{1}{3}(L/r)^2$.

13-70. Solve Problem 13-69 if the load is 300,000 lb, the length of columns is 10 ft, and the A.I.S.C. column formula is used.   *Ans.* Use 6 × 6 × $\frac{9}{16}$ angle.

14

Columns with Eccentric Loads

14-1. Introduction. Many columns in structures support loads that are applied with a considerable amount of eccentricity. A given eccentric load causes greater bending stress than the same load axially applied, and consequently the allowable eccentric load on a column is less than the allowable axial load on the same column.

This chapter will take up first the determination of the allowable eccentric load on a column by methods based on an empirical formula.

Next the theoretically correct secant formula will be derived, and its application to eccentrically loaded columns will be illustrated.

It will then be shown that the secant formula may be used for the design of columns with nominally axial loads by inserting an assumed small eccentricity in the secant formula. The use of the secant formula as a design formula for axially loaded columns is advocated by some engineers.

14-2. Empirical Formulas for Eccentrically Loaded Columns. Several empirical procedures have been followed for the design of columns with eccentric loads. The method given in the A.I.S.C. specifications is widely used and will be discussed.

The basis for the design of axially loaded columns is the requirement that P/A must not exceed F_a, in which F_a is the value found by inserting the proper L/r in the column formula that is being used. Another way of writing this is

$$\frac{P/A}{F_a} \text{ must not exceed unity}$$

The basis for the design of members subject to bending is the requirement that Mc/I must not exceed the specified allowable bending stress. Let this specified allowable bending stress be F_b. Then this requirement may be written

$$\frac{Mc/I}{F_b} \text{ must not exceed unity}$$

In a column with eccentric loads there are both compressive stress due

254

to end loads as in an axially loaded column and also compressive stress resulting from the bending moment caused by the eccentric load.

The A.I.S.C. specifications are based on the assumption that the column will have the desired factor of safety provided that

$$\frac{P/A}{F_a} + \frac{Mc/I}{F_b} \text{ does not exceed unity}$$

The notation used in the A.I.S.C. specifications is as follows:

$$\frac{f_a}{F_a} + \frac{f_b}{F_b} \text{ must not exceed unity} \qquad (14\text{-}1)$$

In this formula f_a is $\Sigma P/A$, in which ΣP is the sum of the loads on the column, both axial and eccentric.   The symbol f_b is the actual value of Pec/I due to the eccentric loading.   In calculating $f_b = Pec/I$, the c and I should be with respect to the axis from which e is measured, that is, the axis about which the bending occurs.   The r used in computing F_a should be the minimum r as in axially loaded columns, regardless of the direction of the eccentricity.   This formula gives satisfactory results for the columns in typical building frames.   It ignores any additional deflection due to the eccentric load which increases e with respect to the cross-sections at the midpoint.   In the case of columns with L/r up to 120 and with the eccentric load causing a moment that is not excessive, the formula is a satisfactory basis for design.   On the other hand, if L/r is very large and Pe is large, the additional deflection due to the eccentric load might not be negligible.   In such a case an approximate value of additional deflection could be found by the area moment method and Pe increased by this additional e.   A second approximation could be made if necessary.   Another procedure would be to use the secant formula (derived in a following article).   The analysis by which the secant formula is derived does not neglect the deflection due to the eccentricity.

Example.   A steel column 21 ft long is to carry an axial load of 160,000 lb and an eccentric load of 80,000 lb applied 2 in. from the face of the flange, as shown in Fig. 14-1.   Select a wide-flange section to carry the loads in accordance with the A.I.S.C. specifications.

Solution: In solving this problem three trials were made.   First a 12-in. WF 99-lb was tried.   For this section $A = 29.09$ sq in., $I/c = 134.7$, and min. $r = 3.09$ in. $L/r = 252/3.09 = 81.5$, $F_a = 17,000 - 0.485(81.5)^2 = 13,780$ psi.

$$\frac{f_a}{F_a} + \frac{f_b}{F_b} = \frac{240,000/29.09}{13,780} + \frac{80,000 \times 8.375/134.7}{20,000}$$

$$= 0.60 + 0.25 = 0.85$$

Next the 12-in. WF 92-lb was tried, and the sum of the two terms was found to be 0.91.

Next the 12-in. WF 85-lb was tried. For this section $A = 24.98$, $I/c = 115.7$, $L/r = 252/3.07 = 82$.

$$F_a = 17,000 - 0.485 \times (82)^2 = 13,740 \text{ psi}$$

$$\frac{f_a}{F_a} + \frac{f_b}{F_b} = \frac{240,000/24.98}{13,740} + \frac{80,000 \times 8.25/115.7}{20,000}$$

$$= 0.70 + 0.286 = 0.986$$

Use the 12-in. WF 85-lb.

As is explained in Art. 19-7, the A.I.S.C. specifications reduce the allowable bending stress from 20,000 to a smaller value for beams that have compression flanges not laterally supported in some cases where there are comparatively thin and wide

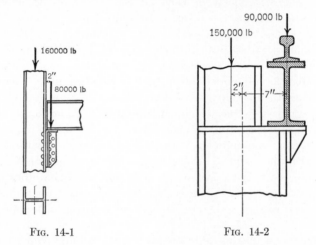

FIG. 14-1   FIG. 14-2

flanges and where the depth of the beam is large. Such a reduction should also be made for columns. The reduction is made if Ld/bt exceeds 600. In this expression L is the unsupported length, d the depth of the beam, b the width of the compression flange, and t the thickness of the compression flange, all in inches. The reduction in F_b should also be made in the case of columns in which Ld/bt exceeds 600.

For the 12-in. WF 85-lb, $t = 0.796$ in., $d = 12.50$ in., and $b = 12.1$ in. With a length of 21 ft the quantity Ld/bt equals 326. Since this is much less than 600 the allowable F_b is 20,000 psi.

PROBLEMS

14-1. A column 24 ft long supports the load from a column above, and also a crane reaction, as shown in Fig. 14-2. Select a 14-in. wide-flanged section to carry the load in accordance with the A.I.S.C. specifications.

Ans. Use 14-in. WF 78-lb.

14-2. A 14-in. WF 103-lb beam used as a column 28 ft long has an eccentric load of 280,000 lb on the Y–Y axis. How far from the X–X axis can this load be and still comply with A.I.S.C. specifications? *Ans.* $e = 3.40$ in.

14-3. A transformer unit weighs 800 lb and is carried on a southern longleaf pine post as shown in Fig. 14-3.   Will a 10 × 10 in. (nominal size) post suffice?   (*Hint:* Use the appropriate Forest Products Laboratory column formula to determine the allowable value of F_a for an axial load.)   Consider the length of the column to be 30 ft.   Assume that the allowable bending stress F_b is 1,600 psi.

14-4. A 12-in. WF 65-lb beam 20 ft long has an axial load of 120,000 lb and an eccentric load of 60,000 lb located on the $Y-Y$ axis.   What eccentricity is permitted by the A.I.S.C. specifications?

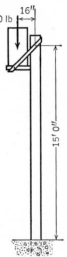

Fig. 14-3

14-3. The Secant Formula. Although eccentrically loaded columns are often designed by approximate methods such as are given in Art. 14-2, a correct analysis for eccentrically loaded columns has been known for some time.   The formula resulting from this analysis is known as the "secant formula."

An ideal column loaded with an initially eccentric load acts quite differently from the same column loaded axially.   Under axial load the column does not begin to bend until (*a*) the critical stress is reached or (*b*) the average compressive stress in the column reaches the proportional limit of the material.   Under an eccentric load, however, the column begins to bend just as soon as any load is applied.

Moreover, the maximum deflection (at the midlength) of an eccentrically loaded column is definite for any given load and initial eccentricity.   This deflection can be computed if the dimensions of the column and the stiffness of the column material are known.   With the deflection known, the moment arm of the load with respect to the centroid of the mid cross-section can be determined, and the maximum compressive stress in the column can be found.   The equation expressing the relationship between the eccentric load and the maximum stress it causes in the column is called the "secant formula."   It is derived as follows:

Suppose a column with ends perfectly free to rotate (round-ended column) to be acted on by a load P, having an eccentricity e, with respect to the centroid of the end cross-section of the column (Fig. 14-4).   Let y be the deflection of the column at a distance x from the end, the origin and axes being taken as shown.   Then, as in the case of a slender column under its critical axial load, the equation of the elastic curve of this column can be written $EI\, d^2y/dx^2 = -Py$.   Multiplied through by $2dy$, this becomes

$$2EI(dy/dx)d(dy/dx) = -2Py\, dy$$

Integrating,

$$EI\,(dy/dx)^2 = -Py^2 + C_1$$

To evaluate C_1, note that, when $dy/dx = 0$, y equals the maximum deflection D. Therefore $C_1 = PD^2$. Substituting this value for C_1, dividing by EI, and taking the square root of both members of the equation,

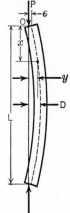

$$dy/dx = (P/EI)^{\frac{1}{2}}\,(D^2 - y^2)^{\frac{1}{2}}$$

or

$$dy/(D^2 - y^2)^{\frac{1}{2}} = (P/EI)^{\frac{1}{2}}\,dx$$

Integrating again,

$$x = \left(\frac{EI}{P}\right)^{\frac{1}{2}}\left(\sin^{-1}\frac{y}{D} + C_2\right)$$

(It may be noted that to this point the derivation of the secant formula is identical with the derivation of Euler's formula.) To evaluate C_2, note that, when $x = 0$, $y = e$. Therefore $C_2 = -\sin^{-1}(e/D)$. Whence

Fig. 14-4

$$x = \left(\frac{EI}{P}\right)^{\frac{1}{2}}\left(\sin^{-1}\frac{y}{D} - \sin^{-1}\frac{e}{D}\right)$$

To evaluate $\sin^{-1}(e/D)$, note that, when $x = L/2$, $y = D$. Then

$$\frac{L}{2} = \left(\frac{EI}{P}\right)^{\frac{1}{2}}\left(\sin^{-1} 1 - \sin^{-1}\frac{e}{D}\right)$$

Whence

$$\sin^{-1}(e/D) = \pi/2 - (PL^2/4EI)^{\frac{1}{2}}$$

Therefore

$$e = D \sin\left[\tfrac{1}{2}\pi - (PL^2/4EI)^{\frac{1}{2}}\right] = D \cos\,(PL^2/4EI)^{\frac{1}{2}}$$

Whence

$$D = e \sec\,(PL^2/4EI)^{\frac{1}{2}}$$

As shown in Chapter 12, the maximum stress S equals $P/A + Mc/I$. The maximum bending moment occurs where the deflection equals D and is PD or $Pe \sec\,(PL^2/4EI)^{\frac{1}{2}}$. Inserting this value, substituting Ar^2 for I, and factoring,

$$S = \frac{P}{A}\left[1 + \frac{ec}{r^2} \sec\frac{L}{r}\left(\frac{P}{4EA}\right)^{\frac{1}{2}}\right]$$

This equation, the *secant formula*, gives the maximum stress S, caused by a load P having an eccentricity e with respect to the centroid of the end section of a round-ended column with length L, area of cross-section

A, radius of gyration r, distance from the neutral axis to the most remote fiber c, and modulus of elasticity E.

The foregoing derivation is rational. For small deflections, such as are encountered in practice, and for stresses within the proportional limit, it gives results that are theoretically correct.   Moreover, careful measurements of the deflections of columns loaded with a measured end-eccentricity have checked the theory satisfactorily, not only as applied to small, nearly "ideal" columns, but for full-sized structural columns as well.[1]   This makes the secant formula a very valuable foundation for practical column analysis and design.

It may be noted that, when L/r approaches zero in the secant formula, S approaches P/A $(1 + ec/r^2)$ or $P/A + Pec/I$, which is the stress in a short, eccentrically loaded compression block.   The quantity ec/r^2 therefore expresses the limiting ratio of the bending stress (caused by the eccentricity) to the direct compressive stress, as the slenderness of the column decreases.   The quantity ec/r^2 is often called the "eccentricity ratio."

PROBLEMS

14-5. A round steel bar, 1 in. in diameter and 52 in. long, carries a load of 5,000 lb applied with an eccentricity of $\frac{1}{16}$ in. at each end.   The ends of the bar are free to rotate.   Calculate the maximum deflection $(D - e)$ which the midpoint of the axis undergoes as the load is applied.

14-6. Using the equation $S = P/A + PDc/I$, find the maximum stress which the 5,000-lb load causes in the column of Problem 14-5.

Ans. $S = 34,470$ psi.

14-7. Use the secant formula as given in Art. 14-3 to check the value obtained for S in Problem 14-6.

14-4. Curves Representing the Secant Formula.

The secant formula is more commonly written

$$\frac{P}{A} = \frac{S}{1 + \left(\dfrac{ec}{r^2}\right) \sec \dfrac{L}{r}\sqrt{\dfrac{P/A}{4E}}}$$

If, in the above formula, S is the yield-point stress of the material, the value given for P/A is that at which failure must occur.

Values of P/A are not easy to calculate by this formula for a given L/r because P/A also occurs under the radical sign in the denominator. For any given value of S and for a given value of ec/r^2, values of L/r can be computed for selected values of P/A.   When these values have

[1] See "Final Report of Special Committee on Steel Column Research," *Trans. A.S.C.E.*, Vol. 98, p. 1460, Conclusion 1.

been found a curve can be plotted having values of P/A as ordinates corresponding to values of L/r. The curves shown in Fig. 14-5 represent the secant formula for $S = 33,000$ psi and $E = 30,000,000$ psi, and for values of ec/r^2 of 0.10, 0.25, and 1.0.

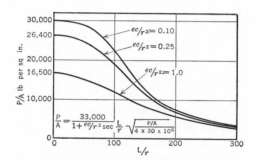

Fig. 14-5. Columns of structural steel with three different eccentricities of load.

The secant curves of Fig. 14-5 show strikingly how greatly initial eccentricity of loading decreases the load which will cause a given maximum stress in a relatively short column. On a very slender column, initial eccentricity has less effect. In engineering work, however, the usual practice calls for values of L/r sufficiently small to make eccentricity of loading very important.

14-5. Secant Formula Applied to Design of Columns. An eccentrically loaded column will certainly fail when the maximum stress equals the yield point of the material. Therefore the secant formula will give the ultimate load for a round-ended column if written

$$\frac{P}{A} = \frac{\text{Yield point of material}}{1 + \left(\frac{ec}{r^2}\right) \sec \frac{L}{r} \sqrt{\frac{P/A}{4E}}}$$

The formula can be modified for other end conditions by substituting for L a length kL, which represents the effective part of the total length.

It is not permissible to convert the buckling load formula into a formula for *allowable* load simply by replacing the yield-point stress with the allowable compressive stress. The reason is that, for a column of any marked slenderness, a given percentage increase in *load* results in a much greater increase in *maximum stress*. To convert the given equation into a working formula, therefore, let the buckling load P be replaced by the allowable load P', times the desired factor of safety f.

Then P/A becomes $P'f/A$, and the equation becomes

$$\frac{P'f}{A} = \frac{\text{Yield point of material}}{1 + \left(\dfrac{ec}{r^2}\right)\sec\dfrac{kL}{r}\sqrt{\dfrac{P'f/A}{4E}}}$$

This can be written

$$\frac{P'}{A} = \frac{(1/f)\ (\text{Yield point of material})}{1 + \left(\dfrac{ec}{r^2}\right)\sec\dfrac{kL}{r}\sqrt{\dfrac{P'/A}{4E/f}}}$$

It is seen therefore that the factor of safety must be applied both to the ultimate strength of the material (in a column the yield point establishes the ultimate strength) and to its stiffness. This is consistent with the fact that the load-carrying capacity of a short column is determined by the strength of the column material, whereas that of a slender column is determined by the stiffness.

The A.R.E.A. specifications (1935) provide that for columns with known eccentricity of loading the following secant formula shall be used:

$$\frac{P}{A} = \frac{(1/f)\ (\text{Yield point of material})}{1 + (ec/r^2 + 0.001L/r)\sec\dfrac{kL}{r}\sqrt{\dfrac{P/A}{4E/f}}}$$

In this formula e is the intentional eccentricity of loading, r is the least radius of gyration of the cross-section in question, and c is the distance of the most remote point on that cross-section from the axis with respect to which r is least.[2] The value of k is $\frac{3}{4}$ for columns with riveted ends and $\frac{7}{8}$ for columns with pinned ends; f is 1.76 for carbon steel with a yield point of 33,000 psi. The term $0.001L/r$ provides for chance eccentricity, such as that due to crookedness of the column, which exists in addition to the intended eccentricity.

When a column carrying both nominally axial and intentionally eccentric loads is to be investigated or designed by means of the secant formula, the two loads are replaced by their resultant.

PROBLEMS

14-8. A 6-in. standard steel pipe projects upward for a length of 10 ft above a concrete foundation in which the lower end is embedded. What eccentricity is permissible for a load of 56,000 lb applied to the upper end? Assume yield point = 33,000 psi, $k = 2$, and $f = 2$. A.R.E.A. specifications.

[2] If the intentional eccentricity is at right angles to the least radius of gyration, this is not a logical procedure, but any error to which it leads is on the "safe" side.

14-9. An 8-in. WF 17-lb section is used as a column 9 ft 6 in. long. It carries a load the resultant of which acts on the axis $Y-Y$ and 1 in. from the axis $X-X$. What may the load be in accordance with the secant equation of the A.R.E.A. specifications? The yield point equals 33,000 psi, $f = 1.76$, $k = \frac{3}{4}$.

14-6. Secant Formula for Axially Loaded Columns.

While formulas of the types discussed in Chapter 13 were in use, the secant analysis showing the effect of an eccentric load on an ideal column was being worked out. In 1912 Professor O. H. Basquin suggested that most of the defects in the fabrication and loading of an actual column could be considered as an "equivalent eccentricity of loading." He proposed that a reasonable value for this equivalent eccentricity be derived from a careful study of column tests and then be inserted in the secant formula for use in the design of structural columns. Subsequently a Special Committee on Steel Column Research was appointed by the American Society of Civil Engineers, and over a period of years this committee made a very careful study of existing column test data, which it supplemented by elaborate additional tests. The result of this investigation was the recommendation by the committee (in 1933) that the equation

$$\frac{P}{A} = \frac{\text{Yield point of material}}{1 + 0.25 \sec \dfrac{kL}{r} \sqrt{\dfrac{P/A}{4E}}}$$

be accepted as a basis for the design of structural columns with nominally axial loads.

This general form of the secant equation is applicable to a column with any end condition when a value of k consistent with the end condition has been introduced. That is, the part of the column length between inflection points acts as a round-ended column, and this part of the length is represented by kL. From its study of column tests the committee recommended that in pinned structures k be taken as $\frac{7}{8}$ and in riveted structures as $\frac{3}{4}$.

The committee recommended the use of 32,000 psi for the yield point and a factor of safety such as to reduce the average stress in a short compression block to 15,000 psi. With the 0.25 eccentricity ratio, this makes the maximum stress $1.25 \times 15,000 = 18,750$ psi. The factor of safety which will make this reduction is $32,000/18,750 = 1.71$. When these substitutions are made and a value of 30,000,000 is assumed for E, the equation for riveted-ended columns becomes

$$\frac{P'}{A} = \frac{18,750}{1 + 0.25 \sec \dfrac{\frac{3}{4}L}{r} \sqrt{\dfrac{P'/A}{4 \times 17.6 \times 10^6}}}$$

Because of the very considerable difficulty in using this formula for the design and investigation of columns, parabolic formulas giving very

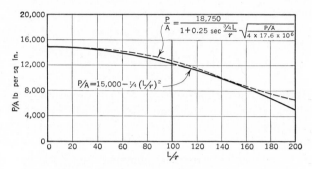

Fig. 14-6. Parabolic formula and secant formula.

nearly the same values of P/A were proposed by the committee. The close agreement of one of these parabolic formulas and a secant formula is shown in Fig. 14-6.

GENERAL PROBLEMS

In each of the following problems a wide-flange beam is to support an eccentric load located on the $Y-Y$ axis of the cross-section. Determine the quantity indicated using the A.I.S.C. specifications. Take $F_b = 20,000$ psi.

14-10. 14-in. WF 150-lb, $L = 30$ ft, $e = 6$ in. Calculate allowable P.

14-11. 14-in. WF 74-lb, $L = 24$ ft, $e = 10$ in. Calculate allowable P.

14-12. 12-in. WF 72-lb, $L = 24$ ft, $e = 4$ in. Calculate allowable P.
$\qquad$ *Ans.* $P = 172,000$ lb.

14-13. 14-in. WF 95-lb, $L = 27$ ft, $P = 280,000$ lb. Calculate allowable e.

14-14. 12-in. WF 65-lb, $L = 20$ ft, $P = 190,000$ lb. Calculate allowable e.

14-15. $L = 22$ ft, $P = 250,000$ lb, $e = 2$ in. Select WF beam.

14-16. $L = 20$ ft, $P = 300,000$ lb, $e = 3$ in. Select WF beam.

15

Combined Stresses

15-1. Introduction. In a beam the tensile stress on a vertical plane at a point y in. from the neutral axis is given by the formula $S = My/I$, and the shearing stress on horizontal and vertical planes through the same point is given by $S_s = VQ/Ib$. It will be shown in this chapter that, at any point in the cross-section of a beam where there are both tensile and shearing stresses, there are greater tensile stresses than the stress found by $S = My/I$. Does this greater tensile stress ever exceed the tension in the extreme fibers?

In a shaft, such as a vertical turbine shaft, subject to axial compressive forces and also subject to torque, there are shearing stresses at the surface (on the transverse and on longitudinal planes) which are given by $S_s = Tc/J$ and compressive stresses on transverse planes equal to P/A. It will be shown that at any point where both these stresses occur there are greater shearing and compressive stresses than those given by the formulas. Can these be disregarded in the design of the shaft?

At a point in the shell of a boiler subject to steam pressure it was found that tensile stresses exist in two directions, the circumferential tension being twice the longitudinal tension. Do still greater stresses on some oblique plane result from the combination of these calculated stresses? These questions and many similar questions can be intelligently answered only if the relationships between given stresses and the resulting maximum stresses are understood. If stresses greater than those commonly calculated exist, the designer should be aware of them.

The term "combined stresses" is commonly used to designate the stresses calculated by combining other stresses. In this chapter are derived relationships existing between given combinations of stress on certain planes at a point, such as the combinations mentioned above, and the stresses that exist on other planes through the same point. Only "two-dimensional" stresses (all forces and stresses being parallel to one plane) will be considered in this chapter.

15-2. Representation of a State of Stress in Body. The state of stress existing at a point in a stressed body is conveniently represented by showing the unit stresses acting on the faces of a small rectangular solid at the point in the body. If the stresses in the body are uniformly distributed, that is, do not vary in intensity from point to point, the rectangular solid may be of any size. However, if, as is common, the stresses vary from point to point, as in a beam, the solid is taken of infinitesimal size so that the stresses may without error be regarded as uniform over its faces.

It is possible to represent the same state of stress in a body in different ways. As an example, consider a prism with axial tensile loading causing a tensile stress of 10,000 psi on all transverse planes. This condition of stress may be represented by an infinite number of different combinations of shearing and tensile stresses on differently inclined

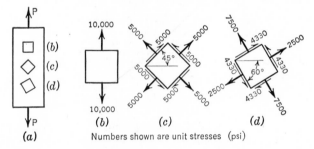

FIG. 15-1.   The same state of stress represented in three ways.

planes. Three of these are shown in Fig. 15-1. Inspection of the stresses shown in *d* does not indicate the identity of this state of stress with that shown in *b*, but, if the "principal stresses" (defined later) for *d* are calculated, they are found to be the stresses shown in *b*.

The principal stresses shown in *b* are no more the "true stresses" than those shown in *c* or *d*, which represent the same state of stress at the given point in the body but show the stresses that exist on other planes.

It is important to keep in mind that stress at a certain point cannot be considered quantitatively without considering a plane (passing through the point) on which the stress acts. On different planes through a given point in a stressed body the stresses differ.

In the following discussion the term *normal stress* will be used to denote either tensile unit stress or compressive unit stress as distinguished from shearing unit stress. Tensile and compressive stresses are "normal" inasmuch as they result from forces acting perpendicular to the plane of stress, whereas shearing stresses result from forces parallel to the plane on which the shearing stresses act. Shearing stresses are sometimes called "tangential" stresses.

15-3. Calculation of Stresses on an Oblique Plane. When known stresses act on mutually perpendicular planes, the stresses on any inclined plane are found by applying the conditions of equilibrium to a wedge-shaped solid two faces of which coincide with the planes of known stress and one face of which is in the direction of the inclined plane.

Example. A steel rod, 1 in. in diameter, fixed at one end, is used as a tension member to carry a load of 12,560 lb and at the same time is subject to a torque of 1,570 lb-in. applied at the end as shown diagrammatically in Fig. 15-2. The tensile stress resulting from this load is 16,000 psi over all transverse sections. Shearing

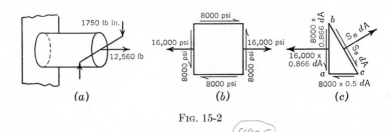

Fig. 15-2

stresses at the surface caused by the torque are 8,000 psi. Calculate the stresses which exist at a point on the surface of the rod on a plane making an angle of 60° with the element of the surface through that point.

Solution: The given tensile and shearing stresses are shown on a cube in Fig. 15-2b.[1] In c is shown a wedge cut from the cube by a plane making an angle of 60° with an element of the cylinder. This wedge is a particle in equilibrium, and the forces holding it in equilibrium result from the given unit stresses and the unknown unit stresses. Equating the sum of the components parallel to bc to zero,

$$S_s\,dA - 16{,}000 \times 0.866dA \times 0.5 + 8{,}000 \times 0.866dA \times 0.866 - 8{,}000 \times 0.5dA \times 0.5 = 0$$

$$S_s = +6{,}930 - 6{,}000 + 2{,}000 = +2{,}930 \text{ psi}$$

The plus sign indicates that the stress on the face bc of the wedge is in the direction assumed when writing the equation.

Equating the sum of the components normal to bc to zero,

$$S_n\,dA - 16{,}000 \times 0.866dA \times 0.866 - 8{,}000 \times 0.866dA \times 0.5 - 8{,}000 \times 0.5dA \times 0.866 = 0$$

$$S_n = 12{,}000 + 3{,}460 + 3{,}460 = +18{,}920 \text{ psi}$$

The plus sign indicates that the normal stress on bc is tensile, as assumed in writing the equation.

[1] The same intensity of shearing stress that acts on the horizontal surfaces of the cube must also act on the vertical surfaces. See Art. 5-5.

PROBLEMS

15-1. By the method used in Art. 15-3 calculate the shearing and normal stresses on a 45° plane which result from the stresses shown in Fig. 15-2b.

15-2. Solve Problem 15-1 if the plane is inclined 135° with horizontal.

15-3. Solve Problem 15-1 if the plane is inclined 30° with horizontal.

15-4. A steel pipe 20 in. in diameter and with a wall thickness of $\frac{1}{4}$ in. has a welded spiral seam which intersects elements of the cylinder at 45° as shown in Fig. 15-3. Allowable tensile stress in the pipe wall where there is no seam is 12,000 psi. Allowable tensile and shearing stresses in the seam are 9,000 and 6,600 psi, respectively. What is the allowable unit pressure in the pipe? Does the presence of the seam affect the allowable pressure (a) if the pipe is a straight pipe joining two large tanks so that there is no longitudinal stress in the

Fig. 15-3

pipe? (b) if the pipe has elbows or closed ends so that there is longitudinal stress? (*Hint:* Consider the forces acting on the small triangular portion of the pipe wall shown.) *Ans.* (b) Allowable R = 300 psi.

15-4. Principal Stresses. The important relationships stated below will be demonstrated in later articles.

1. In a stressed body at a point where there are normal stresses on one or both of two mutually perpendicular given planes and also shearing stress on the same planes there are two other mutually perpendicular planes on one of which the maximum normal stress occurs and on the other the minimum normal stress occurs.

2. On these two planes there are no shearing stresses. *Proof on Page 272*

3. On mutually perpendicular planes inclined 45° to these planes, the maximum shearing stresses occur. *Proof on Page 273 (15-12)*

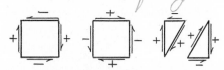

Fig. 15-4

The maximum and minimum normal stresses at a point in a stressed body are called the principal stresses at that point. The planes on which the principal stresses act are known as principal planes of stress.

In this chapter the larger and smaller principal stresses will be represented by the symbols p and q respectively in order to distinguish them from other normal stresses that occur on other planes at the same point.

The algebraically larger of the normal unit stresses occurring on two mutually perpendicular planes that are not principal planes will be designated as S_x and the smaller as S_y.

Tensile normal stress will be considered positive or plus, and com-

Principal Stresses
Larger is P
Smaller is q

pressive normal stress negative or minus. The shearing stress on any face of an elementary body will be considered positive or plus if the moment of the shearing force with respect to a point in the body is clockwise or, in other words, if the shearing force on that face of the body tends to rotate the body in a clockwise direction. Figure 15-4 illustrates this convention for signs of shearing stress. The angle θ between two planes will be considered positive or plus if counterclockwise.

15-5. Normal Stresses Resulting from Two Normal Stresses Combined with Shearing Stresses. In this article a general expression for the normal stress on an inclined plane will be derived. Then expressions for the principal stresses will be found.

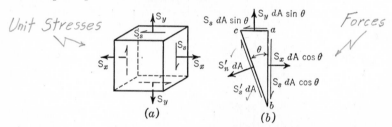

Fig. 15-5

Figure 15-5a shows an elementary cube with the given stresses, and b shows a wedge cut from this cube, the inclined face making an angle θ with the direction of the plane on which S_x acts. On the faces of the cube the given unit stresses are shown, but on the faces of the wedge the *forces* due to these unit stresses are indicated. The forces on the bc face are expressed in terms of the unknown normal unit stress S_n' and the unknown shearing unit stress S_s', expressions for both of which are desired. If the area of the bc face of the wedge is dA, that of the ac face is $dA \sin \theta$ and that of the ad face is $dA \cos \theta$.

Summing up all components normal to bc and placing the sum equal to zero,

$$S_n' dA - S_x dA \cos^2 \theta - S_y dA \sin^2 \theta$$
$$+ S_s dA \sin \theta \cos \theta + S_s dA \sin \theta \cos \theta = 0$$

$$S_n' = S_x \cos^2 \theta + S_y \sin^2 \theta - 2S_s \sin \theta \cos \theta$$

$$= S_x \frac{1 + \cos 2\theta}{2} + S_y \frac{1 - \cos 2\theta}{2} - S_s \sin 2\theta$$

Whence

$$S_n' = \frac{S_x + S_y}{2} + \frac{S_x - S_y}{2} \cos 2\theta - S_s \sin 2\theta \qquad (15\text{-}1)$$

$$\ast \quad \frac{dS_n'}{d\theta} = 0 + \frac{S_x - S_y}{2} \cdot \frac{d}{d\theta} \cos 2\theta - S_s \frac{d}{d\theta} \sin 2\theta = 0$$

$$= 0 + \left(\frac{S_x - S_y}{2}\right)\left(-\sin 2\theta \cdot \frac{d 2\theta}{d\theta}\right) - S_s \cos 2\theta \cdot \frac{d 2\theta}{d\theta} = 0$$

$$\frac{dS_n'}{d\theta} = 0 - 2\left(\frac{S_x - S_y}{2}\right)\sin 2\theta - 2S_s \cos 2\theta = 0$$

which gives the value of the resultant normal stress on a plane inclined at an angle θ with the direction of the given normal stress. The value of θ that will make S_n' maximum is found by putting the derivative of S_n' with respect to θ equal to zero.

$$\frac{dS_n'}{d\theta} = 0 - (S_x - S_y)\sin 2\theta - 2S_s \cos 2\theta = 0$$

from which

$$\tan 2\theta_n = -\frac{2S_s}{S_x - S_y} \qquad (15\text{-}2)$$

There are two values of 2θ, $180°$ apart, for any given value of $\tan 2\theta$. Therefore there are two planes $90°$ apart on one of which the maximum normal stress occurs and on the other the minimum normal stress occurs.

The maximum and minimum values of S_n' are found by substituting in equation 15-1 the values for $\sin 2\theta$ and $\cos 2\theta$ corresponding to $\tan 2\theta_n = -2S_s/(S_x - S_y)$. By constructing the right triangles (Fig. 15-6) with one leg equal to $-S_s$ and one leg equal to $(S_x - S_y)/2$, mak-

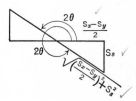

Fig. 15-6

ing $\tan 2\theta = -2S_s/(S_x - S_y)$, the following values are obtained:

$$\sin 2\theta_n = \mp \frac{S_s}{\sqrt{\left(\dfrac{S_x - S_y}{2}\right)^2 + S_s^2}} \quad \text{and} \quad \cos 2\theta_n = \pm \frac{(S_x - S_y)/2}{\sqrt{\left(\dfrac{S_x - S_y}{2}\right)^2 + S_s^2}}$$

Putting these values in equation 15-1,

$$\max S_n' = \frac{S_x + S_y}{2} \pm \frac{\left(\dfrac{S_x - S_y}{2}\right)^2}{\sqrt{\left(\dfrac{S_x - S_y}{2}\right)^2 + S_s^2}} \pm \frac{S_s^2}{\sqrt{\left(\dfrac{S_x - S_y}{2}\right)^2 + S_s^2}}$$

$$= \frac{S_x + S_y}{2} \pm \sqrt{\left(\frac{S_x - S_y}{2}\right)^2 + S_s^2}$$

Letting the letters p and q represent the algebraically larger and smaller principal stresses,

$$p = \frac{S_x + S_y}{2} + \sqrt{\left(\frac{S_x - S_y}{2}\right)^2 + S_s^2} \qquad (15\text{-}3)$$

$$q = \frac{S_x + S_y}{2} - \sqrt{\left(\frac{S_x - S_y}{2}\right)^2 + S_s^2} \qquad (15\text{-}4)$$

Note that, if equations 15-3 and 15-4 are added, the following equation results:

$$p + q = S_x + S_y \qquad (15\text{-}5)$$

Equation 15-5 shows that the *algebraic* sum of the two normal unit stresses on any pair of mutually perpendicular planes at a point equals the algebraic sum of the principal stresses at that point.

In a numerical problem the direction of the plane on which the larger principal stress acts may be determined as follows. Let S_x be the algebraically larger of the two given normal stresses. The angle between the direction of S_x and the direction of p, the algebraically larger principal stress, will always be less than 45°, the smaller of the two values of θ given by equation 15-2.

Equation 15-2 shows that, if the shearing stress S_s on the plane on which S_x acts has the same sign as S_x, tan 2θ will be negative and θ will be clockwise. This means that the direction of p will be clockwise from the direction of S_x. If S_x and the shearing stress S_s on the same plane have opposite signs the direction of p will be counterclockwise from S_x.

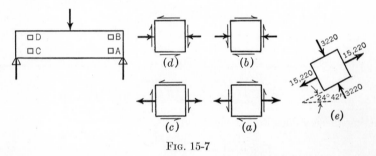

FIG. 15-7

Example. At four different points in a certain beam a normal stress of 12,000 psi acts upon a vertical plane, and shearing stresses of 7,000 psi act on horizontal and vertical planes. The four combinations are shown in Fig. 15-7. Determine the principal stresses and the planes on which the principal stresses act for case (a).

Solution: Case (a). $S_x = +12,000$ psi, $S_y = 0$, $S_s = -7,000$ psi.

$$\max S_n' = (S_x/2) \pm \sqrt{(S_x/2)^2 + S_s^2} = +6,000 \pm \sqrt{6,000^2 + 7,000^2}$$
$$= +6,000 \pm 9,220$$

Hence

$$q = -3,220 \text{ psi (compression)} \qquad \text{and} \qquad p = +15,220 \text{ psi (tension)}$$

The angle with the direction of S_x (horizontal) is found from tan $2\theta = -\dfrac{2S_s}{S_x} =$

$\dfrac{+14,000}{+12,000} = \dfrac{7}{6}$, hence

$$2\theta = 49° 24' \text{ or } 229° 24', \text{ and } \theta = 24° 42' \text{ and } 114° 42'$$

Since p, the algebraically larger principal stress, always makes an angle less than 45° with S_x, the larger normal stress, the principal stresses are on planes, as shown in Fig. 15-7e.

Numerically the principal stresses will be equal at a, b, c, and d. However, p will be compression or negative, and q tension or positive at b and d. At a and d the direction of p will be counterclockwise from S_x, and at b and c the direction of p will be clockwise from S_x.

15-6. Maximum Shearing Stress. The wedge taken as a free body in Art. 15-5 is shown in Fig. 15-8 with the forces acting on the three faces.

Summing up all components parallel to bc and placing the sum equal to zero,

$$S_s'\, dA + S_y\, dA \sin\theta \cos\theta - S_x\, dA \sin\theta \cos\theta$$
$$+ S_s\, dA \sin^2\theta - S_s\, dA \cos^2\theta = 0$$

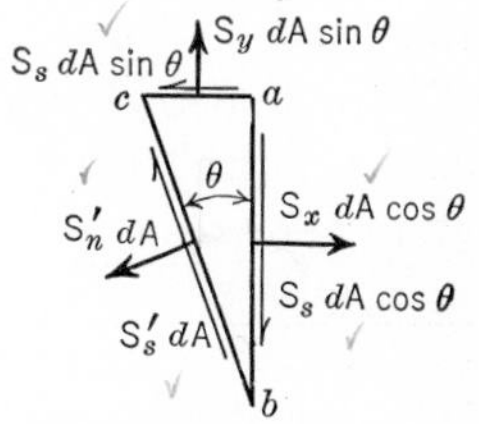

Whence

$$S_s' = (S_x - S_y) \sin\theta \cos\theta + S_s(\cos^2\theta - \sin^2\theta)$$

or

$$S_s' = \frac{(S_x - S_y)}{2} \sin 2\theta + S_s \cos 2\theta \quad (15\text{-}6)$$

Fig. 15-8

which gives the value of the resultant shearing stress on a plane inclined at an angle θ to the direction of the given normal stresses.

The inclination of the planes of maximum shearing stress are found from equation 15-1 by putting the derivative of S_s' with respect to θ equal to zero.

$$\frac{dS_s'}{d\theta} = \frac{S_x - S_y}{2} \cos 2\theta - S_s \sin 2\theta = 0$$

from which

$$\tan 2\theta_s = \frac{S_x - S_y}{2S_s} \quad (15\text{-}7)$$

where θ_s is that value of θ which gives maximum S_s. There are two values of $2\theta_s$, 180° apart, for any given value of $\tan 2\theta_s$; and consequently there are two values of θ_s which differ by 90°. This result is consistent with the fact, previously demonstrated, that equal shearing stresses exist on mutually perpendicular planes at a point.

Tan $2\theta_s$ is seen to be the negative reciprocal of $\tan 2\theta_n$ found in Art. 15-5. Consequently $2\theta_s$ differs from $2\theta_n$ by 90°. It follows that the planes of maximum shearing stress are inclined 45° with the planes of maximum normal stress. It also follows that $\sin 2\theta_s = \cos 2\theta_n$ found in Art. 15-5 and that $\cos 2\theta_s = -\sin 2\theta_n$. Substituting these values in equation 15-6 and simplifying,

For proof see page 415

$$\text{max } S_s' = \sqrt{\left(\frac{S_x - S_y}{2}\right)^2 + S_s^2} \qquad (15\text{-}8)$$

The sign of the shearing stress on an inclined plane is generally unimportant. It may be determined in a numerical problem, however, by substituting values of $\sin 2\theta$ and $\cos 2\theta$ *with their proper signs* in equation 15-6. Another, and perhaps better, way to determine the direction of the shearing stresses is to consider a wedge having the sloping face in the direction given by θ_s. If the sum of all components of force parallel to this surface are put equal to zero, the direction of the shearing stress to cause equilibrium may be found.

Note that this expression for the maximum shearing stress is the same as the radical that occurs in the expressions for p and q in formulas 15-3 and 15-4. It is thus seen that the principal stresses $= \frac{1}{2}(S_x + S_y) \pm$ maximum shearing stresses.

That there is no shearing stress upon the principal planes is shown by equating the expression for the shearing stress (15-6) to zero and solving for $\tan 2\theta$.

$$\frac{(S_x - S_y)}{2} \sin 2\theta + S_s \cos 2\theta = 0$$

Hence
$$\tan 2\theta = \frac{\sin 2\theta}{\cos 2\theta} = -\frac{2S_s}{S_x - S_y}$$

for zero shearing stress. This value of $\tan 2\theta$ is the same as the value for $\tan 2\theta_n$ for the planes of maximum normal stresses. Hence the planes of zero shearing stress are principal planes.

Example. Calculate the maximum shearing stress at points A, B, C, D of the example of Art. 15-5.

Solution: The value of the radical in the example of Art. 15-5 is 9,220 psi, which is the value of the maximum shearing stresses. The planes of maximum shearing stress are inclined 45° to the principal planes and are therefore inclined to the horizontal 69° 42′ and 159° 42′ counterclockwise.

PROBLEMS

15-5. At a point in the web of an I-beam the bending stress is compression and equals 16,250 psi. The shearing stress is 11,400 psi and is the result of negative total shear. Calculate the maximum shearing stress and the principal stresses at this point and the inclinations of the planes on which they exist.

15-6. A 3-in.-diameter solid shaft is subjected to a torque of 42,400 lb-in. and a bending moment of 28,000 lb-in. (*a*) Calculate the maximum shearing stress and the inclinations of the planes of maximum shearing stress. (*b*) Calculate the principal stresses and the inclinations of the principal planes.   Draw a diagram illustrating these stresses.   *Ans.*   (a) $S_s' = 9{,}560$ psi.

15-7. Calculate the principal stresses which exist at a point where the shearing and normal stresses on 30° and 60° planes are those shown in Fig. 15-1d.   Also calculate the maximum shearing stresses.

15-8. For values of S_s/S_x of 0, 0.1, 0.5, 1.0, and 2.0 and $S_y = 0$, calculate values of the principal stresses in terms of the given normal stress.   Show the results in the form of a curve.   *Ans.*   For $S_s/S_x = 1$, $p = 1.618 S_x$.

15-9. In a boiler shell, subject to internal pressure, longitudinal tensile stress exists, and also circumferential stress which is twice the longitudinal stress.   Do stresses greater than the circumferential stress exist?   If so, on what planes?   If not, why not?   Discuss fully.

15-7. Normal Stresses and Shearing Stresses in Terms of Principal Stresses.   The equation

$$S_n' = \frac{S_x + S_y}{2} + \frac{S_x - S_y}{2} \cos 2\theta - S_s \sin 2\theta \qquad (15\text{-}1)$$

was derived in Art. 15-5.   In this equation S_x, S_y, and S_s are the given normal and shearing stresses, and S_n' is the resulting normal stress on an inclined plane.   Now suppose that the planes on which the given stresses act are planes of zero shearing stress and are therefore principal planes.   Then the normal stresses on these planes are principal stresses, and S_x in the equation becomes p, S_y becomes q, and S_n' is the normal stress S_x on the inclined plane.   Making these substitutions, and remembering that $S_s = 0$,

$$S_x = \frac{p + q}{2} + \frac{p - q}{2} \cos 2\theta \qquad (15\text{-}9)$$

On a plane perpendicular to the plane of S_x, the normal stress is S_y, and for this perpendicular plane $\cos 2\theta$ is negative.   Hence

$$S_y = \frac{p + q}{2} - \frac{p - q}{2} \cos 2\theta \qquad (15\text{-}10)$$

Equation 15-6, $S_s' = \dfrac{(S_x - S_y)}{2} \sin 2\theta + S_s \cos 2\theta$, becomes

$$S_s = \frac{p - q}{2} \sin 2\theta \qquad (15\text{-}11)$$

in which S_s is the resulting shearing stress on a plane making an angle of θ with the plane on which p acts.

The maximum value of S_s occurs when $\theta = 45°$, in which case

$$\max S_s = \frac{p - q}{2} \qquad (15\text{-}12)$$

In words, the maximum shearing stress at a given point equals half the difference between the principal stresses. Note that larger shearing stresses result if the principal stresses are of opposite kinds.

15-8. Mohr's Circle for a Case of Plane Stress. The relationships already derived between stresses on different planes at a point are all contained in a graphic diagram known as Mohr's circle, devised by Professor Otto Mohr of Dresden, Germany, about 1880.

From Mohr's circle, drawn to scale, the desired stress values can be measured. However, the diagram has far greater usefulness. This graphic diagram is remarkably simple, and the steps in its construction

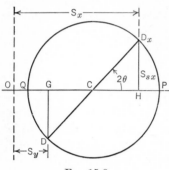

are easily learned and remembered. From a freehand sketch of Mohr's circle the formulas 15-2 to 15-5 and 15-9 to 15-12 can be written. Also from a free-hand sketch numerical values for stresses can be calculated by addition and subtraction after one right triangle has been solved by slide rule. Mohr's circle is, moreover, the basis for other constructions used in more advanced problems.

FIG. 15-9

Let it be assumed that the principal stresses p and q are known and that it is desired to determine the normal and shearing stresses on planes making a given counterclockwise angle θ with the principal planes.

The complete diagram is shown in Fig. 15-9. The steps in drawing Mohr's circle for this case are as follows:

1. On a horizontal axis lay off to some convenient scale a distance OP equal to the unit stress p. Along the same axis lay off OQ equal to the unit stress q.

2. Draw a circle having QP as a diameter.

3. Draw a diameter DD_x making a counterclockwise angle 2θ with QP.

4. Drop a perpendicular D_xH from D_x to QP and a perpendicular DG from D. In this diagram $OH = S_x$, $OG = S_y$, $D_xH = S_{sx}$ (the shearing stress on the plane on which S_x acts), and $DG = S_{sy}$.

Proof: Note in Fig. 15-10 that $OC = (p + q)/2$ and $PC = (p - q)/2$. The radius of the circle is therefore $(p - q)/2$, and hence D_xH is $\dfrac{p - q}{2} \sin 2\theta$, which is the value derived in Art. 15-7 for the shearing stress on the inclined plane. The length CH is $\dfrac{p - q}{2} \cos 2\theta$, and hence

$OH = \dfrac{p+q}{2} + \dfrac{p-q}{2} \cos 2\theta$, which is the same as the value for S_x in formula 15-9.

The angle PCD is 180° greater than PCD_x and consequently is 2θ for the plane perpendicular to the plane of S_x. Therefore OG is the value of the normal unit stress S_y. But $OG = \dfrac{p+q}{2} - \dfrac{p-q}{2} \cos 2\theta$, which agrees with the value for S_y in equation 15-10.

The ordinate $DG = - \dfrac{p-q}{2} \sin 2\theta$, which is the value given by equation 15-11 for S_s. Hence the shearing unit stress S_s on this plane is given by DG and is equal in magnitude to the shearing unit stress

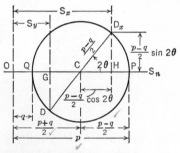

FIG. 15-10. Mohr's circle, positive stresses.

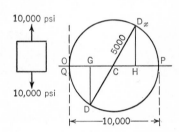

FIG. 15-11

S_{sx} as was shown in Chapter 5 where it was stated that in a stressed body equal shearing unit stresses exist on planes perpendicular to each other.

Example. Verify by calculations based on Mohr's circle the stresses shown in Fig. 15-1d.

Solution: The stress shown in 15-1a is a principal stress because there are no shearing stresses on the planes. It will also be seen that S_y is zero. The upper plane in (d) is inclined 30° to the plane on which S_x acts. The diagram (Fig. 15-11) need not be drawn to scale. Lay off $OP = 1,000$ psi, $OQ = 0$. Draw the diameter DD_x making the angle $D_xCP = 2\theta = 60°$. Then $CD_x = CP = 5,000$ psi, $CH = CG = 2,500$ psi. Hence $S_x = OH = 7,500$ psi. $S_y = OG = 2,500$ psi. The shearing stress $= D_xH = 5,000 \times 0.866 = 4,330$ psi.

15-9. Principal Stresses Found by Mohr's Circle. The problem considered in this article is of frequent occurrence and may be stated thus: given (at a point in a stressed body) normal stresses S_x and S_y on two mutually perpendicular planes and the shearing stress S_s on these two planes, to find the magnitudes of the principal stresses p and q and the directions of the planes on which they act. First it will be shown that Mohr's circle will afford a solution for this problem if numerical values are given and desired. By means of Mohr's circle algebraic expressions can be derived for p, q, and θ, the angle between the given planes and the principal planes.

Mohr's circle as drawn in Fig. 15-12 represents the relationships between S_x, S_y, S_s, θ, p, and q. For the present problem the diagram is drawn as follows.

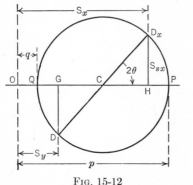
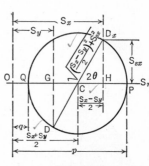

FIG. 15-12   FIG. 15-13

1. Lay off on the horizontal axis OH equal to S_x, the algebraically larger given normal stress, and OG equal to S_y, the smaller given normal stress.

2. Erect perpendiculars HD_x and GD each equal to S_s, the given shearing stress.

3. Draw a circle with D_xD as its diameter intersecting the horizontal axis at P and Q (P being to the right of Q).

Then $OP = p$ and $OQ = q$, the principal stresses. The angle D_xCP is 2θ or twice the angle between the directions of S_x and p. With S_s and S_x both plus, θ is clockwise as shown, which means that P acts in a clockwise direction relative to S_x.

The construction shown in Fig. 15-12 represents graphically the relationships derived analytically in Arts. 15-5 and 15-6. In Fig. 15-13 note that $OC = (S_x + S_y)/2$ and that $CH = (S_x - S_y)/2$. The student should verify the value of CD_x shown in Fig. 15-13 and should write out values for p, q, $\tan 2\theta_n$, and the maximum S_s. These values should be compared with those given in Arts. 15-5 and 15-6.

15-10. Mohr's Circle for Negative Stresses. If S_{sx} is negative, it is measured downward from H (D_x is below the horizontal axis). A negative S_x or S_y is measured to the left from the vertical axis. If P is to the left of 0, p is negative (compressive); if Q is to the left of 0, q

is negative (compressive).   As an example, in Fig. 15-14 Mohr's circle is drawn for a stress in which $S_x = +8{,}000$, $S_y = -3{,}600$, $S_{sx} = -5{,}000$.   From this diagram p scales $+9{,}900$, q scales $-5{,}500$, 2θ scales $40° 48'$.   The maximum shearing stress equals the radius of the circle.   Hence max $S_s = 7{,}660$.   All stresses are pounds per square inch.

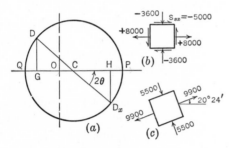

FIG. 15-14.   Mohr's circle for negative S_s and S_y.

The angle D_xCP equals 2θ.   The principal stress p makes a counterclockwise angle with S_x if the radius CP lies in a counterclockwise direction from CD_x as in this example or, in other words, if P is located in a counterclockwise direction around the circle from D_x.

PROBLEMS

15-10. Draw four circles, with diameters of about 2 in., on a page.   On these sketch the construction of Mohr's circle for four different combinations of signs of S_x, S_y, and S_{sx} as follows: $(+ \; + \; +)$, $(+ \; - \; +)$, $(+ \; - \; -)$, $(- \; - \; +)$.   Indicate on a small rectangle the slope and direction of the principal stresses.   Do not take time to lay off values to scale or to scale results.

15-11. Solve Problem 15-10 if the combinations of S_x, S_y, and S_{sx} are $(+ \; + \; -)$, $(+ \; 0 \; -)$, $(- \; - \; -)$, $(+ \; - \; -)$.

15-12. At a point in a body, $p = +16{,}000$ psi and $q = -8{,}000$ psi.   What value of θ will result in $S_{sx} = +6{,}000$ psi, and what will be the value of S_x and S_y on a cube with this inclination?   *Ans.* $\theta = 15°$.

15-13. Solve Problem 15-12 if $q = +2{,}000$ psi.

15-14. Determine p, q, and θ, given $S_x = +12{,}000$, $S_y = +6{,}000$, $S_{sx} = -5{,}000$ psi.

15-15. Determine p, q, and θ, given $S_x = +15{,}000$, $S_y = -6{,}000$, $S_{sx} = +7{,}000$ psi.

15-16. Determine S_x, S_y, and S_{sx} on planes making counterclockwise angles of $40°$ with the plane on which p acts if $p = +20{,}000$ and $q = -12{,}000$ psi.

15-17. Determine S_x, S_y, and S_{sx} on planes making clockwise angles of $32°$ if $p = +18{,}000$ and $q = +6{,}000$ psi.

15-18. Given principal stresses $p = +10{,}000$ psi and $q = -5{,}000$ psi.   Is there a plane on which the normal stress is zero?   If so, what is the angle between that plane and the plane on which p acts?

15-19. Solve Problem 15-18 if $p = +12{,}000$ psi and $q = -4{,}000$ psi.

15-11. Principal Stresses in a Body Subjected to Pure Shear. It is possible for a body to be loaded in such a way that at certain points there are planes on which nothing but shearing stresses exist. This is true of a shaft subjected to torsion only. In that case, there is a shearing stress on transverse planes and on axial planes, but no normal stresses exist on either transverse or axial planes. Another case of shearing stress on planes on which there are no normal stresses occurs in beams. At the neutral axis there are no normal stresses on cross-sections, but shearing stresses occur on the cross-sections and on the neutral surface. At any point where this stress condition occurs, the material is said to be in a state of "pure shear."

Putting S_x and S_y equal to zero in equations 15-3 and 15-4, the principal stresses are $p = +S_s$ and $q = -S_s$. From equation 15-2, $\tan 2\theta_n$ becomes infinity when S_x and S_y are both zero. Hence $2\theta_n$ equals 90° and θ equals 45°. Consequently the following relationship may be stated.

In a body at a point where only shearing stresses exist on two mutually perpendicular planes, there are resulting tensile and compressive principal stresses of the same magnitude as the shearing stresses, on planes making angles of 45° with the planes of shearing stress.

The existence of these tensile and compressive stresses resulting from shear may be visualized by considering the corresponding deformations.

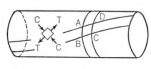

Fig. 15-15

Figure 15-15 represents a cylinder subject to torsion. Upon the surface of this cylinder, before the torsional forces were applied, two parallel lines (elements of the cylindrical surface) were drawn, and two lines were drawn around the cylinder. The included area, $ABCD$, was rectangular before the torsional deformation occurred, but during the deformation the diagonal BD lengthened and AC shortened. These deformations were in the directions of the tensile stress and the compressive stress, respectively.

An example of the effect of such stresses is afforded by the failure under torsional loads of a cylinder made of some material having a tensile strength less than its shearing strength. A common chalk crayon, twisted until it fractures, illustrates this failure. The tensile fracture of a round cast-iron rod tested in torsion is shown in Fig. 15-16.

15-12. Bending Combined with Torsion in a Circular Shaft. The transverse loads due to belt tensions and weights of pulleys and of the shafting itself cause bending stresses which in many instances are not negligible compared with the shearing stresses due to torsion.

Formulas 15-3, 15-4 and 15-8 may be applied to these cases to find the maximum resultant shearing stresses and the maximum resultant tension or compression. However, for circular shafts the solution may be expressed in more convenient formulas.

The shearing stress in the extreme fibers of a circular shaft, as given by the common torsion formula, is $S_s = Tc/J$, and the bending stress

FIG. 15-16.   Tensile failure of a cast-iron torsion specimen.

is $S_b = Mc/I$. In these two formulas $J = 2I$ for either a solid or hollow circular shaft. The maximum resultant shearing stress is

$$\max S_s{}' = \sqrt{\left(\frac{S_b}{2}\right)^2 + S_s{}^2} = \sqrt{\frac{M^2c^2}{J^2} + \frac{T^2c^2}{J^2}} = \frac{c}{J}\sqrt{M^2 + T^2}$$

or

$$J/c = \sqrt{M^2 + T^2}/S_s \qquad (15\text{-}13)$$

in which S_s is the allowable shearing stress. For a shaft so supported or loaded that no bending moment acts on it, this equation reduces to $J/c = T/S_s$, as it should.

The maximum resultant tensile or compressive stress is

$$\max S = \frac{S_b}{2} + \sqrt{\left(\frac{S_b}{2}\right)^2 + S_s{}^2} = \frac{Mc}{2I} + \frac{c}{2I}\sqrt{M^2 + T^2}$$

from which

$$I/c = (M + \sqrt{M^2 + T^2})/2S \qquad (15\text{-}14)$$

in which S is the allowable tensile or compressive stress. This reduces to the flexure formula, $I/c = M/S$, when the torsional moment is reduced to zero.

If, for a given material used as shafting, allowable shearing, tensile, and compressive stresses are specified, the *resultant* maximum shearing and normal stresses as given by the above formulas should not exceed the respective specified allowable stresses.

PROBLEMS

15-20. Determine the size of a solid circular shaft to withstand a torque of 50,000 lb-in. and at the same time a bending moment of 40,000 lb-in. if the maximum shearing stress is not to exceed 8,000 psi and the maximum bending stress is not to exceed 12,000 psi.

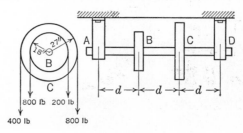

800 ℔   200 lb

400 lb   800 lb

Fig. 15-17

15-21. The shaft AD in Fig. 15-17 is supported at A and D by "self-aligning" bearings that do not fix the direction of the shaft. The shaft is driven by pulley C, and power is taken off at pulley B to drive a machine. The belt pulls are given in the end view. Pulley B weighs 300 lb, pulley C weighs 400 lb, and the distance d is 20 in. What is the required diameter of shaft if allowable stresses of 10,000 psi in bending and 6,000 psi in shearing are not exceeded?   *Ans.* $D = 3.16$ in.

15-22. Solve Problem 15-21 if distance d is 30 in.

15-23. If S_s and S_t are the allowable shearing and tensile stresses, what is the greatest ratio of S_s to S_t in order that the allowable torque and bending moment will be determined by S_s for all allowable combinations of T and M?

Ans. $S_s = 0.5 \, S_t$.

15-24. In the derivation of the formulas of Art. 15-12 no consideration was given to shearing stresses which exist because of beam action, although in cantilever shafts the maximum shear and maximum bending moment may occur at the same section. Is the ignoring of shear due to beam action justified, and if so why?

15-25. A handbook gives for shafting subject to bending moment and torque this formula for determining the diameter:

$$d = \sqrt[3]{(5.1/S)(M + \sqrt{M^2 + T^2})}$$

and adds that for ductile materials it is well to check the value of d by means of

$$d = \sqrt[3]{(5.1/S)\sqrt{M^2 + T^2}}$$

In these formulas S is defined as the "fiber stress in pounds per square inch." Are these formulas rational? Do they apply to hollow shafting? Should S be the same in the two formulas? Discuss fully.

15-26. Calculate the required diameter of a steel shaft if the maximum torque is 36,000 lb-in. and at the same cross-section the bending moment is 50,000 lb-in. Allowable stresses are bending 10,000 psi and shearing 6,000 psi.

15-13. Photoelastic Stress Analysis.

In 1816 Sir David Brewster, a Scottish physicist, observed that certain transparent bodies, stressed by applied forces, showed patterns of colored bands when polarized light was passed through them. The pattern of the bands was evidently related to the distribution of stresses caused by the loads. Many scientists have since contributed to the development of the laws of this phenomenon, and, during the present century, methods have been developed by means of which this phenomenon has become the basis for experimental methods of determining the stress distribution in a body in which a purely mathematical stress analysis would be difficult or even impossible because of the irregular shape and complex loading.

Photograph by Yale Laboratory of Photoelasticity

FIG. 15-18.   Model beams of transparent plastic with symmetrical loading photographed by transmitted polarized light.

A photograph of a small model of two loaded beams made of clear plastic is shown in Fig. 15-18. The alternate dark and light bands or regions are visible only when monochromatic polarized light is passed through the model. By means of these bands it is possible to determine the intensity of stress caused by the applied loads at various points in a model. The same relationship between stresses and loads will exist in a geometrically similar body of another material, similarly loaded, provided that the material of which the body is made follows Hooke's law.

Each band (or "fringe") is the locus of points where the maximum shearing stress has a constant value. In Art. 15-7 it was shown that at a point in a stressed body

$$\max S_s = \tfrac{1}{2}(p - q)$$

It follows, therefore, that each band is also the locus of points where the difference between the principal stresses is constant.

As the load on the model is gradually increased a band appears where high maximum shearing stress exists and this band travels inward. A second band appears where the first one formed when the maximum

shearing stress at that point becomes twice as much as it was when the
first band appeared. Consequently the intensity of the maximum
shearing stress at the point is indicated by the number of bands that
have formed and are visible.

The increase in stress corresponding to each additional fringe in the
plastic body is found by using a model such as the loaded beam shown
in Fig. 15-18. The dimensions are accurately known, and the loads at
which successive fringes occur are observed. The stresses can then be
calculated.

Photoelastic analysis is particularly useful for determining stresses
in machine parts or structures of such intricate shapes that it would be
difficult or impossible to calculate the stresses by purely mathematical
methods. If, in such a case, a plastic model of the machine part is
made to scale and loaded with measured loads, the stresses in the model
corresponding to the loads on the model can be determined by observing
the number of fringes at a highly stressed section. The relationship
between loads and stresses thus obtained in the model can be applied
to the determination of stresses in geometrically similar bodies used in
machines and structures. The theory of photoelasticity is beyond the
scope of this book.[2] The required apparatus is rather elaborate and
not inexpensive, and its use requires skill, experience, and a thorough
knowledge of the underlying theory. The method has made valuable
contributions and is being developed for new applications.

15-14. Transverse Deformation; Poisson's Ratio. When a prism or
other body of elastic material is subjected to compressive loads, not
only do the dimensions in the direction of the loads decrease, but also
the transverse dimensions increase. If the loads are tensile, the length
increases and the transverse dimensions decrease. For stresses within
the range for which S/δ is a constant E, the ratio of the transverse *unit*
deformations to the longitudinal unit deformations is a constant for a
given material. This constant is called Poisson's ratio. In this book
the symbol m is used for this constant. This definition may be represented by the equation

$$m = \frac{\text{Unit transverse contraction}}{\text{Unit axial elongation}} \qquad (15\text{-}15)$$

[2] For a short textbook on this subject see L. G. N. Filon, *A Manual of Photoelasticity for Engineers*, Cambridge University Press, 1936. For a short explanation
see Glenn Murphy, *Advanced Strength of Materials*, Chapter X, McGraw-Hill Book
Co., 1946. A very complete treatise is Max M. Frocht, *Photoelasticity*, 2 vols., John
Wiley & Sons, 1941, 1948.

Values of Poisson's ratio vary considerably, but the following are commonly used values:

Aluminum alloys	0.36
Brass, bronze, copper	0.33
Monel metal	0.25–0.26
Steel	0.25–0.28
Concrete	0.10–0.18

Poisson's ratio for steel is commonly taken as $\frac{1}{4}$.

Example. A steel eyebar 2×6 in. in cross-section is stressed in tension by a total pull of 300,000 lb. What is the change in the 6-in. dimension?

Solution: $S_t = 300,000/12 = 25,000$ psi. The unit longitudinal deformation is $\delta = 25,000/30,000,000 = 0.000833$ in. per in. The transverse unit deformation is $m\delta = \frac{1}{4} \times 0.000833 = 0.000208$ in. per in. In width of 6 in., $\Delta = 6 \times 0.000208 = 0.00125$ in.

The transverse deformations that accompany axial stress do not result from transverse stress and do not cause transverse stress. This fact may be shown by considering a pile of smooth rectangular blocks (Fig. 15-19) loaded in compression. The transverse dimensions, such as AB, of each block increase. If part of the block $ABCD$ cut off by a plane EF at any point is considered a free body, there can be no resultant force on the face EF (and consequently no stress), since there are no horizontal forces on BE, BC, or CF to balance such a force on EF.

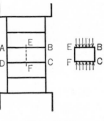

FIG. 15-19

Stresses will result, however, if this transverse deformation is *prevented*, as, for instance, it would be if AD and BC were in contact with rigid surfaces before the loading was applied.

This transverse change in length is somewhat analogous to temperature expansion, which does not cause or result from stresses, but which causes stresses if prevented. It is apparent that the complete stress analysis of a confined or restrained body may involve the use of Poisson's ratio.

When stresses S_x and S_y exist at a point, the strains (or deformations) in the x and y directions are respectively

$$\delta_x = (S_x/E) - m\,S_y/E$$

$$\delta_y = (S_y/E) - m\,S_x/E$$

PROBLEMS

15-27. A round rod of steel 1.50 in. in diameter and 14 in. long was subjected to tensile loads of 61,500 lb in a testing machine. It was observed that a gage length of 2 in. near the midpoint of the rod increased in length 0.0023 in. and the diameter of the rod decreased 0.00043 in. Calculate the modulus of elasticity and Poisson's ratio for this steel.   *Ans.* $m = 0.249$.

15-28. An aluminum-alloy block 1.50 in. thick, 3.00 in. wide, and 4.00 in. long is placed in a testing machine and subjected to compressive loads of 70,000 lb applied to the ends. Calculate the increase in the width and in the thickness on the basis of the value for m given in Art. 15-14 and on the assumption that $E = 10,500,000$ psi.

15-15. E and E_s in Terms of Poisson's Ratio. It is shown in Art. 15-11 that, if shearing stresses alone act on two mutually perpendicular planes, principal stresses of the same intensity as the shearing stresses, and of opposite kinds from one another, act on planes at 45° with the planes of shearing stress. From this fact there may be derived a relation between the modulus of elasticity E and the shearing modulus of elasticity E_s, in terms of Poisson's ratio m. Consider a point in a stressed body, such as a point on the surface of a shaft, where only shearing stresses S_s exist on mutually perpendicular planes (Fig. 15-20a).

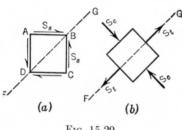
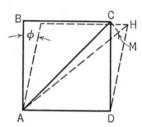

(a)   (b)

Fig. 15-20   Fig. 15-21

Now suppose that at this same point O a cube (Fig. 15-20b) is taken with sides at 45° to those of the previous cube. It has already been shown that on the faces of this cube there will be no shearing stresses and that the tensile and compressive unit stresses will equal the shearing unit stresses at 45° or in other words, S_s, S_t, and S_c are numerically equal. Now in this stressed body a certain *unit* deformation (elongation) occurs along the line FG. This deformation may be regarded as resulting either from the stresses S_s in Fig. 15-20a or from the stresses S_c and S_t in Fig. 15-20b.

The unit elongation in the diagonal direction due to S_s is equal to $S_s/2E_s$. This may be shown as follows: In Fig. 15-21 the total elongation is MH and the unit elongation $= MH/AM$, since the angle is very small. But $MH = CH \cos 45° = CD \times (S_s/E_s) \cos 45°$, and $AC = CD/\cos 45°$. Hence the unit elongation along AC due to S_s is

$$\delta = \frac{MH}{AC} = \frac{CD(S_s/E_s)\cos 45°}{CD/\cos 45°} = \frac{1}{2}\frac{S_s}{E_s}$$

The unit elongation along FG due to S_t and S_c is

$$\delta = (S_t/E) + mS_c/E = (S_s/E) + m\,S_s/E$$

since $S_s = S_t = S_c$. Equating these two different values for the same unit elongation,

$$\tfrac{1}{2}S_s/E_s = (S_s/E) + m\,S_s/E$$

whence

$$E_s = \frac{E}{2(1+m)}$$

if $m = \tfrac{1}{4}$, as is commonly assumed for steel, $E_s = \tfrac{2}{5}E$. The use of $E = 30{,}000{,}000$ psi and $E_s = 12{,}000{,}000$ psi is consistent with this result.

PROBLEM

15-29. Calculate E_s for the following metals:

Aluminum alloy:	$E = 10{,}000{,}000$ psi, $m = 0.36$
Brass:	$E = 16{,}000{,}000$ psi, $m = 0.33$
Monel metal:	$E = 25{,}000{,}000$ psi, $m = 0.26$

15-16. Theories of Failure. As the forces or loads acting on an elastic body are gradually increased, stresses and deformations also increase until, at some point in the body where unit stresses are high and unit deformations are large, failure occurs. Failure as here used means either one of two things. Failure or "elastic breakdown" of a ductile material begins when its elastic behavior ends and permanent set begins. Failure of a brittle material occurs when rupture occurs, which, for a perfectly brittle material, is also when its elastic behavior ends. The body or member as a whole may not have failed, but at some point "elastic breakdown" of the material has begun.

The elastic strength of a material is commonly determined by tests of axially loaded prisms, and in such prisms only a single principal stress exists. The same material used in a member of a machine or structure is, in general, subjected to a much more complicated state of stress. Is it rational to base the design of members subjected to very complex states of stress on the allowable stresses determined from tests involving a much simpler stress? Obviously the answer to this question depends upon a knowledge of the true causes of failure. The conclusions of investigators have been presented as "theories of failure," and a number have been proposed. Five of the best known are presented and discussed here.[3]

[3] For extended discussions see J. Marin, *Trans. A.S.C.E.*, Vol. 101, 1936, p. 1162; J. Marin, *Mechanical Properties and Materials and Design*, McGraw-Hill, 1942; and H. M. Westergaard, *Journal of the Franklin Institute*, Vol. 189, 1920, p. 627.

The Maximum Stress Theory. According to this theory, failure or elastic breakdown occurs when the maximum principal stress becomes equal to the corresponding yield point (or ultimate strength, if the material is brittle). This is the oldest and simplest of the various theories and is sometimes called Rankine's theory of failure. It assumes that the effect of the maximum principal stress is not modified by the presence of the principal stress at right angles. The theory, in the form stated above, will not in general apply to materials having a shearing elastic limit considerably below the tensile (or compressive) elastic limit, for the following reasons. With two principal stresses of opposite sorts (one tension, one compression), the maximum shearing stress equals half the numerical sum of the two principal stresses. Therefore, when loading is such as to cause two nearly equal principal stresses of opposite character, the shearing stress will nearly equal the principal stress. Therefore failure could not occur in the manner specified by the theory unless the material has a shearing elastic limit nearly equal to its tensile and compressive elastic limits. This seems improbable for many materials.

The theory is sometimes stated in the following form, which considerably widens its possible application: Failure will occur when the maximum principal stress equals the corresponding elastic limit, or when the maximum shearing stress equals the shearing elastic limit. This theory is the basis of most structural design as commonly carried out.

The Maximum Shear Theory. According to this theory, generally attributed to J. J. Guest, elastic breakdown occurs (yielding begins) when the maximum shearing stress in a loaded member becomes equal to the maximum shearing stress that exists in a tensile specimen of the same material when stressed to the elastic limit. The maximum shear theory assumes that failure, both in the tensile test specimen and in the member with more complex loading, results from shearing stress.

For principal stresses in two directions the maximum shearing stress is $(p - q)/2$, and for a tensile specimen the maximum shearing stress at the tensile elastic limit is Elastic limit/2. The theory is therefore expressed by the equation

$$\frac{p - q}{2} = \frac{\text{Elastic limit in tension}}{2}$$

If this theory were strictly correct, all tensile specimens should fail on 45° planes. In many ductile materials failure appears to have begun on such planes, and the initial yielding may in fact have occurred on such planes even though the final rupture does not follow these planes.

On the other hand, the rupture of a cylinder made of a brittle material in pure torsion indicates failure in tension and in no way resembes a shear failure, notwithstanding the fact that shearing stresses are equal to the tensile stresses (Fig. 15-16). Also the failure of cast iron and other brittle materials under tensile loading does not suggest a shear failure (Fig. 2-5).

It is rather widely believed that the maximum shear theory applies more or less well to ductile materials but not at all to brittle materials.

The Maximum Strain Theory. This theory is attributed to the French elastician, St. Venant. It states that elastic breakdown in a stressed body occurs when the maximum *unit elongation* becomes equal to the maximum unit elongation existing in a tensile test specimen at the elastic limit or when the maximum unit shortening becomes equal to the maximum unit shortening in a compression member at the elastic limit.

In a stressed body the unit deformation in the direction of the maximum principal stress is $\delta = p/E \pm mq/E$, in which m is Poisson's ratio.

It follows that, if both principal stresses are tensile stresses, failure will not occur until the larger principal stress *exceeds* the tensile elastic limit of the material. On the other hand, if the larger principal stress is tension and the lesser compression, failure will occur even if the larger principal stress is somewhat less than the tensile elastic limit.

The maximum strain theory may be expressed by the following equation:

$$\frac{p}{E} \pm m \frac{q}{E} = \frac{\text{Elastic limit}}{E}$$

The Maximum Energy or Maximum Resilience Theory. According to this theory, elastic breakdown occurs when, at some point in a loaded member, the energy of deformation per unit of volume has become equal to the maximum energy of deformation per unit of volume in a prism of the same material when stressed to the yield point. The magnitude of this limiting energy is the modulus of elastic resilience determined from a simple tension test. For two-dimensional cases of combined stresses, the condition of failure occurs when

$$p^2 - 2mpq + q^2 = (\text{Elastic limit in tension})^2$$

The Maximum Shearing Strain Energy Theory. In this theory (also called the distortion energy theory) it is asserted that failure occurs when the amount of work done in producing change of shape of a unit volume of material attains a limiting value. This differs from the preceding theory by neglecting the portion of the total work that produces volume change only.   Failure takes place when

$$p^2 - pq + q^2 = \text{(Elastic limit in tension)}^2$$

for the two-dimensional case by this criterion.

Theories of Failure; Conclusion. The five theories of failure mentioned are the best known of a number that have been proposed.   It is certain that none of them can be accepted as a true theory of failure for all types of material and of loading.   Experiments with a limited number of combinations of principal stresses indicate both the maximum shearing stress theory and the maximum shearing strain energy theory to be suitable for predicting the elastic breakdown of ductile metals. Both theories are used for designing members subject to combined stresses.

It is desirable that engineering design proceed steadily toward the substitution of rational for empirical processes as rapidly as correct rational processes can be established.   For this reason it is desirable to know exactly what are the conditions of stress and deformation that lead to failure of an elastic material.   However, it should be realized that theories of failure must be based on the assumption of a perfect and homogeneous material.   It seems probable that failure in an actual stressed body will begin at some microscopic flaw, such as a cavity or particle of foreign matter, in the material where stress conditions differ substantially from those calculated by accepted methods.   Furthermore, even in the absence of flaws, actual stresses may differ from calculated stresses because of initial stresses which result from methods of fabrication and which are present even in the unloaded body.

GENERAL PROBLEMS

15-30. A short piece of 2-in. standard pipe with ends sealed is shown in Fig. 15-22. Forces P of 6,400 lb are applied to the ends, and two forces F apply a torque of 3,200 lb-in. to the upper end, the lower end being fixed to prevent rotation.   An internal pressure of 800 psi exists.   Determine the principal stresses and the inclination of the principal planes at a point in the outer surface.   Also calculate the maximum shearing stress at the same point.

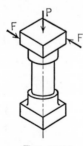

15-31. The load P in Fig. 15-23 is 8,800 lb. The cross-section at AB is rectangular, 2.5 in. by 1 in.   Determine the principal stresses at a point on the cross-section AB which is 0.5 in. from B.   (Note that the shearing stress due to P is not uniform over AB.)

15-32. The longitudinal stress in a boiler shell is 6,000 psi, and the circumferential

FIG. 15-22   FIG. 15-23

stress 12,000 psi. If Poisson's ratio is 0.25, what tensile stress acting alone would produce the same maximum unit elongation?

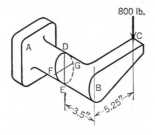

Fig. 15-24.

15-33. The bracket shown in Fig. 15-24 supports a load of 800 lb as shown. The diameter of AB is 2.0 in. Determine the principal stresses and the maximum shearing stresses at D, and the inclinations of the planes on which the stresses act.

Ans. $S_s' = 3,210$ psi.

15-34. Determine the principal stresses and the maximum shearing stresses at F or G (whichever has the larger shearing stresses) in the bracket shown in Fig. 15-24. Note that at F and at G there are shearing stresses due to the action of AB as a cantilever beam.

Proof that $2\theta_s$ differs from $2\theta_n$ by $90°$ (Page 271)

(1) $\tan 2\theta_n = -\dfrac{2S_s}{S_x - S_y}$ (Page 269)

(2) $\tan 2\theta_s = +\dfrac{S_x - S_y}{2S_s}$ (Page 271)

(3) By inspection, $\tan 2\theta_s$ is negative reciprocal of $\tan 2\theta_n$.

(4) At random let $\tan 2\theta_n = -0.5774$

$2\theta_n = 150°$

(5) Then $\tan 2\theta_s = +\dfrac{1}{0.5774} = 1.73$

$2\theta_s = 60°$

(6) $2\theta_n - 2\theta_s = 150° - 60° = \underline{90°}$ Q.E.D.

(7) $\theta_n = \dfrac{150}{2} = 75°$

(8) $\theta_s = \dfrac{60}{2} = 30°$

(9) $\theta_n - \theta_s = 75° - 30° = \underline{45°}$ Q.E.D.

16

Elastic Energy; Stresses Produced by Moving Bodies

16-1. Elastic Energy. An elastic body that is deformed by external force has energy stored within it. This energy is sometimes called "potential energy of deformation." Other names in common use are "internal work," "strain energy," and "elastic energy." The property of a material which makes it capable of storing elastic energy is called resilience.

The ability of a member to store elastic energy is frequently of great importance in situations where the member is called upon to resist moving bodies. In many such cases most of the kinetic energy of a moving body must be transformed into elastic energy of the resisting member. As will become apparent, the design of members called upon to resist moving bodies may be quite different from the design of members which must resist only static or gradually applied loads.

16-2. Forces Exerted on or by a Moving Body. When a moving body is brought to rest by forces acting upon it, *work* (equal to the kinetic energy of the body) is done by the forces. Work is the product of a force and a distance. The greater the distance in which the velocity is reduced to zero, the less is the force required. Therefore the stresses produced are inversely proportional to the distance the body moves while it is being brought to rest.

As an illustration, at the end of a railroad track a "car bumper," frequently consisting of a large block of reinforced concrete, is ordinarily placed to stop cars. If this relatively rigid block and the relatively rigid frame of the car were allowed to come into sudden direct contact, the velocity of the car would be destroyed in such a short distance that a very large force would be exerted between car and bumper and injuriously large stresses would be produced in each. To prevent this, a set of coil springs is used to cushion the impact. These springs cause a gradually increasing force to be exerted on the bumper and on the car frame and permit the car to travel a much greater distance in being brought to rest. The forces and stresses produced are therefore much less than if the car frame came into direct contact with the bumper.

In the design of energy-absorbing members, such as the foregoing spring, it is frequently important that the production of the allowable stress should be accompanied by a large amount of total deformation of the member.

16-3. Elastic Energy under Axial Loads.   Modulus of Resilience. Let a right prism of cross-section A and length L be acted on by axial forces that produce a unit stress of S psi at all points of any cross-section.   Then the unit deformation is S/E (provided that the proportional limit of the material is not exceeded), and the total deformation is SL/E.   If the body was initially unstressed and if the stress increases proportionally with the deformation, the average unit stress is $S/2$, and the average force exerted on the prism is $SA/2$.   Let U be the work done on the prism (or the elastic energy stored in it).   Then $U = (SA/2)(SL/E) = S^2AL/2E$.   But AL = the volume of the prism.   Hence

$$U = \frac{S^2}{2E} \times \textit{Volume of prism} \qquad (16\text{-}1)$$

This shows that the energy which can be absorbed by a prism without exceeding a given unit stress is independent of the relative dimensions of the prism but is a function of the amount of material in it.   The expression $S^2/2E$ gives the energy in inch-pounds per cubic inch.

The amount of energy *per unit of volume* that a given material stores when stressed to the elastic limit is called the *modulus of resilience* of that material.[1]   The modulus of resilience equals $S_e^2/2E$, where S_e is the elastic limit.   Since the modulus of resilience is proportional to the square of the elastic limit and inversely proportional to E, it follows that a material with a high elastic limit and a low modulus of elasticity is capable of storing a large amount of elastic energy or of absorbing a large amount of shock without being damaged thereby.

Example.   Compare the moduli of resilience of two steels with elastic limits of (a) 30,000 and (b) 150,000 psi, respectively, and (c) an aluminum alloy having an elastic limit of 30,000 psi.

Solution: (a) $S_e^2/2E = 30{,}000^2/(2 \times 30{,}000{,}000) = 15.0$ in.-lb per cu in.

(b) $S_e^2/2E = 150{,}000^2/(2 \times 30{,}000{,}000) = 375$ in.-lb per cu in.

(c) $S_e^2/2E = 30{,}000^2/(2 \times 10{,}000{,}000) = 45$ in.-lb per cu in.

[1] In this chapter it is assumed that the proportional limit and the elastic limit of a material have the same value, as is usual.   It is the *elastic* limit that limits resilience, since if a permanent set occurs, some of the stored energy is not returned.   If the stress exceeds the *proportional* limit, however, the expression $S^2/2E$ does not correctly express the amount of the stored energy which equals the area under the stress-strain curve as the unit stress decreases to zero.

The stronger steel, because of its higher elastic limit, has twenty-five times the resilience of the weaker; the aluminum alloy, although no stronger than the weaker steel, has three times the resilience, because it is less stiff.

PROBLEM

16-1. Calculate the modulus of resilience of each of the following materials having the physical properties given (pounds per square inch):

	E	PROPORTIONAL LIMIT
Gray cast iron (tension)	12,000,000	9,000
Gray cast iron (compression)	14,000,000	30,000
Malleable iron	22,000,000	15,000
Hickory	1,800,000	4,000
Spruce	1,200,000	2,500

16-4. Design of Members to Resist Axial Dynamic Loads.

The design of a member which is to resist axial dynamic or moving loads differs in several important ways from the design of a member to receive static loads only. In the first place, Art. 16-2 shows that the amount of energy that a member can store at a given stress is inversely proportional to the modulus of elasticity of the member. If a choice of materials for a member which is to resist dynamic loads is available, the material with the lowest E may be the most desirable on that account. There is no corresponding consideration in the design of members that resist static loads only.

In the second place, although the maximum unit stress in a prismatic member resisting an axial static load is determined by the size of the *cross-section* of the member, the maximum stress in a prismatic member resisting axial dynamic loads is determined not by the cross-section but by the *volume* of the member. In the static load member the only way to reduce the maximum stress is to increase the cross-section. In the member resisting dynamic loads, it is just as effective to increase the *length*. The same amount of energy can be absorbed by a small average force F, coupled with a large total deformation Δ, as by a much larger average force F', coupled with a correspondingly smaller total deformation Δ'. A long member decelerates the moving load less rapidly and therefore absorbs its energy with the exertion of smaller forces on it and consequently with smaller unit stresses. It is sometimes possible to increase the length of a bolt, for example, and thereby materially to decrease the stresses set up in it by a tensile impact load. In Fig. 16-1a a cover, which is subject to dynamic loads, is held to a flange by means of bolts. Most of the energy delivered to these bolts must be absorbed in a length l. By the simple expedient of placing a thick washer under the head and nut of each bolt, as shown in Fig. 16-1b, the length of the bolt material which absorbs most of the energy is increased to l', and materially lower stresses result.

In yet a third way the design of a member to resist dynamic loads differs from the design of the static load member. In both members the maximum stress occurs on the minimum cross-section. In the static load member, however, it is only the *minimum* cross-section that determines the maximum stress. Other cross-sections may have *any* (larger) size, and the maximum stress is unaffected. In a member resisting dynamic loads, however, it is very important that there be *no excess of material* but that the cross-sections throughout the greater part of the length of the member *be not materially greater than the minimum cross-section.* The following example illustrates this fact.

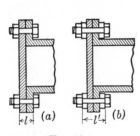

Fig. 16-1

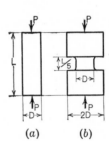

Fig. 16-2

Example. Compare the maximum stresses produced in the two cylindrical bodies shown in Fig. 16-2 by the absorption of U in.-lb of energy.

Solution: For the first body a the relationship derived in Art. 16-3 is

$$U = (S^2/2E) \times AL \quad \text{or} \quad S^2 = 2EU/AL$$

The second body b can be considered to be composed of two cylinders, one with cross-section A and length $0.2L$ and the other with cross-section $4A$ and length $0.8L$. For simplicity assume a uniform stress distribution over all cross-sections of each cylinder. Then, if the unit stress on cross-section A is S', the unit stress on the cross-section with area $4A$ will be $\frac{1}{4}S'$. Therefore the total energy U stored in the two cylinders is

$$U = \frac{S'^2}{2E} \times A \times 0.2L + \frac{(\frac{1}{4}S')^2}{2E} \times 4A \times 0.8L = \frac{S'^2 AL}{10E} + \frac{S'^2 AL}{10E} = \frac{S'^2 AL}{5E}$$

whence $S'^2 = 5EU/AL$. Therefore $S'^2/S^2 = 5/2$, whence $S' = 1.58S$.

It is very interesting to note that, though these two bodies have the same net section, under a dynamic load possessing a given amount of energy the member with the *more* material in it receives 58 per cent higher stress than the member with the less material. The extra material is not only wasted, it is also *definitely disadvantageous.* The reason is, of course, that the part of body b with the larger cross-section receives so small a unit stress and therefore so small a unit deformation that the energy stored in it is very small.   Most of the energy absorbed by b is stored in the small cylinder, which, though it comprises but one-seventeenth of the total volume of b, absorbs one-half of the energy.   The same amount of material in the prism a absorbs only 20 per cent of the

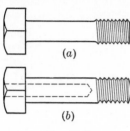

(a)

(b)

Fig. 16-3

energy and is therefore much less highly stressed.   It is quite important that members which are to resist dynamic loads have, so far as practicable, the same amount of material at every cross-section.   Therefore bolts which may have to resist energy loads are often turned down so that their diameter through the greater part of their length is equal to the diameter at the root of the thread, or sometimes a hole is drilled through the head of the

bolt extending down almost to the beginning of the thread and of such size that the cross-section of the remaining body of the bolt equals the cross-section at the root of the thread (Fig. 16-3).

The shorter the length of the part of a tensile or compressive member which has a reduced cross-section, the more severe is the effect in raising the stress under shock loads.   A tensile member punched or drilled at the ends for rivets or bolts may be stressed very highly at the reduced cross-sections when subjected to dynamic loading, even though its total length is so great that it could absorb a considerable amount of energy with low stress, had it a uniform cross-section throughout.   Serious failures have sometimes resulted from disregard of this fact.

PROBLEMS

16-2. In the example of Art. 16-4, what would be the ratio of maximum stresses in bodies a and b if one-half the length of the large cylinder were turned down to diameter D?

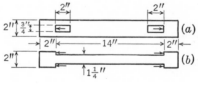

Fig. 16-4

16-3. A machine part is required to resist variable forces causing a certain amount of energy load in each cycle of operation of the machine.   Two possible designs are shown in Fig. 16-4a and b.   If the factor of safety of design a is 5, what is the factor of safety of design b?   How do the weights compare?   Both bars are $\frac{1}{4}$ in. thick.

16-4. What must be the length of a carbon steel rod, 1 in. in diameter, if, owing to the application of an axial tensile load, it is to absorb 600 in.-lb of energy without exceeding the proportional limit of 30,000 psi?   *Ans. L = 51 in.*

16-5. What diameter must a nickel-steel bar 54 in. long have to absorb 600 in.-lb of energy without being stressed above the proportional limit of 50,000 psi?

16-5. Elastic Energy of Bending.

The amount of elastic energy of bending that is stored in a beam in equilibrium under an applied load is determined as follows. A slice of a beam between two transverse planes a distance dx apart, as shown in Fig. 16-5, is considered. The bending moment at the point in the beam where the slice is taken is M and may be regarded as constant throughout the length dx. Consider a "fiber" extending from one plane to the other. Let dA be cross-sectional area and y its distance from the neutral surface. On this fiber the unit stress is My/I, and the total force is $My\,dA/I$. The change in length due to the bending stress is $My\,dx/EI$. As

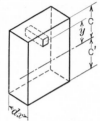

Fig. 16-5

the moment at this section has increased from zero to M, the force on the ends of the fiber has varied from zero to $My\,dA/I$. The work done on the fiber is

$$\frac{My\,dA}{2I} \times \frac{My\,dx}{EI} = \frac{M^2\,dxy^2\,dA}{2EI^2} \quad \checkmark$$

On the entire slice the work done is

$$\frac{M^2\,dx}{2EI^2} \int_{-c}^{c} y^2\,dA = \frac{M^2\,dx}{2EI} \quad \checkmark$$

For the entire beam,

$$U = \int_0^L \frac{M^2\,dx}{2EI} \tag{16-2}$$

To evaluate this for a given beam it is necessary to express M as a function of x, assuming E and I to be constant.

Usually there is an additional amount of elastic energy of shearing deformation in the beam. In Art. 19-5 it is stated that shearing deflections of beams are ordinarily small in comparison with deflections caused by bending. The same statement is true of the energies stored by shearing and bending deformations.

Example. Calculate the elastic energy of bending stored in a cantilever beam by a load P at the end.

Solution: $M = Px$ at a distance x from the load.

$$U = \int_0^L \frac{M^2\,dx}{2EI} = \int_0^L \frac{P^2x^2\,dx}{2EI} = \frac{P^2}{2EI} \frac{x^3}{3}\Big]_0^L = \frac{P^2L^3}{6EI}$$

The maximum stress $= PLc/I$. Therefore

$$U = S^2 LI/6Ec^2$$

Also the maximum stress in this beam is

$$S = \sqrt{6Ec^2 U/LI}$$

For a cantilever beam of *rectangular* cross-section with a load P at the end

$$U = \frac{S^2 L (bh^3/12)}{6E(h^2/4)} = \frac{S^2}{2E} \times \frac{\text{Volume}}{9}$$

indicating that in this case the energy stored for a given maximum stress is $\frac{1}{9}$ of that stored in a tension or compression member of the same volume and with stress equal to the maximum of the beam.

PROBLEM

16-6. Derive an expression for the elastic energy of bending in a uniformly loaded cantilever beam, the load being w lb per in.   *Ans.* $U = w^2 L^5/40EI$.

16-6. Calculation of Beam Deflections by Energy Relations.

In Art. 16-5 it was shown that the elastic energy of bending stored in a prismatic cantilever beam with a load P at the end is $P^2 L^3/6EI$. This must equal the work done by the load, as the end of the beam moves through the distance Δ, the deflection due to bending. The force exerted on the end of the beam has increased from 0 to the value P and has an average value of $P/2$. Therefore the work done on the beam by the load is $P\Delta/2$. Equating the work and energy, $P\Delta/2 = P^2 L^3/6EI$, whence $\Delta = PL^3/3EI$, the same value as was obtained for this beam and loading by the double-integration and area-moment methods. In a similar way, expressions for the bending deflections of prismatic beams with other loadings can be obtained.

PROBLEM

16-7. Calculate the midpoint deflection of a simply supported beam of span L due to a load P at the midpoint by equating the work done by the load P with the energy stored in the beam as it bends.

16-7. Beams of Constant Strength.

If I/c for every cross-section of a beam is proportional to the bending moment at that section, evidently $M/(I/c)$ will be a constant. That is, a beam having its section modulus varied in this way would have the same maximum fiber stress at every cross-section. Such a beam is called a beam of constant strength.

Consider a cantilever beam with a concentrated load P at the end. Then $M = Px$. If this beam is to have constant strength, the I/c of any cross-section must be proportional to the distance of that section from the free end of the beam. If the successive cross-sections are rectangular, for each, $I/c = bd^2/6$. Therefore bd^2 must vary as x. This can be accomplished by varying either the width or the depth of the sections. If the depth is made constant, the width must vary as x; that is, the beam will be triangular in plan. If the width is made constant, the d^2 must vary as x, or $d^2 = qx$, where q is a constant. The depth must therefore vary as the ordinates of a parabola (Fig. 16-6).

For any type of beam and loading, uniformity of strength is accomplished by setting up the equation $I/c = M/S$, regarding S as constant, and making I/c vary as M.

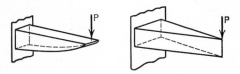

FIG. 16-6.   Cantilever beams of constant strength.

Beams with exactly constant strength are impractical. For example, in the cantilever with a concentrated load at the end, the bending moment decreases to zero at the load. Close to the load the cross-sections that are sufficient for bending will be overstressed in shear. Where bending moments are small, the cross-section must be of such size that the allowable shearing stress is not exceeded. The beam cannot be allowed to taper to an actual edge. In forged and cast beams, however, it is practical to vary the cross-section so as roughly to *approximate* a beam of uniform strength. Where such beams are used under conditions that make it necessary for the beam to absorb shock loads, as in axles, the cross-section is often varied in such a way as to diminish the differences between the maximum bending stresses on different cross-sections.

16-8. Elastic Energy of Beams of Constant Strength.   Since at every cross-section of a beam of constant strength the maximum fiber stress is the same, it follows that, for a given maximum stress and a given volume of material, a beam of constant strength will store more elastic energy than a prismatic beam. In Art. 16-5 it was shown that the energy stored in a "slice" of a beam is

$$U = \frac{M^2 \, dx}{2EI}$$

This may be expressed in terms of the maximum bending stress on the cross-section by substituting SI/c for M, whence

$$U = \frac{S^2 I^2 \, dx}{2EIc^2} = \frac{S^2}{2E} \times \frac{I \, dx}{c^2}$$

For a beam of rectangular cross-section $I/c = bh^2/6$ and $h/c = 2$. Making these substitutions

$$U = \frac{S^2}{2E} \times \frac{bh\,dx}{3}$$

In a beam of constant strength S is the same for all cross-sections. For the entire rectangular beam of constant strength

$$U = \frac{S^2}{2E} \int_0^L \frac{bh\,dx}{3} = \frac{S^2}{2E} \times \frac{\text{Volume}}{3} \qquad (16\text{-}3)$$

Example. A cantilever beam made of spring steel has the dimensions shown in Fig. 16-7 and carries a load of 250 lb at the end. (a) What maximum bending stress does this load cause, and how much elastic energy of bending does it store? (b) What is the deflection of the free end of the beam? (c) Calculate the amount of the stored energy in a beam of 12-in. constant width, all other dimensions and the load being the same as in Fig. 16-7.

Solution: (a) For the cross-section at the face of the wall, $\dfrac{I}{c} = \dfrac{bd^2}{6} = \dfrac{12 \times (\frac{5}{16})^2}{6}$

$$= 0.195 \text{ in.}^3 \quad S = M/(I/c). \quad \text{Therefore}$$

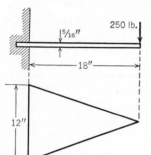

$$S = \frac{250 \times 18}{0.195} = 23{,}050 \text{ psi}$$

The volume of the beam is

$$\frac{12 \times 18}{2} \times \frac{5}{16} = 33.75 \text{ cu in.}$$

$$U = \frac{S^2}{2E} \times \frac{\text{Volume}}{3} = \frac{(23{,}050)^2}{2 \times 30{,}000{,}000} \times \frac{33.75}{3}$$

Fig. 16-7 $= 99.6$ in.-lb

(b) The work done on the beam by the load $= 250\Delta/2$ in.-lb. Therefore

$$250\Delta/2 = 99.6, \quad \text{and} \quad \Delta = 0.80 \text{ in.}$$

(c) If the beam has a constant width of 12 in., the stored energy will be given by the formula of Art. 16-5 and will be

$$U = \frac{S^2}{2E} \times \frac{\text{Volume}}{9} = \frac{(23{,}050)^2 \times 67.50}{2 \times 30{,}000{,}000 \times 9} = 66.4 \text{ in.-lb}$$

Therefore the tapering beam of constant strength absorbs 1.5 times as much energy as the prismatic beam.

PROBLEM

16-8. A steel cantilever beam is 60 in. long, 1 in. thick, and 8 in. wide at the fixed end and tapers to a point at the other end. Calculate the amount of the concentrated load at the small end that will cause a maximum bending stress of 18,000 psi. Calculate the energy stored in the beam when so loaded, and calculate the end deflection.

16-9. Leaf Springs.   The advantage of a beam of constant strength for absorbing work or storing energy is shown by the example of Art. 16-8. The ordinary leaf spring used for cushioning the travel of vehicles is an approximation to a beam of constant strength.   Leaf 1 of the spring shown in Fig. 16-8a contains the same material as the middle strip (numbered 1) of the beam shown in b.   Leaf 2 is the equivalent of the two strips numbered 2 in b.   In the same way it is seen that all the

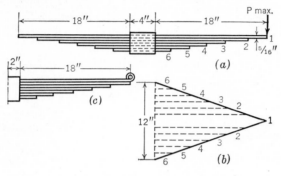

FIG. 16-8

leaves in the right-hand arm of the spring shown in a are together equivalent to the beam of constant strength shown in b.   It is also commonly assumed that the stress in the extreme fibers at all cross-sections of all leaves is the same as it is in the extreme fibers of the beam of constant strength.

For practical reasons there is usually added another full-length leaf forged at the ends to form eyes for the bolts attaching the springs to the vehicle (Fig. 16-8c).   The design of leaf springs is a specialized field in machine design.[2]   The materials for automobile leaf springs are high-strength alloy steels, carefully heat-treated, and maximum stresses in service are very high.

In actual use an appreciable amount of energy is absorbed by the work of friction between the leaves of a spring.

16-10. Elastic Energy of Bodies Uniformly Stressed in Shear.   For a body uniformly stressed in shear it may be shown, in exactly the same way as for tensile or compressive stress, that for stresses below the elastic limit the elastic energy is $U = \dfrac{S_s^2}{2E_s} \times$ Volume.   This expression is in the same form as that for the elastic energy of tension or compression.

[2] For a fuller discussion of leaf springs see books on machine design, such as Norman, Ault, and Zarobsky, *Machine Design*, The Macmillan Co.

It should be kept in mind, however, that, for equal stresses and a given material, the elastic energy for shear is greater per unit volume, since E_s is less than E.   On the other hand, the elastic limit in shear is generally less than that in tension or compression.

A good example of the absorption of energy through shearing deformation is furnished by the rubber spring or "sandwich" shown in Fig. 16-9.

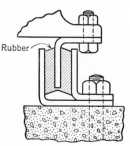

An energy load applied to the central plate is absorbed by the layers of rubber.[3]

16-11. Elastic Energy of Torsion; Helical Springs.   When a bar is subjected to a torque, a twisting deformation results.   The work done on the bar by the applied torque equals the elastic energy stored in the bar, if the stresses produced do not exceed the elastic limit of the material.

Fig. 16-9

Let U be the number of inch-pounds of work done by a gradually applied external torque whose maximum value is T, acting through an angle θ and acting on a cylindrical bar with polar moment of inertia J, length L, and modulus of rigidity E_s.   Then $U = T\theta/2$, since $T/2$ is the average torque twisting the bar.   But $\theta = TL/E_sJ$.   Therefore $U = T^2L/2E_sJ$.

The relationship between the elastic energy stored in the bar, its dimensions and torsional stiffness, and the maximum stress in it is found by substituting the value S_sJ/c for T.   This gives

$$U = S_s{}^2JL/2E_sc^2 \qquad (16\text{-}4)$$

Since J for a solid bar equals $\pi c^4/2 = c^2A/2$, the above equation becomes

$$U = \frac{S_s{}^2}{2E_s} \times \tfrac{1}{2} \text{ Volume} \qquad (16\text{-}5)$$

For the absorption of energy loads, helical springs are often used. Equations 16-4 and 16-5 apply to such springs, which are bars subjected to torsional stress.   Equation 16-5 shows that the capacity of a helical spring to store energy at a given stress is directly proportional to the volume of the spring.   The relative values of length, cross-section, and radius of coil, however, determine the amount of deformation which will accompany the storing of any given amount of energy at a given stress.

The deformation of a helical spring is given by the equation $\Delta =$

[3] For an interesting discussion of the use of rubber in absorbing shocks and vibration, see Walter C. Keys, "Rubber Springs," *Mechanical Engineering*, May, 1937.

PR^2L/E_sJ (Art. 6-9), where R is the mean radius of the helix and P is the load causing the deformation. The work done in deforming the spring, however, is $U = P\Delta/2$. Therefore $\Delta^2 = 2UR^2L/E_sJ$, or, for a solid circular wire,

$$\Delta^2 = 4UR^2L/\pi E_s c^4$$

Eliminating L between the last equation and 16-4,

$$c^3 = 4UR/\pi \Delta S_s \quad \text{or} \quad c = \sqrt[3]{4UR/\pi \Delta S_s} \qquad (16\text{-}6)$$

This equation can be used to determine the necessary radius of wire for a spring to absorb any given amount of energy with a given maximum stress and deformation, the radius of the helix being known. After the diameter of the wire has been determined, the length which it must have is found from equation 16-5. If the spring is to absorb tensile loads, it will probably be close-coiled, and the length will be $2\pi RN$ (very closely), where N is the number of coils. If the spring is to absorb compressive loads, it must be open-coiled, and the length will be $2\pi RN/\cos \phi$, where ϕ is the pitch angle of the helix.

Example. A helical spring, made of a round bar of spring steel, is to have a mean radius of 5 in. and is to absorb 6,000 ft-lb of energy, given it by compressive forces. The allowable stress is 60,000 psi, and the allowable deformation is to be approximately 8 in. Determine the required radius of the bar, the number of coils required, and the "pitch" of the helix.

Solution: Since $c = \sqrt[3]{4UR/\pi \Delta S_s}$

$$c = \sqrt[3]{\frac{4 \times (6,000 \times 12) \times 5}{\pi \times 8 \times 60,000}} = \sqrt[3]{0.955} = 0.986 \text{ in.}$$

Let the diameter of the bar be 2 in. From equation 16-5, the necessary volume of the bar must be $4UE_s/S^2$, and this must also equal $\pi c^2 L$. Therefore

$$L = \frac{4UE_s}{\pi c^2 S_s{}^2} = \frac{4 \times 72,000 \times 12,000,000}{\pi \times 1 \times 60,000 \times 60,000} = 306 \text{ in.}$$

Although this must be an open-coiled spring, the pitch of the helix will be small, and no material error will result from considering the length of the spring to be $2\pi RN$. Therefore $N = 306/(2\pi \times 5) = 9.74$ turns; say 10 turns. The spring must be capable of compressing 8 in. in 10 turns, or 0.8 in. per turn. Therefore the pitch of the helix must be 2.8 in., and the helix will be 28 in. long.

Since neither the bar diameter nor the number of coils is exactly what the equations call for, the spring will not be stressed to precisely 60,000 psi when it absorbs 6,000 ft-lb of energy, nor will it be compressed exactly 8 in.

This discussion has not taken into account the "direct" shearing stress in the helical spring. The direct shearing stress is generally small in comparison with the torsional stress and in practice is almost always disregarded.

PROBLEMS

16-9. A steel spring is made of 10 turns of 1-in.-diameter rod in a coil having an outside diameter of 5 in. Calculate the torsional stress and deformation when 7,400 in.-lb of energy is stored in it.   *Ans.* S_s = 60,000 psi.

16-10. Calculate the torsional stress and the energy stored when the spring of Problem 16-9 is compressed 3.5 in.

16-11. The spring of Problem 16-9 is made with a clear space of $\frac{1}{2}$ in. between coils. Calculate the torsional stress and the energy stored when it is closed solid.

STRESSES PRODUCED BY MOVING BODIES

16-12. Introduction. Up to this point in this chapter, consideration has been limited to the relationship between the energy stored in a member and the accompanying stresses and deformations. The energy stored has been recognized as having been transmitted to the member by some moving body which has come in contact with the member; but it has not been necessary to consider what fraction of the energy possessed by the moving body has been stored in the member as elastic energy. The only thing that has been considered is the effect, in stressing and deforming the member, *of that amount of energy which has been stored.*

The articles immediately following this one will make the assumption that all the energy possessed by a moving load is transmitted to the resisting member as elastic energy. On the basis of that assumption, these articles will connect the weight of a moving body and either the vertical distance through which it falls onto a resisting member or the velocity which it has when it comes in contact with the resisting member, with the stresses and deformations produced. A convenient form of equation is one in which the "dynamic" stresses and deformations produced by the moving weight are related to the stresses and deformations which the same amount of weight, acting as a static load, would produce. Such equations will be derived.

The equations derived are never absolutely accurate, since it is never true that all the energy possessed by a moving load is stored as elastic energy in a resisting body. For many situations, however, the equations are sufficiently close to the truth to be acceptable and useful. After the equations have been derived, the limitations of their application to various situations will be discussed in Art. 16-16.

16-13. Gradually Applied Load and Suddenly Applied Load. Suppose that a load W is hung on the end of a cantilever beam (Fig. 16-10). If "gradually applied" to the beam, it is first entirely supported by something other than the beam (the hand, in the picture). As the external support is gradually lowered, the stiffness of the beam causes more and

more of the load to be resisted by the beam, until eventually the beam
carries the entire load W. Since the accompanying deflection is that
due to the static load W, let it be called Δ_{st}. The average load on the
beam during the production of this
deflection Δ_{st} has been $W/2$, and the
work done on the beam by the load
(or done on the load by the beam) has
been $(W/2)\Delta_{st}$.

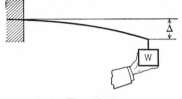

FIG. 16-10

The force exerted on the load by
the hand has decreased, in proportion
to the deflection, from W to 0, and the
work the hand has done on the load has been $(W/2)\Delta_{st}$. The beam
and the hand together have done work on the load equal to the work
of gravity, or the loss of potential energy, which is $W\Delta_{st}$.

Suppose now that the weight is brought just in contact with the undeflected beam and then *suddenly* released. Call the deflection of the
beam when the weight is brought to rest Δ_1. The force exerted on the
weight by the beam at that instant is $(\Delta_1/\Delta_{st})W$, since the force W of the
static load deflected the beam Δ_{st} in. and since forces are proportional
to the deflections they produce. The work done on the load by the
beam during the deflection Δ_1 equals

$$\frac{1}{2}\frac{\Delta_1}{\Delta_{st}} W \times \Delta_1 \qquad \text{or} \qquad \frac{1}{2}\frac{\Delta_1{}^2}{\Delta_{st}} W$$

This equals the work done on the load by gravity. Therefore

$$\frac{1}{2}\frac{\Delta_1{}^2 W}{\Delta_{st}} = \Delta_1 W$$

whence $\Delta_1 = 2\Delta_{st}$. Since the stresses are proportional to the deflections,
a suddenly applied load causes twice the stress that the same load does
if gradually applied. It is also true that the maximum force which the
load exerts on the beam is twice the weight of the load.

Although these relations between a gradually applied load and a
sudden load have been worked out for a beam, nothing in the derivation
limits them to beams. For an axially loaded member, Δ_1 and Δ_{st}
represent total *deformations*; for a shaft they represent total torsional
deformations, which are proportional to angles of twist; for a helical
spring, they represent the shortening or elongation of the spring, etc.
In any elastic body a suddenly applied load causes twice the stress and
twice the deformation (or deflection) as the same load applied gradually.

Suddenly applied loads may cause vibrations which are generally
undesirable and which sometimes have injurious effects. As an illustra-

tion of vibration a beam is shown in Fig. 16-11 with a weight attached to the end. First assume that the weight is entirely supported by a cord and that the beam is undeflected. If the cord is cut, the load is suddenly applied to the beam and the beam deflects a distance Δ_1, which, as shown above, is twice the deflection Δ_{st} that would occur if the load were gradually applied.

Until the deflection equals Δ_{st}, the pressure of the beam on the body is less than the weight and the body has downward acceleration. The weight has downward velocity when the deflection is Δ_{st}. As the deflection increases, the force exerted by the beam on the body exceeds the weight and the body slows down and comes to rest when $\Delta_1 = 2\Delta_{st}$. But now the upward force exerted on the body by the beam is twice the

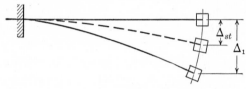

FIG. 16-11

weight, and hence upward acceleration occurs until the deflection is Δ_{st}, and then downward acceleration occurs until the body again comes to rest with the beam straight. This cycle of motion would be repeated indefinitely except for energy losses which gradually reduce the amplitude and finally bring the body to rest with the deflection of the beam equal to Δ_{st}.

16-14. Weight Falling a Height h. If the weight W is dropped a distance h before striking the beam or other elastic member, the beam will deflect a distance Δ which is greater than either Δ_{st} or Δ_1. The work done on the weight by gravity is equaled by the work done on it by the beam, or

$$W(h + \Delta) = \frac{1}{2} \frac{\Delta}{\Delta_{st}} W \times \Delta = \frac{1}{2} \frac{\Delta^2}{\Delta_{st}} W$$

or

$$h + \Delta = \frac{1}{2} \frac{\Delta^2}{\Delta_{st}}$$

whence

$$\Delta - \Delta_{st} = \sqrt{2\Delta_{st}h + \Delta_{st}{}^2}$$

and

$$\Delta = \Delta_{st} + \Delta_{st}\sqrt{\frac{2h}{\Delta_{st}} + 1} = \Delta_{st}\left(1 + \sqrt{\frac{2h}{\Delta_{st}} + 1}\right) \qquad (16\text{-}7)$$

It is also true, since stresses are proportional to deformations or deflections, that

$$S = S_{st}\left(1 + \sqrt{\frac{2h}{\Delta_{st}} + 1}\right) \tag{16-8}$$

in which S_{st} is the static stress due to a gradually applied weight and S is the stress due to the same weight falling a height h and striking the beam. Note that, if $h = 0$, equations 16-7 and 16-8 give values of $2\Delta_{st}$ for Δ and $2S_{st}$ for S, as found in Art. 16-13.

In equations 16-7 and 16-8 if Δ_{st} is small in comparison with h, as it often is (especially for members loaded axially), with negligible error

$$\Delta = \Delta_{st}\,(1 + \sqrt{2h/\Delta_{st}}) \qquad \text{and} \qquad S = S_{st}\,(1 + \sqrt{2h/\Delta_{st}}) \tag{16-9}$$

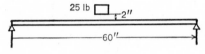

FIG. 16-12

Example 1. A 1-in. square beam (Fig. 16-12) is 60 in. long and rests on supports at the ends. A 25-lb weight falls 2 in., striking the beam at its midpoint. What stress is caused (a) if the beam is steel? (b) if the beam is made of an aluminum alloy?

Solution: (a) For the steel beam

$$\Delta_{st} = \frac{PL^3}{48EI} = \frac{25 \times 60^3}{48 \times 30,000,000 \times \frac{1}{12}} = 0.045 \text{ in.}$$

$$S_{st} = \frac{Mc}{I} = \frac{375}{\frac{1}{6}} = 2,250 \text{ psi (for static load)}$$

Therefore

$$S = 2,250 + 2,250\sqrt{\frac{4}{0.045} + 1} = 2,250 + 2,250\sqrt{89 + 1} = 2,250 + 2,250 \times 9.5$$
$$= 2,250 + 21,400 = 23,650 \text{ psi}$$

and

$$\Delta = 0.045 \times 10.5 = 0.473 \text{ in.}$$

(b) For the aluminum-alloy beam, $E = 10,000,000$ psi

$$\Delta_{st} = 0.045 \times 3 = 0.135 \text{ in.}$$

$$S_{st} = 2,250 \text{ psi (for static load)}$$

$$S = 2,250 + 2,250\sqrt{\frac{4}{0.135} + 1} = 2,250 + 2,250\sqrt{30.6} = 2,250 + 2,250 \times 5.54$$
$$= 2,250 + 12,500 = 14,750 \text{ psi}$$

If grades of steel and aluminum alloy having the same strength are used, the aluminum-alloy beam has a considerably higher factor of safety. It may be noted, however, that, if the load were suddenly applied (without falling, or $h = 0$), the stress in either beam would be simply twice 2,250 psi, the stress due to static load, or 4,500 psi.

Example 2. If the steel beam in Example 1 is 66 in. long instead of 60 in. but other conditions remain the same, what is the stress?

$$\Delta_{st} = \frac{PL^3}{48EI} = \frac{25 \times 66^3}{48 \times 30,000,000 \times \frac{1}{12}} = 0.060 \text{ in.}$$

$$S_{st} = 33 \times 12.5 \times 6 = 2,480 \text{ psi}$$

$$S = 2,480 + 2,480 \sqrt{\frac{4}{0.060} + 1} = 2,480 + 2,480 \times 8.2 = 22,800 \text{ psi.}$$

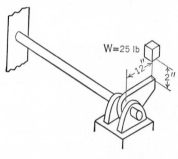

W=25 lb

Note that this is a smaller stress than that resulting in the shorter beam of the same cross-section and with the same loading. The stress is the sum of the stresses due to a static load plus that same stress multiplied by a coefficient which is $\sqrt{(2h/\Delta_{st}) + 1}$. By lengthening the beam a certain amount, this coefficient is reduced enough (from 9.5 to 8.2) to make the total stress less in spite of the greater amount of the "static" stress.

Example 3. A 1-in.-diameter steel shaft (Fig. 16-13) 60 in. long and adequately supported to prevent bending is fixed at one end and carries a 12-in. rigid arm fixed to the other end. A weight of 25 lb falls 2 in., hitting the arm. What stress results in the shaft?

Fig. 16-13

Solution: The static stress due to the 25-lb weight acting with a moment arm of 12 in. is

$$S_{st} = \frac{Tc}{J} = \frac{300 \times \frac{1}{2} \times 2}{\pi \times (\frac{1}{2})^4} = 1,530 \text{ psi}$$

$$\theta_{st} = \frac{TL}{E_s J} = \frac{300 \times 60 \times 2}{12,000,000 \times \pi \times (\frac{1}{2})^4} = 0.0153 \text{ radian}$$

$$\Delta_{st} = 12\theta_{st} = 0.184 \text{ in.}$$

Therefore the resulting stress $S = 1,530\left(1 + \sqrt{\frac{4}{0.184} + 1}\right) = 1,530 \ (1 + 4.8)$

$$= 8,880 \text{ psi}$$

PROBLEMS

16-12. In Example 3 let the moment arm be 6 in., other quantities remaining unchanged. Calculate the stress produced in the shaft. The static stress will have been halved. Why will the total stress not have been more greatly reduced?

16-13. In Example 3 calculate the stress in the shaft if the length of the shaft is 100 in., other quantities remaining unchanged.

16-14. In Example 3 assume the shaft to be fixed at both ends, and the 12-in. arm to be supported at the midpoint in such a way as to prevent bending of the shaft. Other conditions remaining unchanged, what is the resulting stress?

16-15. In Example 1 assume all conditions to remain unchanged except the length of the beam. Find the stress resulting from the falling weight when the length is 48 in.

16-16. In the example of Art. 16-8 find from what height the 250-lb load must fall on the spring to stress it to 60,000 psi.

16-15. Stresses Produced by a Body of Weight W Moving with a Velocity of v Ft per Sec.

For a falling body $v^2 = 2gh$ or h (ft) $= v^2/2g$, whence $h(\text{in.}) = 6v^2/g$, where v is in feet per second and g is in feet per second per second. If this value for h is substituted in equation 16-8,

Art. 16-14, there results $S = S_{st}\left(1 + \sqrt{\dfrac{12v^2}{g\Delta_{st}} + 1}\right)$, for the stress produced by the moving body in terms of the stress produced by a gradually applied force equal to the weight.

If, instead of falling on the resisting member, the moving body is traveling horizontally so that there is no gravitational effect but all stress in the resisting member is caused by the kinetic energy of the moving body, it can be shown that

$$S = S_{st}\sqrt{12v^2/g\Delta_{st}} = 0.61 S_{st}\sqrt{v^2/\Delta_{st}} \qquad (16\text{-}10)$$

PROBLEM

16-17. Prove the truth of the foregoing equation.

16-16. Limitations of the Foregoing Expressions.

In deriving the expressions relating the energy of moving bodies and the stresses caused in elastic members that are hit by the bodies, it was assumed that all the kinetic energy of the moving body is stored in the resisting member as elastic energy of direct elongation or compression, of bending, or of torsion in the cases of axially loaded members, beams, and shafts or helical springs, respectively. This assumption will never be entirely true, and may be far from true. If the velocity of impact is great, the rate of deceleration is likely to be so great that high local stresses and deformations will be produced, and in extreme cases, as when a lead bullet strikes a steel beam, almost all the kinetic energy may be transformed into energy of local deformation, largely inelastic, of both the moving body and the resisting member. Even when the velocity of impact is small, if the dimensions of the resisting member are such as to give it a large amount of *stiffness*, the same thing will result. Finally, if the mass of the resisting member is large in comparison with that of the moving body, the *inertia* of the resisting member may cause a considerable part of the kinetic energy to be consumed in the production of local deformations of the moving body and the resisting member.

All three of these invalidating conditions imply large values of $2h/\Delta_{st}$. A high velocity of impact is consistent with a large value of h. Also, generally speaking, the greater the stiffness or the greater the mass of the resisting member, the less will be the value of Δ_{st}. The formulas are therefore more accurate for small values of $2h/\Delta_{st}$ or of $12v^2/g\Delta_{st}$, than for large values. Wherever this ratio is less than 100, values of Δ and S computed from the equations will probably not be in error by more than about 10 per cent.[4]

There is another condition which the equations assume, and which is never present, although frequently it may be closely approximated. That condition is immovability of the supports of the member. If the supports are yielding and permit the resisting member to be displaced as a whole, the resisting member simply transmits to the supports a part of the energy of the moving load. If the member itself is very rigid in comparison with the supports, almost all the energy of the moving load may simply pass through the member to the supports. This fact is utilized when machine parts subject to shock are held in rubber mountings. In such cases the stresses produced by an impact load may be only a small fraction of their values as computed by the foregoing equations.

Because of all these circumstances the equations need to be applied with care and judgment.

16-17. "Equivalent Static Loads"; Impact Formulas. It has been noted that, whatever the nature of a moving load and whatever the nature of the resisting member, the maximum stresses and deformations of the member are the direct result of the maximum *forces* exerted on the member. For many members on which moving loads act, there is inevitably a great deal of uncertainty concerning both the amount of energy given up by the moving load and the proportion of this energy that is stored elastically in the resisting member. In such cases satisfactory application of the equations developed in the preceding articles of this chapter would be very difficult, and the results would necessarily be uncertain. As an alternative procedure, it is a common practice to assume some relation between the moving load and the greatest *force* which the moving load exerts on the member. This is accomplished by assuming that the force exerted by the moving load equals the weight of the moving load plus that weight multiplied by some factor. Such a factor is called an "impact factor." The value assumed for it is usually

---

[4] For a discussion of the effect of the inertia of the resisting member, see S. Timoshenko, *Vibration Problems in Engineering*, D. Van Nostrand Co.

empirical and is based on a consideration of similar members in existing machines or structures.

As an illustration of this procedure, the supports for an elevator hoist may have to carry "dead" (or non-moving) loads of 4,000 lb, consisting of the weight of the beams that carry the operating motors and the weight of the operating motors themselves; and "live" loads of 5,000 lb, consisting of the elevator car, the load carried by it, the cables, etc. The supports then might be designed for a total load of 14,000 lb made up as follows:

Dead load	4,000 lb
Live load	5,000 lb
Impact	5,000 lb

Here the impact factor is 1. This is equivalent to assuming that the force exerted on the supports by the live load may reach twice the static weight of the live load, or that the supporting beams may have to decelerate the downward-moving live load (or accelerate the upward-moving live load) at a rate equal to that of gravity.

GENERAL PROBLEMS

16-18. A 12-lb weight falls 36 in. onto the head of the bolt shown in Fig. 16-14. Assuming all the energy to be absorbed by the bolt, what is the maximum tensile stress produced in it? What is the maximum shearing stress on the cylindrical surface where the head joins the body of the bolt? How much is the bolt elongated?

16-19. Suppose that a $1\frac{1}{4}$-in. diameter coiled spring consisting of 6 turns of $\frac{1}{4}$-in. diameter wire is placed on the head of the bolt in Problem 16-18 to cushion the blow. The spring shortens 1.2 in. as it is closed tight. To what is the maximum tensile stress in the bolt reduced? What is the maximum torsional stress in the spring?

16-20. A round carbon-steel bar, 1 in. in diameter, is used as a cantilever beam 48 in. long and carries a static load P at the end which causes a maximum stress equal to the proportional limit of 30,000 psi. (a) What is the minimum diameter of a nickel-steel bar which will absorb the same amount of energy if loaded in the same way without stress above the proportional limit of 54,000 psi? (b) Which of the bars will support the greater static load at the end if stressed to the proportional limit? *Ans.* (a) $d = 0.56$ in.

16-21. A steel block falls 3 in. and strikes the side of the unloaded beam of Problem 16-20 at the free end. Calculate the weight of the block if it causes a maximum stress of 30,000 psi in the beam.

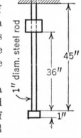

Fig. 16-14

17

Continuous Beams

17-1. Definition. A continuous beam is one which rests upon more than two supports, as in Fig. 17-1. Such beams occur frequently in modern structures. There is usually some economy of material in the use of a continuous beam, as compared with a series of simple beams over the same spans. In this book the consideration of continuous beams will be limited to beams in which E and I are constant from end to end and which have all the supports on the same level.

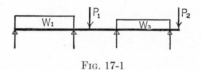

Fig. 17-1

17-2. Theorem of Three Moments. Continuous beams are statically indeterminate structures, and therefore the external reactions cannot be found by the conditions of static equilibrium alone. A very convenient method of finding bending moments in continuous beams is by means of a relation that exists between the bending moments at the three supports of any two adjacent spans of a continuous beam. This relation is expressed as an equation and is commonly called the *theorem of three moments*. By use of this theorem or equation the bending moments at all the supports of a continuous beam can be found. When these are known it is possible to determine the shears and bending moments at all points and to draw the shear and bending-moment diagrams.

The theorem of three moments is commonly ascribed to the French engineer E. Clapeyron, who published one form of it in 1857. The derivation of this equation expressing the relation that always exists between the bending moments at three consecutive supports is based on conditions of deflection and continuity of the elastic curve. The equations expressing these conditions are the necessary additional equations for the solution of this indeterminate type of structure.

It will be seen that, if there are n spans in a continuous beam, there

are $n + 1$ supports.[1] The bending moment at an end support is zero
if the beam does not overhang the end.   If it does overhang, the bending
moment at the end support can be calculated.   There are therefore
$n - 1$ unknown bending moments at the $n - 1$ intermediate supports.

If a "three-moment equation" is written for each group of three
consecutive supports, there will be $n - 1$ such equations, which are just
sufficient for finding the $n - 1$ bending moments.

17-3. Derivation of Theorem of Three Moments.   The derivation of
the theorem of three moments is based upon relationships that exist
between deflections and slopes in the elastic curve of the beam over any
two adjacent spans.   Such relationships may be established by area-
moments, by double integration, or by "superposition," making use of
previously calculated values.   The desired relationships are readily
found by the area-moment method, which will be used because of its
simplicity.   Figure 17-2a represents any two adjacent spans of a continuous beam.   The loads shown rep-
resent *any system of loads.*   Figure
17-2b represents the deflected elastic
curve.   The shape of this is unknown,
and it is unnecessary at present to
know its exact form.   Since the beam
is *continuous,* there is one and only
one tangent at B.   This is shown sloping downward to the right consistent
with the assumed elastic curve.   Since
this derivation is confined to the case
where the supports remain at the same
level, A, B, and C in Fig. 17-2b are on

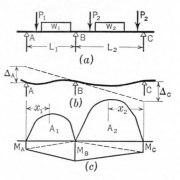

FIG. 17-2

the original straight, horizontal line. Δ_A is the displacement of A from
the tangent at B, and Δ_C is the displacement of C from the same
tangent.   By similar triangles

$$\Delta_A/L_1 = -\Delta_C/L_2$$

The minus sign must precede one of the members of this equation because the displacements Δ_A and Δ_C are in opposite directions.   This
equation introduces two conditions: continuity, and no settlement of
supports.   The similar triangles do not exist unless both these conditions
exist. Δ_A and Δ_C are easily expressed in terms of the bending-moment
diagrams for the left and right spans, respectively, by means of the
second area-moment proposition.

[1] It is assumed that these are "knife-edge" supports; that is, that the supports
themselves exert no restraint on the beam, although in general, at the supports,
there will be bending moments that are due to the continuity of the beam.

In Art. 11-12 it was shown that a loaded beam fixed at the ends is equivalent to a simple beam having the same span and load, and also having applied to it end moments of such magnitude as to make the tangents at the ends of the span horizontal. In a continuous beam, the tangents at the end of a span are not, in general, horizontal. Any span of a continuous beam, however, can be considered equivalent to a simple beam having the same span and load and acted on by end moments of sufficient amount to give the tangents at the ends of the beam the slope which the elastic curve of the continuous beam has at the supports in question. Since this is true, the bending-moment diagram for each of the spans under consideration may be drawn in two parts. One part is the M diagram for a simple beam with the given loading. Since the bending moment is always positive in a simple beam with downward loads, this part is shown above the base line in Fig. 17-2c. The other part of the diagram represents the bending moment throughout the beam caused by the restraint or bending moments at the supports. The magnitude of these moments not being known, this part of the diagram cannot be drawn to scale (which does not interfere with its use for the present purpose). The sign of these moments is also unknown, although they are generally negative. In the equations below they will be assumed positive, and the sign resulting from the solution of the equations will then be the true sign. To simplify the appearance of the diagram, these areas are drawn below the base line.

Let A_1 be the area of the positive part of the M diagram for the left span, and let x_1 be the distance to its centroid from support A (the support which is displaced from the tangent). A_2 and x_2 are corresponding values for the right span.

By the second area-moment proposition,

$$\Delta_A = \left(A_1 x_1 + M_A \times \frac{L_1}{2} \times \frac{L_1}{3} + M_B \times \frac{L_1}{2} \times \frac{2L_1}{3} \right) \frac{1}{EI}$$

$$\frac{\Delta_A}{L_1} = \left(\frac{A_1 x_1}{L_1} + \frac{M_A L_1}{6} + \frac{M_B L_1}{3} \right) \frac{1}{EI}$$

In the same way

$$\frac{\Delta_C}{L_2} = \left(\frac{A_2 x_2}{L_2} + \frac{M_C L_2}{6} + \frac{M_B L_2}{3} \right) \frac{1}{EI}$$

since

$$\Delta_A / L_1 = - \Delta_C / L_2$$

$$\frac{A_1 x_1}{L_1} + \frac{M_A L_1}{6} + \frac{M_B L_1}{3} = - \left(\frac{A_2 x_2}{L_2} + \frac{M_C L_2}{6} + \frac{M_B L_2}{3} \right)$$

Multiplying by 6 and collecting terms,

$$M_A L_1 + 2M_B(L_1 + L_2) + M_C L_2 = -\frac{6A_1 x_1}{L_1} - \frac{6A_2 x_2}{L_2} \quad (17\text{-}1)$$

This is a form of the theorem of three moments which applies to *any type of loading whatever*, provided that the three supports are on a straight line and EI is constant throughout both spans.

17-4. Theorem of Three Moments for Specific Loadings. For any given type of loading, the theorem of three moments is obtained from the foregoing equation by substituting for $6A_1 x_1/L_1$ and $6A_2 x_2/L_2$ expressions giving their values for that particular loading. The table gives such expressions for several common types of loading.

LOADING	$-\dfrac{6A_1 x_1}{L_1}$	$-\dfrac{6A_2 x_2}{L_2}$
	$-\dfrac{w_1 L_1^3}{4}$	$-\dfrac{w_2 L_2^3}{4}$
	$-\dfrac{P_1 a}{L_1}(L_1^2 - a^2)$	$-\dfrac{P_2 b}{L_2}(L_2^2 - b^2)$
	$-\dfrac{7W_1 L_1^2}{30} = -\dfrac{7w_1 L_1^3}{60}$	$-\dfrac{7W_2 L_2^2}{30} = -\dfrac{7w_2 L_2^3}{60}$
	$-\dfrac{4W_1 L_1^2}{15} = -\dfrac{2w_1 L_1^3}{15}$	$-\dfrac{4W_2 L_2^2}{15} = -\dfrac{2w_2 L_2^3}{15}$
	Trapezoidal loading. Divide into uniform load plus a triangular load. Use values above.	

When values given in this table are substituted in equation 17-1, the common forms of the theorem of three moments given below are obtained.

Uniform loads (w_1 lb per ft on left span, w_2 lb per ft on right span):

$$M_A L_1 + 2M_B(L_1 + L_2) + M_C L_2 = -\frac{w_1 L_1^3}{4} - \frac{w_2 L_2^3}{4} \quad (17\text{-}2)$$

For equal spans and the same uniform load covering all spans the foregoing equation becomes:

$$M_A + 4M_B + M_C = -\frac{wL^2}{2} \tag{17-3}$$

Uniform load and one or more concentrated loads on each span:

$$M_A L_1 + 2M_B(L_1 + L_2) + M_C L_2 = -\sum \frac{P_1 a}{L_1}(L_1{}^2 - a^2)$$

$$-\sum \frac{P_2 b}{L_2}(L_2{}^2 - b^2) - \frac{w_1 L_1{}^3}{4} - \frac{w_2 L_2{}^3}{4} \tag{17-4}$$

In the above formula Σ indicates that this term is to be written for each concentrated load in a span. The use of the foregoing formulas will be illustrated by examples.

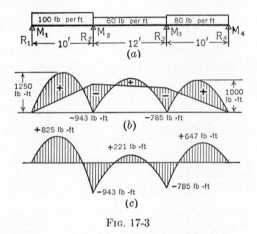

Fig. 17-3

Example 1. Calculate the bending moments at the supports of the continuous beam shown in Fig. 17-3.

Solution: The "three-moment equation" for uniform loads given above is written for the first two spans:

$$M_A L_1 + 2M_B(L_1 + L_2) + M_C L_2 = -\frac{w_1 L_1{}^3}{4} - \frac{w_2 L_2{}^3}{4}$$

$$10 \times 0 + 2M_2(10 + 12) + 12M_3 = -\frac{100 \times 1,000}{4} - \frac{60 \times 1,728}{4}$$

Whence $\qquad\qquad 44M_2 + 12M_3 = -25,000 - 25,920 = -50,920$

Dividing by 12, $\qquad\qquad 3.67M_2 + M_3 = -4,243$ lb-ft $\qquad\qquad(1)$

The equation written for the second two spans is

$$12M_2 + 2M_3(12 + 10) + 10 \times 0 = -\frac{60 \times 1,728}{4} - \frac{80 \times 1,000}{4}$$

Whence $\qquad\qquad$ $12M_2 + 44M_3 = -25,920 - 20,000 = -45,920$ lb-ft

Dividing by 44, $\qquad$ $0.273M_2 + M_3 = -1,042$ lb-ft $\qquad\qquad\qquad$ (2)

Subtracting (2) from (1),

$$3.397M_2 = -3,201$$

$$M_2 = -943 \text{ lb-ft}$$

$$M_3 = -1,042 + 0.273 \times 943 = -785 \text{ lb-ft}$$

The bending moments at the two intermediate supports M_2 and M_3 having been determined, it is possible to calculate the shear at various points, the four reactions, and the bending moments at all points. Methods for performing these calculations will be given later.

The bending-moment diagram for a continuous beam may be drawn by making use of a procedure suggested in Art. 11-12. It was there shown that the bending-moment diagram for a beam with any loading and with end moments of M_A and M_B at the respective ends can be drawn by starting with the bending-moment diagram for a simply supported beam with the same loading. Across this is drawn a straight line with ordinates of M_A at the A end and M_B at the B end.

By use of this procedure, the bending-moment diagram for the continuous beam of the above example is obtained and is shown in Fig. 17-3b. The bending-moment diagrams were first drawn for each span as if it were a simply supported beam. A straight line was drawn across each of these diagrams with ordinates at the supports equal to the calculated moments. The area below these straight lines is the negative bending-moment diagram resulting from the end moments of each span. By superimposing this negative area over the positive area, the algebraic sum of the plus and minus ordinates is automatically obtained. It is also possible to calculate maximum plus bending moments and other values, and plot a bending-moment diagram of the conventional type as shown in c. The two diagrams are equivalent.

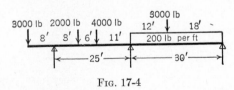

FIG. 17-4

Example 2. A beam continuous over two spans is shown in Fig. 17-4. Calculate the moments at the supports caused by the loads shown.

Solution: The moment $M_A = -24,000$ lb-ft, and the moment M_C equals zero. Hence the only unknown is M_B, and the three-moment equation written for the two spans may be solved for M_B.

$$M_A L_1 + 2M_B(L_1 + L_2) + M_C L_2$$

$$= -\Sigma \frac{P_1 a}{L_1}(L_1{}^2 - a^2) - \Sigma \frac{P_2 b}{L_2}(L_2{}^2 - b^2) - \frac{w_1 L_1{}^3}{4} - \frac{w_2 L_2{}^3}{4}$$

Substituting numerical values,

$$-24{,}000 \times 25 + 2M_B \times 55 + 0 = -\frac{2{,}000 \times 8}{25}(25^2 - 8^2)$$

$$-\frac{4{,}000 \times 14}{25}(25^2 - 14^2) - 0 - \frac{3{,}000 \times 18}{30}(30^2 - 18^2) - \frac{200 \times 30^3}{4}$$

Whence

$$-600{,}000 + 110 M_B = -359{,}000 - 961{,}000 - 1{,}037{,}000 - 1{,}350{,}000$$

Hence

$$M_B = -\frac{3{,}107{,}000}{110} = -28{,}250 \text{ lb-ft}$$

PROBLEM

17-1. Calculate the moments at the supports of the beam shown in Fig. 17-5. (Loads are given in thousands of pounds.)

17-5. Symmetrical Beams. If a beam is symmetrical in all respects, the bending moments at symmetrically located supports are equal. This condition reduces the number of unknowns (unless the beam has but two spans) and the number of equations required. In such cases the equal bending moments should be given the same subscripts in writing the equation.

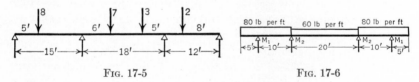

FIG. 17-5   FIG. 17-6

Example 1. Calculate the moments at the supports of the beam shown in Fig. 17-6.

Solution:

$$M_1 = -400 \times 2.5 = -1{,}000 \text{ lb-ft}$$

$$M_A L_1 + 2M_B(L_1 + L_2) + M_C L_2 = -\frac{w_1 L_1{}^3}{4} - \frac{w_2 L_2{}^3}{4}$$

$$-1{,}000 \times 10 + 2M_2 \times 30 + 20M_2 = -\frac{80 \times 1{,}000}{4} - \frac{60 \times 8{,}000}{4}$$

$$-10{,}000 + 80M_2 = -20{,}000 - 120{,}000 = -140{,}000$$

$$80M_2 = -130{,}000$$

$$M_2 = -1{,}625 \text{ lb-ft}$$

Example 2. Calculate the moments at the supports of the beam shown in Fig. 17-7.

Solution: From the table of Art. 17-4, the value of the term representing a triangular load with the heavy end toward the middle support is found to be $-4W_1L_1^2/15$. Since no load occurs in the span BC, the three-moment equation for the first two spans becomes

$$M_A L + 2M_B\left(L + \frac{L}{4}\right) + M_C \frac{L}{4} = -\frac{4WL^2}{15}$$

But M_A equals zero and M_C equals M_B, and the equation becomes

$$2M_B\left(L + \frac{L}{4}\right) + \frac{M_B L}{4} = -\frac{4WL^2}{15}$$

$$\frac{11 M_B L}{4} = -\frac{4WL^2}{15}$$

$$M_B = -\frac{16}{165}WL$$

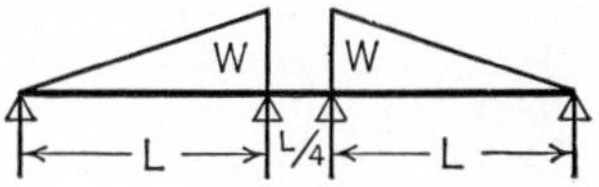

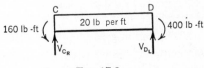

FIG. 17-7

PROBLEMS

17-2. A continuous beam of four equal spans of L ft each overhangs $0.4L$ ft at each end and carries a uniform load of w lb per ft. Calculate the moments at the supports.

Ans. $M_B = -0.084\ wL^2$.

17-3. A continuous beam of four equal spans of L ft each carries a load of P lb at the midpoint of each span. Calculate the moments at the supports.

17-6. Calculation of Shears and Reactions.

The bending moments at all supports having been calculated, it is possible to compute the shears at either end of a span by applying $\Sigma M = 0$, with the other end of the span as the moment center. The shear at a reaction will be designated by a large V with two subscripts, the first being

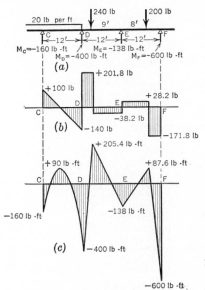

FIG. 17-8

FIG. 17-9

the letter of the reaction and the second being R or L, indicating whether the shear is just to the right or to the left of the reaction.

Example. Three spans of a continuous beam are shown in Fig. 17-8a. The bending moments at the supports have been found by the theorem of three moments. Calculate all the shears and the reactions at D and E.

Solution: Consider as a free body the length of beam between supports C and D. Since the bending moments at C and D are negative, the couples acting on the ends of the segment are as shown (Fig. 17-9).

Since $\Sigma M_D = 0$, $12V_{CR} + 400 - 160 - (20 \times 12)\ 6 = 0$.

Whence $V_{CR} = +100$ lb. Then

$$V_{DL} = +100 - 240 = -140 \text{ lb}$$

This is the *external shear* at D and is minus in accordance with the convention given in Art. 7-5. This negative external shear is consistent with the upward *resisting shear* that acts on the segment just to the left of D.

If the segment between supports D and E is considered as a free body, $\Sigma M_E = 0$ gives $12V_{DR} + 138 - 400 - 240 \times 9 = 0$. Whence $V_{DR} = +201.8$ lb. Then

$$V_{EL} = +201.8 - 240 = -38.2 \text{ lb}$$

By similar procedures V_{ER} may be found to be $+28.2$ lb, and V_{FL}, -171.8 lb. (The student should verify these figures.) With these values known, the shear diagram can be drawn for the three spans. It is shown in Fig. 17-8b.

The reaction $R_D = 140 + 201.8 = 341.8$ lb.

Equilibrium of the short length of beam over a support establishes the amount of the reaction as the *numerical* sum of the shears on either side of the reaction, if the shears on the two sides are of opposite sign, as they usually are. If the shears are of the same sign, the reaction equals their numerical difference.

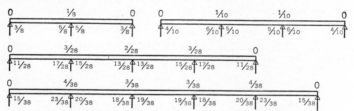

Coefficients for Moments at Reactions and Shears at ends of Spans for Continuous Beams with Equal Spans and same Uniform Load over all Spans.

Fig. 17-10. Coefficients above the beams multiplied by wL^2 give the bending moments at the supports. Coefficients below the beams multiplied by wL give the shears.

17-7. Bending Moments at Intermediate Points. If the shears and moments at supports are known, the bending moment at any intermediate point is easily determined by applying the definition of bending moment to the segment of the beam extending from one of the adjacent supports to the point in question. In the example of Art. 17-6 the maximum bending moment in the CD span occurs where the shear changes sign, 5 ft from C. At this point

$$M_5 = -160 + 100 \times 5 - 100 \times 2.5 = -160 + 250 = +90 \text{ lb-ft}$$

In the DE span the maximum positive bending moment occurs at the concentrated load and is 205.4 lb-ft. The student should verify this figure and the value of $+87.6$ lb-ft for the bending moment at the concentrated load in the EF span.

The bending-moment diagram for these three spans is shown in Fig. 17-8c.

Coefficients for shears and bending moments in uniformly loaded beams of equal spans are given in Fig. 17-10.

PROBLEMS

17-4. Calculate the shears and bending moments, and draw shear diagram and bending-moment diagram for the span of a continuous beam shown in Fig. 17-11.

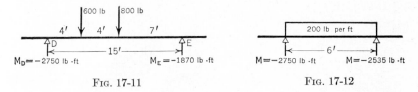

FIG. 17-11   FIG. 17-12

17-5. Calculate the shears and bending moments, and draw shear diagram and combined bending-moment diagram for the span of a continuous beam shown in Fig. 17-12.

17-6. Calculate shears and bending moments, and draw shear and bending moment diagrams for the beam of Fig. 17-6. For bending moments at the supports, use the values found in the example.

17-8. Continuous Beams Fixed at Ends. The continuous beams so far considered were assumed to be completely unrestrained at all supports. It sometimes happens that one or both ends of a continuous beam are fixed. Restraint at one end adds one unknown moment and requires an additional equation. If the beam is completely fixed at the end, the additional equation may be based on the fact that the deflection of the next support from the tangent at the end is zero.

Example. Calculate the moments at the supports of the beam shown in Fig. 17-13a. The beam is fixed at A.

Solution: The three-moment equations written for the first two and the second two spans, respectively, are as follows:

$$M_A + 4M_B + M_C = -wL^2/2 \tag{1}$$

$$M_B + 4M_C + 0 = -wL^2/2 \tag{2}$$

A bending-moment diagram for the span AB is shown in Fig. 17-13b. The moment of this area with respect to B equals zero, since the deflection of B from the tangent at A is zero. From this fact a third equation results.

$$M_A \times \frac{L}{2} \times \frac{2}{3}L + M_B \times \frac{L}{2} \times \frac{L}{3} + \frac{wL^2}{8} \times \frac{2}{3}L \times \frac{L}{2} = 0$$

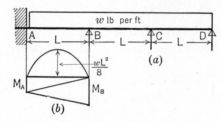

FIG. 17-13

Whence

$$2M_A + M_B = -wL^2/4 \qquad\qquad (3)$$

If equations 1, 2, and 3 are solved simultaneously, the following values are obtained:

$$M_A = -9wL^2/104 \qquad M_B = -wL^2/13 \qquad M_C = -11wL^2/104$$

PROBLEMS

17-7. The beam shown in Fig. 17-14 is continuous over two spans and is fixed at A. Calculate the bending moments at A, B, and C. Draw shear and bending-moment diagrams.

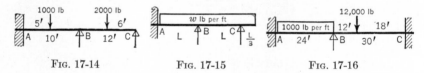

FIG. 17-14   FIG. 17-15   FIG. 17-16

17-8. The beam shown in Fig. 17-15 is continuous over two spans, is fixed at A, and overhangs at C. Calculate the moments at the supports, and draw shear and bending-moment diagrams.

17-9. The beam shown in Fig. 17-16 is continuous over two spans and is fixed at A and C. Calculate the moments at A, B, and C, and draw shear and bending-moment diagrams.

GENERAL PROBLEMS

For each of the beams shown below, calculate the bending moments at the supports. Find the shears, reactions, and intermediate bending moments. Draw shear and bending-moment diagrams. (Each problem should be done on a single sheet of paper.)

17-10. Figure 17-17.   *Ans.* $M_B = -585$ lb-ft.

17-11. Figure 17-18. Beam is 12-in. 40.8-lb I-beam. Weight of beam is included in given loads.   *Ans.* $M_B = -40,100$ lb-ft.

17-12. An 8-in. WF 17-lb beam is continuous over three spans of 20 ft each. It carries a uniformly distributed load of 600 lb per ft, which includes the weight of the beam. (*a*) Using values given in Fig. 17-10, calculate the maximum bending stress. (*b*) If three separate beams were used, what would the maximum bending stress be?

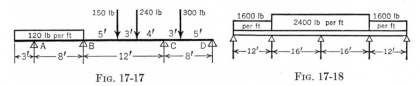

FIG. 17-17   FIG. 17-18

17-13. A continuous beam rests on three supports without overhang. The length of the left-hand span is *L* ft, and of the right-hand span 0.4*L* ft. A load *P* is applied at the midpoint of the left-hand span. How much greater is the reaction of the intermediate support than it would be if the right-hand reaction did not exist?

17-14. A continuous beam of four spans of 30 ft each has a uniform load of 1,200 lb per ft over its entire length. (*a*) Calculate the total weight of a wide-flange beam to carry this loading with an allowable stress of 18,000 psi. See Fig. 17-10 for the maximum bending moments. (*b*) If four separate 30-ft beams were used instead of a continuous beam, what total weight of steel would be required?

18

Beams of Two Materials

18-1. Introduction. Concrete and steel are very often used together in beams. Some use is also made of wood beams strengthened with strips of steel and of beams made of two different metals (Fig. 18-1). If

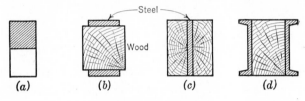

Fɪɢ. 18-1

the two materials are attached to each other so that no slipping can occur, there is a definite distribution of stress, which can be determined. A convenient way of attacking such problems is by a method which may be called "equivalent areas."

18-2. Equivalent Area in Bending. Figure 18-2a is a cross-section of a beam made of wood and steel. The common assumption that a plane

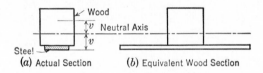

(a) Actual Section (b) Equivalent Wood Section

Fɪɢ. 18-2

section before bending remains a plane after bending is made for this type of beam. It follows that the unit stress in any fiber of the wood is proportional to its distance from the neutral axis.

Let $E_s/E_w = n$, the ratio of the modulus of elasticity of the steel to that of the wood.

A "fiber" of steel v in. from the neutral axis will have the same unit deformation as a fiber of wood v in. from the neutral axis. Consequently the unit stress in any steel fiber will be n times the unit stress in a fiber of the wood which is the same distance from the neutral axis. A unit area of steel therefore has n times as much total stress as a unit area of wood the same distance from the neutral axis. If for the area of steel at a given distance from the neutral axis there were substituted n times that area of wood (at the same distance from the neutral axis), the resisting moment of the beam would be the same. The deformations of the substituted fibers would also be the same as the deformation of the actual steel fibers.

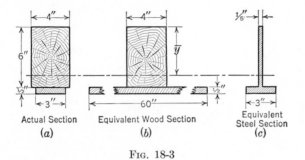

Actual Section   Equivalent Wood Section   Equivalent Steel Section
   (a)   (b)   (c)

FIG. 18-3

From these facts it follows that the position of the neutral axis and the stresses (or resisting moment) may be found by using an equivalent section of one material, as shown in Fig. 18-3b. The value of I for this equivalent section can be used in the relation $S = Mc/I$.

Example. Calculate the allowable bending moment for a beam made of a 4×6 in. timber with a $3 \times \frac{1}{2}$ in. steel strap adequately fastened to the under side, as shown in Fig. 18-3a. How does this compare with the allowable bending moment for the timber alone? Assume that allowable stresses are 1,200 psi for wood and 18,000 psi for steel. E for wood $= 1,500,000$ psi; E for steel $= 30,000,000$ psi.

Solution: Either the equivalent wood section or the equivalent steel section may be used to calculate the stresses. Using the equivalent wood section in Fig. 18-3b,

$$\bar{y} = \frac{24 \times 3 + 30 \times 6.25}{54} = \frac{72 + 187.5}{54} = 4.81 \text{ in.}$$

$$I_0 = \frac{4 \times 6 \times 6 \times 6}{12} + 24 \times 1.81^2 + \frac{60 \times \frac{1}{2} \times \frac{1}{2} \times \frac{1}{2}}{12} + 30 \times 1.44^2$$

$$= 72 + 78.7 + 0.6 + 62.2 = 213.5 \text{ in.}^4$$

This bending moment must not be greater than that which would cause a stress of 1,200 psi on the most remote fiber of the wood. The bending moment causing this stress is

$$M = \frac{SI}{c} = \frac{1,200 \times 213.5}{4.81} = 53,300 \text{ lb-in.}$$

This bending moment may be applied to the beam, provided it does not cause a stress in the steel in excess of 18,000 psi. The stress in the lowest wood fiber of the equivalent section which results from a bending moment of 53,300 lb-in. is 53,300 × (6.5 − 4.81)/213.5 = 422 psi. Since $E_s/E_w = 20$, the bending moment causing a stress of 422 psi in the wood would cause a stress of 422 × 20 = 8,440 psi in the steel, which is satisfactory. The bending moment could be increased in the ratio 18,000/8,440 without causing excessive stress in the steel, but any increase above 53,300 lb-in. would cause stresses greater than 1,200 psi in the wood fibers at the top of the beam.

For the plain timber used as a beam,

$$\frac{I}{c} = \frac{4 \times 6 \times 6}{6} = 24 \text{ in.}^3$$

$M = 1,200 \times 24 = 28,800$ lb-in., which is only about 54 per cent of the allowable bending moment for the reinforced beam.

The device of an equivalent section can be used just as effectively if the adjoining surfaces of the two materials lie in a plane parallel to the line of action of the loads, as in Fig. 18-1c and d.

PROBLEMS

18-1. A wood beam 10 × 16 in. in cross-section is reinforced by securely bolting a 6 × $\frac{1}{2}$ in. steel plate of the same length to the lower 10-in. face of the beam. Calculate the allowable bending moment if the stress in the wood is not to exceed 1,200 psi and the stress in the steel is not to exceed 15,000 psi. Assume E for the wood to be 1,200,000 psi.

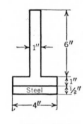

Ans. $M = 705,000$ lb-in.

18-2. Calculate the allowable bending moment if a 3 × $\frac{1}{2}$ in. plate is added to the top of the beam in Problem 18-1.

18-3. A beam is made by adequately attaching a 4 × $\frac{1}{2}$ in. steel plate to a T-section of cast iron. The cross-section is shown in Fig. 18-4. The steel is on the tension side. Calculate the maximum tensile and compressive stresses in the cast iron and the maximum tensile stress in the steel caused by a bending moment of 100,000 lb-in. Assume E for cast iron to be 0.4 of E for steel.

FIG. 18-4

18-4. Two 8-in. 13.75-lb channels are adequately bolted to an 8 × 8 in. (actual size) oak beam as shown in Fig. 18-1d. If E for oak is 1,500,000 psi, calculate the allowable bending moment. Allowable stresses are: for steel, 18,000 psi; for oak, 800 psi.   *Ans.* $M = 355,000$ lb-in.

18-3. Shearing Stress in Beams of Two Materials.

An equation giving the shearing unit stresses, horizontal and vertical, at any point in any cross-section of a beam was derived in Chapter 8. This equation, $S_s = VQ/Ib$, can also be applied to beams of two materials, by using the equivalent cross-section for a beam of one of the two materials, as explained in Art. 18-2. The reason is as follows:

In deriving the equation for shearing unit stresses, the shearing *force* on the horizontal surface of a block (which was taken as a free body) was equated to the difference between the forces exerted by the bending stresses on the ends of the block. Since the *forces* on the equivalent cross-section are the same as the forces on the cross-section of the original beam, it is apparent that the equation for shearing unit stress may be used in connection with an equivalent section.

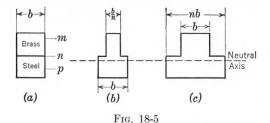

FIG. 18-5

Example. As an example, let Fig. 18-5a be the cross-section of a composite beam of brass and steel, for which values of E may be taken as 15,000,000 psi and 30,000,000 psi, respectively. The equivalent cross-section for a steel beam is shown in Fig. 18-5b, and the equivalent cross-section for a brass beam is shown in Fig. 18-5c. The neutral axes of the two equivalent cross-sections are shown and are necessarily at the same distance from the lower edges of the cross-sections.

The equation $S_s = VQ/Ib$ may be applied to *either* equivalent section, but it is somewhat simpler to use the equivalent section which has the width of the original beam at the point where the shearing stress is desired. Thus, to calculate shearing stresses at m and n, the section shown in Fig. 18-5c should be used. To calculate the shearing stress at p, the section shown in Fig. 18-5b should be used.

PROBLEM

18-5. Calculate the allowable total shear in a beam with the cross-section shown in Fig. 18-3 if the allowable shearing stress along the grain for the wood is 120 psi.

18-4. Deflection of Beams of Two Materials.
The curvature of a beam may be regarded as the result of the changes in length of the "fibers" in the beam. Since the fibers at any point in a beam of two materials change in length by the same amount as the fibers at the corresponding point in the beam of one material with "equivalent cross-section," it follows that the deflections of the two beams are the same. Consequently the deflection at any point of a beam of two materials may be found by calculating the deflection of a beam of equivalent cross-section of one material.

The methods used in this book for calculating deflections of beams are based on the relationship expressed by the equation $1/\rho = M/EI$, in which EI is a function involving the shape and size of the cross-section and the stiffness of the material. Figure 18-6 shows in (a) the cross-section of a beam of two materials (say brass and steel), in (b) the equivalent cross-section of a steel beam, and in (c) the equivalent cross-section of a brass beam. By considering elementary strips such as the one shown at a distance v from the neutral axis, it is apparent that EI for the steel beam in (b) equals EI for the brass beam in (c) and that this value of EI also equals the E for brass times the I (with respect to the neutral axis) of the area of brass plus the E for steel times the I (with

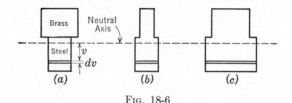

Fig. 18-6

respect to the neutral axis) of the area of steel.   The quantity EI can therefore be computed from either of the equivalent sections or from the cross-section of the actual beam after the neutral axis has been found from an equivalent cross-section.

PROBLEM

18-6. The beam shown in Fig. 18-3 is 12 ft long and carries a uniform load of 250 lb per ft.   Calculate the deflection at the midpoint. $E = 1,500,000$ psi for the wood.

18-5. Reinforced-Concrete Beams.   The most common use of two materials in beams occurs in reinforced-concrete construction.   Concrete beams without reinforcing could be used only for relatively short spans and light loads because of the weakness of concrete in tension.

In reinforced-concrete construction the reinforcing steel is placed in the forms before the concrete is poured.   When the concrete sets, it adheres very firmly to the steel.   This adherence is called "bond." Fortunately, steel and concrete contract and expand about the same amount with change in temperature.   The firm bond and the roughly equal thermal expansion of steel and concrete are both essential to the success of reinforced concrete.

Reinforcing steel is generally in the form of bars, which may be round or square, or twisted, or otherwise "deformed."   Sometimes wire mesh, welded wire mesh, or "expanded" metal is used as reinforcing.

18-6. Assumptions in Reinforced Concrete.   Because of the low tensile strength of concrete it is common practice to assume that the concrete in a reinforced-concrete beam carries *no tensile stress at all*.   It is also generally assumed that the compressive unit stress in the concrete at a given cross-section is proportional to the distance from the neutral axis.   The steel at a given cross-section is assumed to be uniformly stressed, since it is so placed that all of it is at nearly the same distance

from the neutral axis.   The force exerted by the steel is therefore the
product of the stress in the steel and the cross-sectional area of the steel
and is assumed to act at the center of the cross-section of the steel.
These assumptions are not exact but are probably as near to the truth as
the assumed values for strength and modulus of elasticity of concrete.

18-7. Resisting Moment.   The result of the assumptions made is
illustrated in Fig. 18-7b.   The unit stress in the concrete varies from
zero at the neutral axis to a maximum at the top of the beam.   This
variation of stresses is represented by short arrows, increasing in length

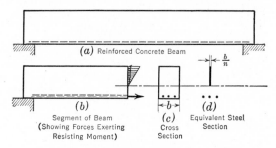

(a) Reinforced Concrete Beam

(b)
Segment of Beam
(Showing Forces Exerting
Resisting Moment)

(c)
Cross
Section

(d)
Equivalent Steel
Section

Fig. 18-7

from the neutral axis to the top.   The distance from the top of the beam
to the resultant compressive force is one-third of the distance from the
top of the beam to the neutral axis.   The resultant force equals the
product of the *average* unit compressive stress in the concrete (which is
one-half the maximum compressive stress) and the area of the cross-
section above the neutral axis.   The amount and position of this resultant as here stated occur in the solution of any problems and should
be kept in mind.   The resisting moment at any section may be regarded
as a couple.   One of the forces is the resultant of the compressive
stresses in the concrete, and the other force is the resultant of the tensile
stress in the steel.

The equivalent steel section is shown in Fig. 18-7d.   This consists of
the actual cross-sectional area of the reinforcing steel and the steel
equivalent of the concrete above the neutral axis.   This is a rectangle
with a width $1/n$ times the width of the beam.   The position of the
neutral axis of the cross-section must be computed.   It does not pass
through the centroid of the actual cross-section of the beam, but through
the centroid of the equivalent steel section.

18-8. Investigation of a Rectangular Reinforced-Concrete Beam.
The steps that are taken in the investigation of a reinforced-concrete
beam will be illustrated with a numerical example.   Let the assumed

beam be $6 \times 11\frac{1}{2}$ in. in cross-section. The reinforcing consists of three $\frac{1}{2}$-in. round rods 10 in. below the top of the beam as shown in Fig. 18-8a. Assume $E_s = 30,000,000$ and $E_c = 3,000,000$ psi, making $n = 10$. It is desired to find the maximum stress in the concrete and the stress in the steel which result from a bending moment of 95,000 lb-in. The area of steel $= 3 \times 0.196 = 0.60$ sq in.

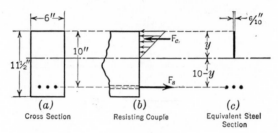

(a)
Cross Section

(b)
Resisting Couple

(c)
Equivalent Steel Section

FIG. 18-8

The position of the neutral axis is most easily found by determining the position of the centroid of the equivalent steel section, shown in Fig. 18-8c. The moment of the area above the neutral axis equals the moment of the area below it. Whence

$$\frac{6}{10} y \times \frac{y}{2} = 0.60 \, (10 - y)$$

$$0.3y^2 = 6.0 - 0.60y$$

$$y^2 + 2.0y = 20$$

Whence

$$y = 3.58 \text{ in.}$$

The resultant compressive force acts $y/3$ in. below the top of the beam. The distance between F_c and F_s is $10 - \dfrac{3.58}{3} = 10 - 1.19 =$ 8.81 in. The resisting moment equals $8.81F_c = 8.81F_s$. For the given bending moment of 95,000 lb-in.,

$$F_c = F_s = 95,000/8.81 = 10,780 \text{ lb}$$

The stress in the steel is

$$S_s = 10,780/0.60 = 17,970 \text{ psi}$$

The stress in the equivalent steel section at the top may be calculated by proportion.

$$\frac{S_s'}{S_s} = \frac{3.58}{6.42} \qquad S_s' = 17,970 \times \frac{3.58}{6.42} = 10,030 \text{ psi}$$

The actual stress in the concrete at the top of the beam is $\frac{1}{10}$ of the stress at the top of the equivalent steel section.

$$S_c = 10,030/10 = 1,003 \text{ psi}$$

The stress in the steel and in the concrete are reasonable stresses, as may be seen by referring to the table of allowable stresses in Art. 18-10.

18-9. Determination of Cross-Section of a Rectangular Reinforced-Concrete Beam. At the cross-section of maximum bending moment, safety requires that the materials in a concrete beam be not over-stressed, and economy requires that they be not greatly understressed. The designer should meet both these conditions. A method of determining a suitable cross-section to resist a given bending moment will now be illustrated.

Let it be assumed that the beam is required to carry a bending moment of 418,000 lb-in. Allowable stresses are 1,000 psi compression in concrete and 18,000 psi tension in steel. Use $n = E_s/E_c = 10$.

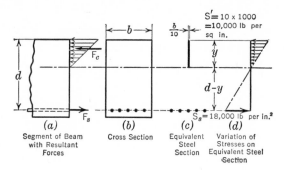

(a) Segment of Beam with Resultant Forces   (b) Cross Section   (c) Equivalent Steel Section   (d) Variation of Stresses on Equivalent Steel Section

FIG. 18-9

Let y in. be the unknown depth from the top of the cross-section to the neutral axis. The equivalent steel section is shown in Fig. 18-9c, and the corresponding stresses are shown in Fig. 18-9d. The stress in the equivalent steel at the top of the beam would be $10 \times 1,000 = 10,000$ psi compression, if the actual stress in the concrete is 1,000 psi.

Since a plane section before bending remains a plane after bending, it follows that the stress at any point in the equivalent steel section is proportional to the distance from the neutral axis. In this beam the position of the neutral axis is determined by the fact that the stress at the top of the section will be 10,000 psi when the stress in steel is 18,000 psi, and by the additional fact that both these stresses are proportional to the distances from the neutral axis.

Hence, by similar triangles, as shown in Fig. 18-9d,

$$\frac{y}{d-y} = \frac{10,000}{18,000}$$

$$18,000y = 10,000d - 10,000y$$

$$28,000y = 10,000d$$

$$y = \frac{10,000}{28,000}d = 0.357d \text{ in.}$$

The distance between the resultant compressive force F_c and the tensile force F_s is

$$d - \frac{y}{3} = d - 0.119d = 0.881d \text{ in.}$$

The resultant compressive force is

$$F_c = \frac{10,000}{2} \times \frac{b}{10} \times 0.357d = 178bd$$

The resisting moment is F_c times the distance between F_c and F_s. This must equal 418,000 lb-in.

Therefore $178bd \times 0.881d = 418,000.$

$$bd^2 = \frac{418,000}{178 \times 0.881} = 2,660 \text{ in.}^3$$

Any cross-section for which $bd^2 = 2,660$ will meet the requirements. It is apparent, however, that, the deeper the beam, the larger will be the moment arm of the resisting moment and the smaller the force.   A deep beam will therefore require less steel and less concrete than a shallower beam.   There are practical limits to the depth.   These will not be discussed here.   A satisfactory cross-section which is practicable and reasonably economical is one in which d is about $1\frac{1}{2}b$.

If these proportions are chosen,

$$bd^2 = \tfrac{9}{4}b^3 = 2,660$$

$$b^3 = 1,182$$

$$b = 10.6$$

If b is made 11 in. even,

$$d^2 = 2,660/11 = 242$$

$$d = 15.6 \text{ in. from top of beam to } center \ of \ steel$$

The moment arm of the resisting couple is $0.881 \times 15.6 = 13.74$ in.

The cross-sectional area of steel can be calculated from the relation $18,000A_s \times 13.74 = 418,000$, giving

$$A_s = 418,000/(18,000 \times 13.74) = 1.69 \text{ sq in.}$$

If round rods are used (the available diameters being in multiples of $\frac{1}{8}$ in.), it may not be possible to provide exactly 1.69 sq in. of steel. For three suitable sizes of round rods the areas of steel that can be used are:

6 rods $\frac{5}{8}$ in. in diameter $= 1.86$ sq in.

4 rods $\frac{3}{4}$ in. in diameter $= 1.76$ sq in.

3 rods $\frac{7}{8}$ in. in diameter $= 1.80$ sq in.

If the rods $\frac{3}{4}$ in. in diameter are selected, there is a very slight excess of steel. The resulting unit stress in the steel will be slightly less than 18,000 psi, the stress in the concrete will be slightly less than 1,000 psi, and the position of the neutral axis will be lowered a little. These changes are very small and may be neglected. There should be $1\frac{1}{2}$ in. of concrete below the rods to insure adequate "bond" and protection to the reinforcing. The total depth of the beam will be $15.6 + \frac{3}{8} + 1.5 = 17.5$ in.

PROBLEMS

18-7. A rectangular reinforced-concrete beam is 10 in. wide, 20 in. deep. There are four $\frac{3}{4}$-in. square reinforcing rods 18.25 in. below the top of the beam. Calculate, by the method of Art. 18-8, the allowable bending moment if stress in the concrete is not to exceed 1,000 psi and stress in the steel is not to exceed 18,000 psi ($n = 10$).

18-8. By the method of Art. 18-9, find the dimensions of the cross-section of a reinforced-concrete beam to carry a bending moment of 260,000 lb-in. Also select suitable square steel rods for reinforcing. (The bottom of the rods is to be $1\frac{1}{4}$ in. above the bottom of the beam.) Allowable stresses are 18,000 psi for steel, and 1,000 psi for concrete ($n = 12$). Make depth of beam approximately twice width. Compare the weight of this beam with the weight of a steel I-beam which will carry this bending moment with a stress not exceeding 18,000 psi.

18-10. Allowable Stresses for Reinforced-Concrete Beams. Concrete can be made of different strengths by varying the proportions of cement, aggregate, and water. In general, the allowable stress depends on the specified strength of the concrete. There are also different grades of steel used for reinforcing bars. As an example of allowable stresses those specified by the American Concrete Institute in the A.C.I. Building Code (1951) are tabulated.

Compressive strength of concrete f_c'	2,000	2,500	3,000	3,750
$n = 30,000/f_c'$	15	12	10	8
Allowable compressive stress $f_c = 0.45f_c'$	900	1,125	1,350	1,688
Allowable shearing stress V_c (beams with no web reinforcement)	60	75	90	113
Allowable shearing stress (beams with properly designed web reinforcement)	240	300	360	450

Reinforcing bars, hard grades, allowable tensile stress = 20,000 psi.
Reinforcing bars, structural grades, allowable tensile stress = 18,000 psi.

18-11. Formulas for Reinforced-Concrete Beams. Although the method developed in Arts. 18-8 and 18-9 can be used in the design and investigation of concrete beams, it is customary in practice to make use of a number of formulas which are derived from the principles just developed. If specific values for known quantities are substituted in these formulas, required values can be found. The terminology and symbols used are quite well established. The principles discussed in the preceding articles will now be applied to the derivation of some of these formulas, in order that the student may become familiar with them and with the symbols.

Study of the following articles will not qualify one to design concrete structures, but it should form a foundation for a more intelligent reading of the literature of the subject and for further study.

The following notation is commonly used:

b = width of beam (inches).

d = depth of beam *to center of reinforcing* (inches).

A_s = area of cross-section of reinforcing steel (square inches).

p = "per cent" of reinforcing. Actually not a percentage, but the ratio of the area of reinforcing steel to the area bd. Hence $A_s = pbd$.

kd = distance from top of beam to neutral axis (inches).

jd = moment arm of resisting couple, or distance (inches) between resultant compressive force and resultant tensile force.

$n = E_s/E_c$, the ratio of the modulus of elasticity of steel to that of concrete.

f_c = compressive unit stress in the extreme fibers of concrete.

f_s = tensile unit stress in reinforcing steel.

(Note that k and j are always less than unity.)

18-12. Position of Neutral Axis, Given *n* and *p*. For a given n (ratio of E_s to E_c) and a given "percentage" p of steel there is a definite value of k. When this is found, the distance from the top of the beam to the neutral axis is determined by multiplying the depth of the beam (to the center of the steel) by k. A formula will now be derived which gives the value of k in terms of n and p. In Fig. 18-10a a typical cross-section of a reinforced-concrete beam is shown, and the resisting moment or couple is shown in Fig. 18-10b.

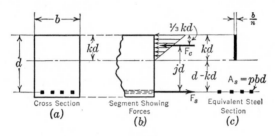

FIG. 18-10

Since $\Sigma H = 0$, $F_c = F_s$. Therefore $kbdf_c/2 = pbdf_s$, from which

$$f_c/f_s = 2p/k$$

Since, in the equivalent steel section, the stress is proportional to the distance from the neutral axis,

$$\frac{nf_c}{f_s} = \frac{kd}{d - kd} = \frac{k}{1 - k} \qquad \text{or} \qquad \frac{f_c}{f_s} = \frac{k}{n(1 - k)}$$

Equating these values of f_c/f_s,

$$\frac{k}{n(1 - k)} = \frac{2p}{k}$$

whence

$$k^2 = 2pn - 2pnk$$

Solving,

$$k = \sqrt{2pn + p^2n^2} - pn$$

(18-1)

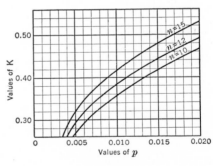

FIG. 18-11

Values of n corresponding to different strengths of concrete as specified by the A.C.I. Building Code are given in the table in Art. 18-10.

Values of n of 10, 12, or 15 apply to the concrete usually specified in reinforced-concrete construction.

In the diagram (Fig. 18-11) values of k are plotted for different values of p and for values of n of 10, 12, and 15. From this diagram, values of k can be found without calculation with sufficient accuracy.

18-13. Balanced Reinforcing. Building codes and other specifications state allowable stresses for reinforcing steel and for concrete of given strength or proportions. If the percentage of reinforcing steel is chosen at random, the bending moment which stresses the concrete to the specified value will cause a stress in the steel more or less than the specified allowable stress for steel.

For a given value of n there is only one value of p which will result in a beam section in which the allowable bending moment causes the allowable stresses in both the steel and the concrete. This value of p gives the most economical cross-section, since both materials are working at the allowed limit. This value of p can be found as follows: In Art. 18-12 it was shown that

$$\frac{f_c}{f_s} = \frac{k}{n(1-k)}$$

from which $kf_s = nf_c - nkf_c$. Dividing by nf_c and solving for k,

$$k = \frac{1}{(f_s/nf_c) + 1} \tag{18-2}$$

The requirement of statics that $F_c = F_s$ gives

$$kdbf_c/2 = pbdf_s$$

from which
$$p = kf_c/2f_s \tag{18-3}$$

From equation 18-2, k for balanced reinforcing is calculated. The value of p may then be read from the curve of Fig. 18-11 or calculated from equation 18-3.

18-14. Formulas for Investigation of a Beam. Several formulas can be derived for the allowable resisting moment (which equals the allowable bending moment) in a concrete beam of given cross-section and with a given amount of reinforcing, provided the value of n is known or assumed. Since the amount of reinforcing is known, the value of p can be determined. The value of p and n fix the value of k, as shown in Art. 18-12. With these terms known, the allowable bending moment can be expressed either in terms of the allowable stress in the steel or of the allowable stress in the concrete. For a given unit stress in the steel the resisting moment equals the resultant force exerted by the steel multiplied by the distance between the resultant tensile and compressive forces. Hence

$$M = F_s jd = f_s A_s jd$$

But

$$A_s = pbd \qquad \text{so that} \qquad M = f_s pbjd^2$$

Substituting $1 - k/3$ for j (see Fig. 18-10),

$$M = f_s p b d^2 \left(1 - \frac{k}{3}\right)$$

In a similar way the resisting moment in terms of the maximum stress in the concrete is

$$M = F_c j d = \frac{f_c}{2} b k d (jd) = \frac{1}{2} f_c k j (b d^2) \tag{18-4}$$

These two equations for the bending moment can, of course, be used for the determination of the stresses caused in the steel and the concrete of a given beam by a given bending moment.

18-15. Steps in the Design of a Concrete Beam. The starting point in the design of a reinforced-concrete beam which is to resist a known bending moment is the selection of the allowable stresses to be used and a decision as to the most probable value of n. Generally these stresses and n are prescribed by a building code or some other specification. Sometimes the designer must himself decide on appropriate values. When the allowable stresses and the value of n have been decided, the value of p for greatest economy can be determined from the equations of Art. 18-13. When the value of p has been selected, the value of k is found by the formula developed in Art. 18-12, or it may be read from Fig. 18-11. With all the foregoing quantities known, the next step in the design is the determination of the dimensions b and d of the concrete cross-section. (These determine the cross-section of the steel, since p is known.) Either of the foregoing formulas may be used to determine the product $b d^2$. With this product found, an assumption can be made as to the relative values of b and d and each dimension determined. With b, d, and p known, suitable reinforcing bars are selected. After this is done, shearing and bond stresses must also be investigated and provided for. These steps are not within the scope of this book.

The design of a concrete structure is complicated by many considerations which cannot be taken up in a book of this scope. The foregoing articles have developed the relationships which determine the tensile stress in the steel and the compressive stress in the concrete due to the bending of a rectangular beam. There is not space here to do more than merely mention other problems in concrete design, such as provision of reinforcement to help resist the shearing stress in a beam, methods of securing proper bond between steel and concrete to keep the steel from slipping, and the design of beams having a T-shaped cross-section.

PROBLEMS

18-9. A rectangular concrete beam, shown in Fig. 18-12, is 14 in. wide and d is 24 in. At the center cross-section there are four steel rods, 1 in. square. Calculate the maximum bending moment for stresses not exceeding 18,000 psi in the steel and 1,000 psi in the concrete. Assume $n = 10$.

Fig. 18-12

Ans. $M = 1,350,000$ lb-in.

18-10. Solve Problem 18-9 if the beam has five rods 1 in. square, instead of four.

18-11. Calculate the depth and the number of square inches of reinforcing steel for a beam 10 in. wide which is to resist a bending moment of 35,000 lb-ft. Allowable stresses are $f_c = 1,000$ psi, and $f_s = 18,000$ psi. Assume $n = 10$. Use balanced reinforcing.

18-12. In Fig. 18-12 the depth $d = 14$ in., $b = 10$ in., and the reinforcing consists of three rods $\frac{3}{4}$ in. square. Allowable stresses are $f_c = 1,125$ psi, $f_s = 18,000$ psi, $n = 12$. Calculate the allowable M.

18-13. In Fig. 18-12 the depth $d = 20$ in., $b = 12$ in., and the reinforcing consists of four rods $\frac{3}{4}$ in. square. Allowable $f_c = 900$ psi, $f_s = 18,000$ psi, $n = 15$. Calculate the allowable M.

18-14. Calculate the area of steel for balanced reinforcing if, in Fig. 18-12, $b = 12$ in., $d = 18$ in., $f_c = 1,125$ psi, $f_s = 20,000$ psi, $n = 12$. With this area of steel calculate the allowable M.   *Ans.* $M = 765,000$ lb-in.

18-15. Same as Problem 18-14 but $f_c = 900$ psi, $f_s = 18,000$ psi, and $n = 15$.

18-16. A beam is to carry a bending moment of 58,000 lb-ft. Depth $d = 18$ in., $f_c = 1,000$ psi, $f_s = 18,000$ psi, $n = 12$. Calculate the area of steel for balanced reinforcing and the width b of the beam.

19

Beams (Additional Topics)

19-1. Introduction. This chapter is divided into the following parts:

Maximum Normal and Shearing Stresses in Beams.
Longitudinal Shear in "Built-up" Beams.
Shearing Deflection of Beams.
Beams of Materials That Do Not Follow Hooke's Law.
Buckling of Beam Flanges and Webs.
Curved Beams.
Beams with Loads Inclined to The Principal Axes of Inertia.
Beams with Cross-Sections Having No Vertical Axis of Symmetry;
   Shear Center.

The first three of these divisions treat problems in the design or use of beams that were not considered sufficiently fundamental for inclusion in the chapters where ordinary problems in beam stresses and deflections were discussed. The remaining five divisions discuss situations to which the ordinary flexure formula, $S = Mc/I$, does not apply, and present modifications of the basic formula or present supplemental formulas that must also be used; or they specify and discuss the conditions that must be introduced if the ordinary formula is to be valid.

MAXIMUM NORMAL AND SHEARING STRESSES IN BEAMS

19-2. Maximum Stresses in Beams. It is evident from the results of Art. 15-5 that the "bending stress" at a given point in a beam calculated by the flexure formula is not the maximum stress at that point if shearing stress exists at that point. It is also true that the shearing unit stress, horizontal and vertical, at a point in a beam calculated from $S_s = VQ/Ib$ is not the maximum shearing stress at that point if tensile or compressive stress exists at that point.

Before discussing the importance of these maximum stresses, an example will be solved to illustrate the calculation of maximum stresses in a steel beam.

Example. An 18-in. WF 96-lb beam is used as a cantilever projecting 4.96 ft and carrying a uniformly distributed total load of 111,600 lb. Determine the maximum normal and shearing stresses at the fixed end. (This loading is such as to give a maximum bending stress of 18,000 psi and a shearing stress on the gross area of the web of 12,000 psi, which are the allowable stresses of the New York City Building Code of 1945.)

Solution: The dimensions and properties of this beam are as follows: depth of beam, 18.16 in.; width of flange, 11.75 in.; thickness of web, 0.512 in.; thickness of flange, 0.831 in.; I_1, 1,674.7 in.[4]; I/c, 184.4 in.[3].

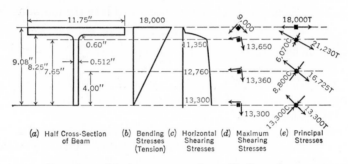

| (a) Half Cross-Section of Beam | (b) Bending Stresses (Tension) | (c) Horizontal Shearing Stresses | (d) Maximum Shearing Stresses | (e) Principal Stresses |

FIG. 19–1.   Maximum stresses in a wide-flange beam.

Figure 19-1a shows the upper half of the cross-section of the beam; in (b) is shown the variation of the bending stress; and in (c), the variation of the horizontal shearing stress. For four points on the cross-section the maximum normal stresses (principal stresses) are shown in (e), and for the same four points the maximum shearing stresses are shown in (d).

The computations for these values at the point on the web where the fillets begin will be shown. The other values are found in a similar way.

$$S_s = \frac{VQ}{Ib} = \frac{111,600(11.75 \times 0.831 \times 8.664 + 0.60 \times 0.512 \times 7.949)}{1,674.7 \times 0.512}$$

$$= 11,350 \text{ psi}$$

$$S_t = \frac{My}{I} = \frac{3,320,000 \times 7.649}{1,674.7} = 15,170 \text{ psi}$$

$$S_{s \text{ max}} = \sqrt{(S_t/2)^2 + S_s^2} = \sqrt{7,585^2 + 11,350^2} = 13,650 \text{ psi}$$

$$S_n = \frac{S_t}{2} \pm S_{s \text{ max}} = 7,580 \pm 13,650 = +21,230 \text{ psi, in tension}$$

$$\text{or} = -6,070 \text{ psi, compression}$$

It will be noticed that, although this beam is not overstressed according to the New York City Building Code of 1945, the maximum tensile stress calculated above exceeds the allowable bending stress by 18 per cent. Structural specifications do not specify that the maximum tensile stress in a beam shall not exceed the specified allowable stress, but instead it is specified that the maximum *bending stress on the extreme fibers* shall not exceed a stated allowable stress (by *bending stress* is meant the stress computed by $S = Mc/I$). This may be regarded as one example of stresses greater than the nominal bending and shear stresses usually calculated and limited by design specifications. The factor of safety may be expected to provide for such higher stresses in ordinary circumstances.

Although the loading assumed above may occur, as in footings, in the majority of beams such unfavorable combinations of large bending moment and large shear on the same cross-section are not found. For many beams supported at the ends the shear is small at points where bending moments are large, and vice versa. Furthermore, on any cross-section of most beams the shearing stress is small at points where bending stresses are large. (The wide-flange beam considered in the

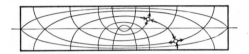

FIG. 19–2.   Directions of principal stresses.

example has exceptionally high shearing stresses in the web near the flanges because it combines heavy flanges with a thin web.) In the majority of beams, because of the conditions just mentioned, the maximum bending stresses in the extreme fibers are, in fact, the maximum principal stresses.

Also in the majority of beams the maximum *total shear* occurs at a section where the bending moment is small; and on the cross-section where the greatest total shear occurs the maximum shearing stress occurs at the neutral axis, where there is no bending stress. Consequently, in the majority of beams the maximum longitudinal (and vertical) shearing stress is, in fact, the maximum shearing stress in the beam. A designer should know when this will not be true.

A more general study of the principal stresses in beams is of help in understanding the behavior of beams and their possible failure. Figure 19-2 represents a side view of a beam of rectangular cross-section carrying a uniformly distributed load. For simplicity it will be assumed that the load carried by the beam is its own weight only and that it is supported at the ends without concentrated reactions.[1]

---

[1] Concentrated loads and reactions cause local stresses which will not be considered here. A uniformly distributed load resting on the top of a beam also causes compressive stresses on the top surface which extend into the beam. In order to avoid for the present the complication of local stresses due to reactions, the beam may be thought of as the middle segment of a beam fixed at both ends, the segment extending between the two points of zero bending moment.

The lines drawn on the face of the beam indicate the direction of the principal stresses, the tangent and normal to a curve at any point being the direction of the two principal stresses at that point. The curves concave downward indicate the directions of compressive principal stresses (there is tensile stress normal to the curve at every point, its magnitude being zero at all points above the neutral axis on a vertical line at the midpoint of the beam). In the same way the curves concave upward follow the direction of tensile principal stresses. Wherever a curve of one set crosses a curve of the other set, the intersection is necessarily at a right angle. The shear being zero at the midsection of the beam, the principal stresses at the midsection are the bending stresses calculated from $S = My/I$. Therefore all curves are horizontal at the midpoint of the beam. At the end of the beam the bending moment is zero, and the principal stresses are those resulting from shearing stresses on vertical and horizontal planes. These principal stresses are inclined 45° to the horizontal and vertical and are equal in intensity to the unit shearing stress at any point. Since bending stresses are zero along the neutral axis, the principal stresses there result from shear alone, and all the lines cross the neutral axis with an inclination of 45°. It should be kept clearly in mind that these lines are not lines of constant intensity of stress.

The occurrence of the tensile principal stresses inclined 45° at the ends of the beam is of significance in beams of materials with low tensile strength, such as concrete. In rein-forced-concrete beams steel rods are embedded in the concrete to carry the tensile stresses. These are placed near the bottom of the beam, if the bending moment is positive. Near the ends, some are bent upwards at an angle of about 45°, as shown in Fig. 19-3.

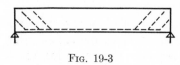

FIG. 19-3

This inclined reinforcing is commonly called "shear" reinforcing, but it actually resists the tensile stresses resulting from shearing stresses. The concrete itself has ample compressive strength to resist the compression stresses caused by the shear.

It should be understood that the distribution of stresses in a composite beam is not exactly the same as in a beam of homogeneous material.

PROBLEM

19-1. Calculate the maximum shearing and normal stress at a point 6.5 in. above the neutral axis at the cross-section of the beam considered in the example of Art. 19-2. Also calculate the inclinations of the planes on which these stresses act, and represent stresses as acting on small cubes properly oriented.

19-3. Connection of Cover Plates to Flanges. Figure 19-4a represents the cross-section of an I-beam with a cover plate riveted to each flange to increase the section modulus of the beam, a method frequently used. As the beam bends (it may be assumed that the loads are applied to the web of the I-beam), the compressive stresses in the top cover plate are the result of the forces exerted on it by the rivets, which

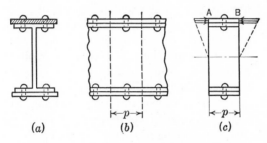

FIG. 19-4.   Rolled beam with cover plates.

serve the same function as the longitudinal shearing stresses in a beam made of one piece.   The problem is to determine the necessary spacing of the rivets.

It follows from the relation already established (Chapter 8) between the vertical shear V and the longitudinal shearing stresses that the rivets should be most closely spaced where the vertical shear V is greatest.

As shown in Art. 8-7, the force on the B end of the segment of cover plate (Fig. 19-4c) is $F_B = M_B Q/I$, where Q is the statical moment of the cross-section of the cover plate with respect to the neutral axis of the entire cross-section.[2] On the A end the force $F_A = M_A Q/I$. Hence the force which the rivets between A and B must exert is $F_B - F_A = (M_B - M_A)Q/I$. Since the change in bending moment equals the area of the shear diagram between the two points A and B, $M_B - M_A = pV_{av}$, in which V_{av} is the average value of V in the distance AB. Hence, $F_B - F_A = pV_{av}Q/I$.   This gives the value of the force which must be supplied by the rivets in a distance of p in.   If R is the value of one rivet in shear or bearing (whichever is least), and if there are n rivets in a group ($n = 2$, in the case illustrated), $nR = pV_{av}Q/I$, or $p = nRI/V_{av}Q$ for the distance between groups of rivets.

Practical considerations limit the distance between rivet groups where the vertical shear is small.   Specifications for structural details

[2] Q is computed from the gross area of the cross-section of the cover plate, making no allowance for the rivet holes.

contain rules governing such matters. For instance, it is frequently specified that for $\frac{7}{8}$- or $\frac{3}{4}$-in. rivets the pitch shall not exceed 6 in., or 16 times the thickness of the cover plate, whichever is less.

When a cover plate is to be *welded* to the flange of an I-beam, the welds must furnish the force provided by the rivets in the foregoing discussion. If p, the unit length of flange to be considered, is taken as 1 ft or 12 in., and R is the allowable load on 1 in. of fillet

of a given size, then n, the number of inches of fillet per foot length of flange, is given by $n = 12V_{av}Q/RI$. Specifications establish minimum allowable lengths of fillet and maximum spacings between welds.

19-4. Connection of Flange to Web of Girder. A plate girder is a "built-up" beam consisting of a web plate to which angles and generally one or more cover plates are attached to form each flange (Fig. 19-5). If loads are applied to the web of the girder, as in Art. 19-3, the spacing of rivets is given by the same equation

FIG. 19-5. Plate girder.

$p = nRI/V_{av}Q$ (in this case, of course, Q is the statical moment of the cross-section of the entire flange). It should be remembered that the rivets are in double shear. The value of a rivet will generally be determined by bearing against the web.

PROBLEMS

19-2. A plate girder is made up of a $48 \times \frac{1}{2}$ in. web plate, and each flange consists of two angles $6 \times 6 \times \frac{3}{4}$ in. and one cover plate 14×1 in. arranged as in Fig. 19-5. At a section where the total shear is 256,000 lb, determine the required spacing of the pairs of rivets connecting the cover plate to the angles. Rivets are $\frac{7}{8}$ in.; $S_s = 13,500$ psi; and $S_c = 27,000$ psi. The distance "back to back of angles" is $48\frac{1}{2}$ in.

19-3. Calculate the required distance between the rivets connecting the flange to the web of the girder of Problem 19-2.

19-4. A 14×1 in. cover plate is to be welded to each flange of a 16-in. WF 78-lb beam. Calculate the length of $\frac{5}{16}$-in. fillet required per foot of beam to attach one cover plate if the shear causes an average stress of 12,000 psi over the web.

Ans. $n = 16.0$ in.

SHEARING DEFLECTION OF BEAMS

19-5. Shearing Deflection of Beams. The methods of calculating beam deflections which were explained in Chapter 10 give the deflection due to bending only. Additional deflections result from shearing deformation. Usually these deflections due to shear are so small in comparison with deflections due to bending that they can be disregarded. In short, deep beams, however, the deflections due to shear may sometimes be important.

Shearing deflections of beams are more difficult to calculate than bending deflections. One method is to equate the work done by the load as the shearing deflection takes place to the strain energy in the beam due to shearing stresses and deformations.

For a beam of rectangular cross-section the maximum shearing stress is $\frac{3}{2}V/A$ at the neutral axis. The stress varies to zero at the top and bottom of the cross-section.

In Art. 16-10 it was shown that the energy of deformation in a unit volume subject to shearing stress is $U = S_s{}^2/2E_s$. For an elementary volume dv the energy is $S_s{}^2\, dv/2E_s$. The shear energy in a "slice" of a rectangular beam can be calculated by integrating $S_s{}^2\, dv/2E_s$ so as to include all elementary volumes that make up the slice. In doing this S_s may be expressed as a function of y, the distance from the neutral axis to a point in the cross-section. The distance y is the variable. It is thus found that the shear energy stored in such a slice of a rectangular beam is $\dfrac{3V^2\, dx}{5bhE_s}$, in which dx is the thickness of the slice and V is the shear at the cross-section.

To compute the shearing deflection Δ_s at the end of a cantilever beam of rectangular cross-section with a load P at the end it should be noted that $V = P$ for all cross-sections of the beam. Equating the "external" work with the strain energy,

$$\frac{P\Delta_s}{2} = \frac{3P^2}{5bhE_s}\int_0^L dx = \frac{3P^2L}{5bhE_s}$$

hence

$$\Delta_s = 6PL/5bhE_s$$

It is useful to compare this shearing deflection with the bending deflection Δ_b for the same beam and loading, which is $\Delta_b = PL^3/3EI$. For a rectangular cross-section $I = bh^3/12$. Hence

$$\frac{\Delta_s}{\Delta_b} = \frac{6PL/5bhE_s}{12PL^3/3Ebh^3} = \frac{3E}{10E_s}\left(\frac{h}{L}\right)^2$$

This shows that the relative importance of shearing deflection decreases very rapidly as the slenderness of the beam increases.

The expression $\Delta_s/\Delta_b = k(E/E_s)(d/L)^2$ is a general expression true for all beams of constant cross-section. The value of k is determined by the shape of the cross-section, the arrangement of the supports, and the kind of loading. Values of k for four cases are tabulated below.[3]

[3] Maurer and Withey, *Strength of Materials*, John Wiley & Sons.

	Cross-sections	
	Circular	Rectangular
Cantilever beam, load at end	$k = \frac{5}{24}$	$k = \frac{3}{10}$
Simple beam, load at midpoint	$k = \frac{5}{6}$	$k = \frac{6}{5}$

PROBLEM

19-5. Two aluminum beams each 3×4 in. in cross-section rest on supports which are 20 in. and 40 in. apart, respectively. Each carries a load of 12,000 lb at the midpoint. Calculate the deflection due to bending and the deflection due to shearing for each beam. Assume 4-in. sides vertical. $E = 10,600,000$ psi, $E_s = 4,000,000$ psi.

BEAMS OF MATERIALS THAT DO NOT FOLLOW HOOKE'S LAW

19-6. Beams of Materials That Do Not Follow Hooke's Law. Beams made of materials, for example cast iron or concrete, for which the stress-strain diagram is not a straight line, or beams stressed beyond the proportional limit, do not conform to the common theory of flexure, and the stresses are not correctly given by the common flexure formula.

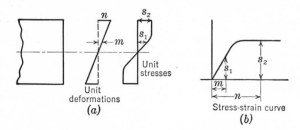

Fig. 19-6. Stress distribution in beam of ductile steel, stressed above point.

The assumption that transverse sections which were planes before bending remain planes after bending is made for beams of such materials and is closely true. It follows from this assumption that deformations of fibers vary directly as their distances from the neutral axis. However, since in the cases under consideration the stresses are not proportional to the deformations, the variation of the tensile and compressive stresses is not the straight-line variation that follows from the same assumption in the common beam theory.

In Fig. 19-6 is shown a stress-variation diagram for a steel beam stressed beyond the yield point. For ductile steel with a pronounced yield point the unit stress remains constant for a considerable increase in unit deformation after the yield point has been reached. After the stress in the extreme fibers in a beam of this steel reaches the yield point, considerable further bending does not increase the stress, but more and more of the cross-section is stressed to the yield point as the bending moment increases. The resisting moment increases only slightly as this change takes place. This results in a large increase in deflection with small increase in load; or, in other words, there is a yielding in bending analogous to that in tension.

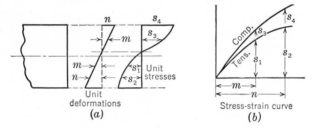

FIG. 19-7. Shift of neutral axis in beam of material with different moduli of elasticity in tension and compression.

The tensile and compressive stress-strain curves for a cast iron are shown in Fig. 19-7, together with diagrams showing deformation and bending stresses in a cast-iron beam. Since for cast iron the modulus of elasticity is greater in compression than in tension, it follows that, for the same unit deformation, the compressive stress is greater than the tensile stress. The sum of the tensile forces, however, equals the sum of the compressive forces, and consequently the neutral axis shifts so as to decrease the area in compression and increase the area in tension as shown in Fig. 19-7a.

BUCKLING OF BEAM FLANGES AND WEBS

19-7. Sidewise Buckling of Compression Flange. If a long beam with a compression flange which is not supported against sidewise deflection is gradually loaded until it fails, it is probable that the failure will result from a sidewise "buckling" of the compressive flange. This can be illustrated by a simple experiment. The ends of a thin wooden yardstick are rested on two tables about 30 in. apart. The stick is kept resting on its edge by holding the ends. A downward force is applied at the midpoint by pulling vertically on a string tied around the yardstick. (The string is used because it offers no lateral support.) As the pull increases, the top surface of the stick will rather suddenly deflect sidewise. This sidewise buckling is greatest at the midpoint, decreasing toward the ends.

An unsupported compression flange of a beam is somewhat comparable to a column, stiffened in the direction of its least r by the web of the beam. (The web, in addition, stiffens the flange somewhat against sidewise deflection, but only slightly.) The loading is not that of the columns considered in Chapter 12, since, instead of being applied at the ends and therefore being the same at all cross-sections, the load is applied all along the length of the flange and the load on any cross-section of the flange is proportional to the bending moment at that section. The theoretical analysis of the stress in such a flange is very complex, and in the design of beams with unsupported compression flanges, an empirical procedure analogous to that used in column design is ordinarily resorted to.

Because of the great complexity of the situation presented by an unsupported compression flange, it is difficult to say just what reduction should be made in the *average* stress in any flange in order to have some particular *maximum* stress value. This is the same difficulty that exists in column design. More important than making just the proper reduction is recognition of the danger inherent in a narrow (easily deflected) unsupported compression flange, the avoidance of such flanges where possible, and the making of an adequate allowance for the condition where it cannot be avoided.

The American Railway Engineering Association specifications for steel building frames (1951) provide that for structural steel beams no reduction in compression flange stress need be made in beams in which the ratio L/b (the unsupported length of the flange divided by the flange width) is less than 15. It is also specified that no beam with L/b greater than 40 shall be used. In designing or investigating beams with value of L/b between 15 and 40, the allowable compressive bending stress is given by the formula

$$S = \frac{22,500}{1 + (1/1,800)(L/b)^2}$$

In this equation S is the stress to be used in the formula $I/c = M/S$. For $L/b = 15$, this formula gives $S = 20,000$ psi, which is the allowable bending stress for beams with the compression flange adequately supported. This equation is similar in form to a Rankine column formula.

The 1947 specifications of the American Institute of Steel Construction permit allowable compressive stresses on extreme fibers of rolled sections, plate girders, and built-up members as follows:

If $\dfrac{ld}{bt}$ does not exceed 600, allowable $S = 20,000$ psi

If $\dfrac{ld}{bt}$ exceeds 600, allowable $S = \dfrac{12,000,000}{ld/bt}$

in which l is the unsupported length of the compression flange in inches, d is the depth of the member, b is the width of the compression flange, and t is the thickness of the compression flange.   The depth of the beam is introduced because a deep beam is more likely to deflect sidewise than a shallow beam of the same width and length.   The thickness of the flange is introduced because a compression flange that is very thin relative to its projecting width may fail by "wrinkling" or bending locally where the stress is high.   The outer edge of the thin flange acts somewhat like a slender column.   The A.I.S.C. handbook gives, for all wide-flange beams, curves in which abscissas are unsupported lengths and ordinates are allowable net bending moments (above that due to the weight of the beam) as limited by reduced compressive stress.

Example 1.   An 18-in. WF 50-lb beam is simply supported and has a span of 22 ft.   If the top flange is not braced laterally, find the greatest bending moment to which the beam may be subjected, using the A.R.E.A. formula.

Solution: For this beam $b = 7\frac{1}{2}$ in., and therefore $\dfrac{L}{b} = \dfrac{22 \times 12}{7.5} = 35.2$.   Therefore the allowable compressive bending stress is to be limited to

$$S = \frac{22,500}{1 + (1/1800)\,(35.2)^2} = 13,300 \text{ psi}$$

For this beam $I/c = 89.0$ in.[3]   Hence the allowable bending moment is

$$M = SI/c = 13,300 \times 89.0 = 1,180,000 \text{ lb-in.} = 98,600 \text{ lb-ft}$$

Because of lack of support of the compression flange, the capacity of the beam is only 67 per cent of that of a beam with L/b of 15 or less.

Example 2.   Determine the bending moment permitted by the A.I.S.C. specifications in the beam described in Example 1.

From the A.I.S.C. handbook the thickness of the flange of this beam is found to be 0.570 in.   Hence

$$\frac{12,000,000}{ld/bt} = \frac{12,000,000}{22 \times 12 \times 18.0/(7.5 \times 0.570)} = 10,800 \text{ psi}$$

$$M = SI/c = 10,800 \times 89.0 = 962,000 \text{ lb-in.} = 80,200 \text{ lb-ft}$$

The ratio of the allowable bending moment for the unsupported beam to the allowable bending moment for the same beam with the compression flange adequately supported is $10,800/20,000 = 0.54$ according to the A.I.S.C. specifications.

As in the case of a column, the *design* of a beam with an unsupported compression flange must be carried out by a process of trial and correction.

Fortunately in most structures the beams are well supported laterally. In buildings, the floor (or roof) generally rests on and supports the compression flange.   Where this is not the situation, it is often possible to

provide bracing between two beams so that the two beams, together
with the system of bracing, form a sufficiently rigid horizontal truss,
which furnishes the lateral support.   Where there is a single beam or
where bracing or other supports are not feasible, it is necessary to reduce
the bending stress.   Sometimes a built-up section of I-beam and channel
is used to stiffen the compression flange (Fig. 9-7).

PROBLEMS

19-6. If a $9 \times \frac{1}{2}$ in. plate is riveted to the compression flange of the beam in
Example 1, what does the allowable moment become?   (*Hint:* In this case it is
possible that the allowable moment will be limited by tension in the bottom flange or
by compression in the top flange.   Investigate both possibilities.)

19-7. A 12-in., 40.8-lb American standard beam rests on supports 14 ft 0 in.
center to center.   Calculate the allowable uniform load (*a*) if the top flange is not
laterally supported; (*b*) if the top flange is supported at the midpoint; (*c*) if the top
flange is supported at the "third-points."   Use A.R.E.A. formula.

Ans.   (a)   w = 2,180 lb per ft.

19-8. Buckling of Beam Webs.   If the web of a beam is thin in relation to the depth of the beam, there is a tendency for the web to buckle.
This tendency may be serious in some beams.

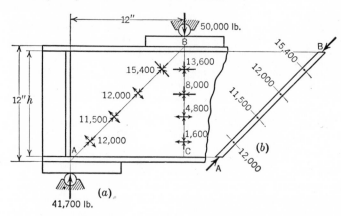

FIG. 19–8.   Measured principal stresses near load and reaction.

To illustrate the tendency of a thin web to buckle, Fig. 19-8 shows
the loading and some of the principal stresses in the web of a beam
under concentrated load.[4]   These stresses were determined by actual
strain gage measurements.   Now suppose that a narrow strip of the
web having the line *AB* as its longitudinal axis is considered (Fig. 19-8*b*).

[4] See discussions by R. L. Moore and E. C. Hartman, *Trans. A.S.C.E.*, Vol. 100,
1935, p. 696.

It may be seen that compressive stresses of considerable magnitude exist on successive cross-sections of the strip. This small part of the beam web is therefore somewhat similar to a column completely braced in one direction by the adjacent web material, but only slightly restrained in a direction prependicular to the plane of the web. If the web is sufficiently thin in relation to its length, the strip is likely to deflect laterally. If this lateral deflection becomes sufficiently great, the web may fail through elastic instability somewhat as a slender column fails.

In standard rolled steel I-beams or wide-flange beams the ratio of web thickness to depth is such that the beams are safe against buckling of the web as described if the average web shear does not exceed 13,000 psi. The average web shear is limited to 13,000 psi in the A.I.S.C. specifications.

19-9. Web "Crippling" under a Concentrated Load. Reference to Fig. 19-8a shows that in the web directly under the concentrated load there are compressive stresses which become increasingly large as the flange is approached. Very close to the junction of flange and web the compression in the web on planes parallel to the axis of the beam may become so great as to lead to a horizontal wrinkling or "crippling" of the web. The shorter the length of the beam along which a concentrated load is applied to the web, the higher is the compressive stress in the web and the greater is the danger of this crippling. Therefore it is necessary that the load be applied along a sufficiently great length of the beam. The same condition exists with respect to a reaction.

In determining the minimum allowable length of end bearing for a reaction or the minimum length of bearing plate through which a load is transmitted to a beam, it has been found experimentally[5] that the load may be assumed to "spread" through the thickness of the flange on a 45° plane (Fig.

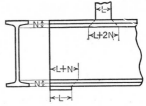

FIG. 19-9

19-9). Therefore the necessary length of a bearing plate under a concentrated load is given by $L = (P/S_c t) - 2N$, where L is the required length of bearing plate, N is the flange thickness (to the toe of the fillet), P is the load, t is the web thickness, and S_c is the allowable compressive stress in resisting this type of failure. An end reaction should be distributed over a length $L = (P/S_c t) - N$. The specifications of the American Institute of Steel Construction permit S_c to have a value of 24,000 psi.

[5] I. Lyse and H. J. Godfrey, "Web Buckling in Steel Beams" (discussion), *Trans. A.S.C.E.*, Vol. 100 (1935), p. 706.

CURVED BEAMS

19-10. Curved Beams. The term "curved beam" is applied to a beam in which the neutral surface of the *unloaded* beam is not a plane surface. The slight deflection of ordinary beams under load is not sufficient to make them "curved beams."

The common flexure formula is not theoretically correct when applied to curved beams. Nevertheless, it may be applied to some of them without causing prohibitive errors. For instance, if the inner radius is four times the depth of the beam, the maximum stresses as calculated from the common flexure formula will be too small by about 10 per cent. If the ratio of radius of curvature to depth is greater, the error is less. On the other hand, as the ratio of inner radius to depth decreases, the error resulting from use of the common flexure formula increases rapidly.

The reason for the failure of the common flexure formula to apply to curved beams is evident from consideration of the diagram in Fig. 19-10. This shows part of a curved beam subject to a bending moment of value M. The assumption is made (and has been experimentally verified) that every plane radial surface remains a plane after bending. This is the same assumption that is the basis of the common flexure formula. It follows that in a curved beam subjected to bending moment the *total* deformations of the various fibers are proportional to the distances of these fibers from the neutral axis or surface. Since, however, the lengths of the fibers between two radial planes such as AB and DC are not all the same, it follows that in a curved beam the unit deformations and consequently the unit stresses do not vary as the total deformations. In a curved beam the fibers at the concave surface are shorter than those fibers which are the same distance from the neutral axis on the convex side. Consequently, at a given distance from the neutral axis *toward* the center of curvature, the unit deformations and consequently the unit stresses are greater than they are at the same distance from the neutral axis *away* from the center of curvature. The manner of stress variation is indicated in Fig. 19-10b.

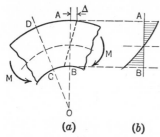

FIG. 19-10. Variation of bending stress in a curved beam.

(a)   *(b)*

The laws of equilibrium require the total tensile force on one face of a radial segment to equal the total compressive force. Since the unit stresses increase more rapidly from the neutral surface toward the center of curvature than they do from the neutral surface away from the center of curvature, it follows that the neutral axis for a curved beam is shifted from the centroid of the cross-section toward the center of curvature.

19-11. The Flexure Formula for Curved Beams.   Figure 19-11 represents part of a curved beam subjected to bending moment M, represented by couples.   Consider a segment between two radial planes (AB and FG), the distance between the planes at the neutral surface being L. The total change in length of the fiber AF at the convex surface is Δ

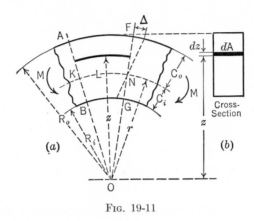

Fig. 19-11

(shown as elongation in the diagram).   The change in curvature of the beam due to bending is not shown.   The length AF equals LR_0/r, in which r is the radius to the neutral surface.   (An expression for the value of r will be found later.)   The stress at the outer fibers, S_0, equals $\delta E = \dfrac{\Delta E}{LR_0/r}$.   The elongation of a fiber at a distance z from O is $\dfrac{z - r}{c_0}\,\Delta$, and the unit stress S_z at any distance z is

$$S_z = \frac{\dfrac{z - r}{c_0}\,\Delta E}{Lz/r}$$

Therefore

$$\frac{S_z}{S_0} = \frac{R_0}{c_0}\frac{z - r}{z} \quad \text{or} \quad S_z = \frac{S_0 R_0}{c_0}\frac{z - r}{z}$$

The force on an area dA of the cross-section at distance z from O equals $\dfrac{S_0 R_0}{c_0}\dfrac{z - r}{z}\,dA$.   Taking moments with respect to O, the resisting moment

$$M = \frac{S_0 R_0}{c_0} \int_{R_i}^{R_0} (z - r) dA = \frac{S_0 R_0}{c_0} \left[\int_{R_i}^{R_0} z \, dA - \int_{R_i}^{R_0} r \, dA \right]$$

But $\int_{R_i}^{R_0} z \, dA$ is the moment of the cross-section with respect to O. If $\bar{R}$ is the distance to the centroid,

$$\int_{R_i}^{R_0} z \, dA = \bar{R}A \qquad \text{also} \qquad \int_{R_i}^{R_0} r \, dA = rA$$

Hence

$$M = \frac{S_0 R_0}{c_0} (\bar{R}A - rA) = \frac{S_0 R_0}{c_0} (\bar{R} - r)A$$

But $(\bar{R} - r)$ is the shift or displacement of the neutral axis due to curvature.   Let $\bar{R} - r = j$.   Then

$$\boldsymbol{M = \frac{S_0 R_0 jA}{c_0}}$$

which is the flexure formula for curved beams, giving M in terms of the stress in the extreme (convex) fibers.   In the same way, or by substituting for S_0 its value in terms of S_i, there results

$$\boldsymbol{M = \frac{S_i R_i jA}{c_i}}$$

Note that these formulas are analogous to $M = SI/c = SAk^2/c$, but with $R_0 j$ and $R_i j$ taking the place of k^2 (k = radius of gyration).

Before stresses or resisting moments can be calculated by the foregoing formulas, it is necessary to determine j for the beam in question. As in straight beams the neutral axis is so placed that the tensile force on one side equals the compressive force on the other side, or the total force on one end of any segment is zero.   Since $S_z = \dfrac{S_0 R_0}{c_0} \dfrac{z - r}{z}$, the total force on the cross-section equals

$$\int S_z \, dA = \frac{S_0 R_0}{c_0} \int_{R_i}^{R_0} \frac{z - r}{z} dA = 0$$

Therefore

$$\int_{R_i}^{R_0} dA - r \int_{R_i}^{R_0} \frac{dA}{z} = 0$$

whence

$$r = \frac{\displaystyle\int_{R_i}^{R_0} dA}{\displaystyle\int_{R_i}^{R_0} \frac{dA}{z}} = \frac{A}{\displaystyle\int_{R_i}^{R_0} \frac{dA}{z}}$$

which, evaluated for a particular cross-section, gives the distance from the center of curvature to the neutral axis. After r is found, j is found by $j = \bar{R} - r$.

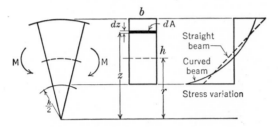

FIG. 19–12.   Shift of neutral axis in a curved beam.

Example. Figure 19-12 shows a beam of rectangular cross-section the depth of which is twice the inner radius. The beam is bent by couples of M lb-in. applied to its end. Calculate the unit stresses at the concave and convex surfaces, and compare them with the maximum bending stress in a straight beam of the same cross-section and subject to the same moment.

Solution: The distance to the neutral axis is

$$r = \frac{A}{\displaystyle\int_{R_i}^{R_0} \frac{dA}{z}} = \frac{bh}{\displaystyle\int_{R_i}^{R_0} \frac{bdz}{z}} = \frac{h}{\log_e z \Big]_{R_i}^{R_0}} = \frac{h}{\log_e \dfrac{R_0}{R_i}}$$

For the beam in this example $R_0/R_i = 3$. Therefore $r = h/\log_e 3 = h/1.09862 = 0.9103h$; whence $j = \bar{R} - r = h - 0.9103h = 0.0897h$.

The unit stress at the concave inner surface is

$$S_i = \frac{Mc_i}{R_i j A} = \frac{M(0.5 - 0.0897)h}{0.5h \times 0.0897h \times bh} = \frac{9.14M}{bh^2}$$

The unit stress at the convex surface is

$$S_0 = \frac{Mc_0}{R_0 j A} = \frac{M(0.5 + 0.0897)h}{1.5h \times 0.0897h \times bh} = \frac{4.38M}{bh^2}$$

In a straight beam the unit stress in the extreme fibers is

$$S = Mc/I = 6M/bh^2$$

Because of the curvature, the stress at the inner (concave fibers) is about 52 per cent greater than the stress in a straight beam, and the stress at the outer fibers is only 73 per cent of the stress in a straight beam.

For beams of rectangular and circular cross-sections, Fig. 19-13 gives, for different ratios of depth to inner radius, the ratios of the stress in a curved beam to that in a straight beam.

Values for the distance r from the axis of curvature to the neutral axis are tabulated for several types of cross-sections.

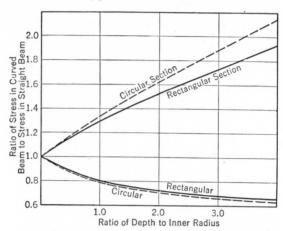

FIG. 19–13. Ratios of stresses in curved beams to stresses in straight beams. Upper curves are stresses on concave surface.

PROBLEM

19-8. A beam of circular cross-section is curved so that the inner radius equals the radius of the cross-section. Calculate the stress on the inner and on the outer fibers caused by a bending moment of M lb-in. Compare these stresses with the maximum bending stresses in a straight beam of the same cross-section with the same bending moment.

19-12. Curved Beams Subject to Bending Combined with Direct Stress.

Curved beams subject to bending moment alone are of rare occurrence, but curved beams subject to bending and direct stress are numerous. Hooks, rings or other links, frames of machines, "C" clamps, and tools of various sorts are common examples.

The stress at any point on a cross-section of such a member is the algebraic sum of the direct stress and the stress due to the bending moment, as in straight beams or prisms with eccentric loads. For curved beams this resultant stress is given by these formulas:

At the inner surface, $S_i = \pm P/A \pm Mc_i/R_i jA$.

At the outer surface, $S_0 = \pm P/A \pm Mc_0/R_0 jA$.

These formulas are analogous to $S = \pm P/A \pm Mc/I$.

Curved Beams

Values of $r = \dfrac{A}{\displaystyle\int \frac{dA}{z}}$ (r is distance from axis of curvature of beam to neutral axis of cross-section)

$$r = \frac{h}{\log_e \dfrac{R_0}{R_i}} = \frac{h}{2.303 \log \dfrac{R_0}{R_i}}$$

$$r = \frac{b_1 h_1 + b_2 h_2}{2.303 \left(b_1 \log \dfrac{R_i + h_1}{R_i} + b_2 \log \dfrac{R_0}{R_i + h_1} \right)}$$

$$r = \frac{b_1 h_1 + b_2 h_2 + b_3 h_3}{2.303 \left(b_1 \log \dfrac{R_i + h_1}{R_i} + b_2 \log \dfrac{R_0 - h_3}{R_i + h_1} + b_3 \log \dfrac{R_0}{R_0 - h_3} \right)}$$

$$r = \frac{\dfrac{h}{2}(b_1 + b_2)}{b_2 - b_1 + \left(b_2 + \dfrac{R_0}{h}(b_1 - b_2) \right) \times 2.303 \log \dfrac{R_0}{R_i}}$$

$$r = \frac{F + \sqrt{F^2 - a^2}}{2}$$

$$j = F - r = \frac{F - \sqrt{F^2 - a^2}}{2}$$

Triangular section: Put b_2 equal to zero in trapezoid.

In the solution of problems involving curved beams, a question arises as to the correct moment arm to use in calculating M. In straight beams this moment arm is the distance from the line of action of the load to the centroid of the cross-section and also to the neutral axis, which passes through the centroid. In curved beams the moment arm is the distance from the line of action of the load to the centroid of the cross-section and not to the neutral axis. The actual load P is regarded as equivalent to an imaginary load P at some point on the cross-section and a couple or bending moment Pe (Fig. 19-14). If this imaginary load is to produce uniformly distributed stress on the cross-section, it must act through the centroid, and consequently e must be measured from the centroid.

Example. A small hand press for performing odd jobs in a machine shop (Greenerd arbor press) has a cast-iron frame with the dimensions shown in Fig. 19-15. (*a*) Calculate the stresses which a load P of 1,000 lb causes to act on a radial section A–A',

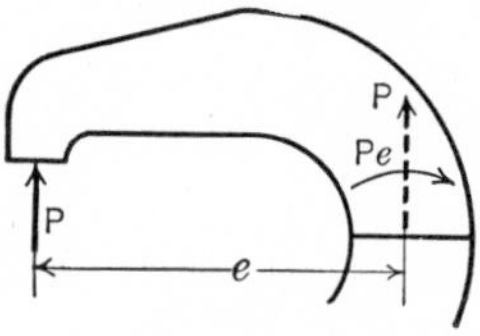

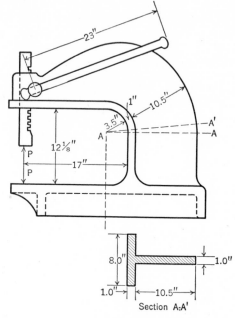

FIG. 19-14

FIG. 19-15

making a small angle with A–A, the end of the straight part of the frame. (*b*) Compare these stresses with those in the straight part of the frame.

Solution: (*a*) The distance r from the center of curvature to the neutral axis of the section A–A' is given by

$$r = \frac{b_1 h_1 + b_2 h_2}{2.303 \left(b_1 \log \dfrac{R_i + h_1}{R_i} + b_2 \log \dfrac{R_0}{R_i + h_1} \right)}$$

$$\frac{R_i + h_1}{R_i} = \frac{3.5 + 1}{3.5} = 1.285 \qquad \frac{R_0}{R_i + h_1} = \frac{15}{3.5 + 1} = 3.333$$

Therefore

$$r = \frac{8 \times 1 + 10.5 \times 1}{2.303 \,(8 \times 0.1089 + 1 \times 0.5224)} = \frac{18.5}{2.30 \times 1.392} = 5.74 \text{ in.}$$

The distance from the center of curvature to the centroid of the cross-section is

$$\bar{R} = \frac{8 \times 4 + 10.5 \times 9.75}{18.5} = 7.26 \text{ in.}$$

Therefore $j = 7.26 - 5.74 = 1.52$ in. Also

$$c_i = 3.76 - 1.52 = 2.24 \text{ in.}$$

$$c_0 = 11.5 - 2.24 = 9.26 \text{ in.}$$

Moment arm of load P with respect to centroid of cross-section $= 17.0 + 3.76 = 20.76$ in. Therefore the bending moment of the load $P = 1{,}000 \times 20.76 = 20{,}760$ lb-in. Whence

$$S_i = \frac{Mc_i}{R_i jA} + \frac{P}{A} = +\frac{20{,}760 \times 2.24}{3.5 \times 1.52 \times 18.5} + \frac{1{,}000}{18.5} = +472 + 54$$
$$= 526 \text{ psi (tension)}$$

$$S_0 = -\frac{Mc_0}{R_0 jA} + \frac{P}{A} = -\frac{20{,}760 \times 9.26}{15.0 \times 1.52 \times 18.5} + \frac{1{,}000}{18.5}$$
$$= -456 + 54 = -402 \text{ psi (compression)}$$

(b) The moment of inertia of the cross-section with respect to the centroidal axis, which is also the neutral axis of the straight part of the frame, $= 243$ in.[4] Therefore

$$S_i = \frac{20{,}760 \times 3.76}{243} + \frac{1{,}000}{18.5} = +321 + 54 = 375 \text{ psi (tension)}$$

$$S_0 = \frac{-20{,}760 \times 7.74}{243} + \frac{1{,}000}{18.5} = -660 + 54 = -606 \text{ psi (compression)}$$

The maximum tensile stress in the curved part of the frame is 40 per cent greater than in the straight part; the maximum compressive stress is 34 per cent less.

PROBLEMS

19-9. Figure 19-16 shows one of a pair of hooks used for lifting the 125-ton ladles in a steel works. The width w of the hook is 16.8 in., and the thickness of the metal is 5.2 in. The inner radius r is 6.1 in. Calculate the maximum stress in the hook if the load on the hook is 135,000 lb.   *Ans.* $S_i = 14{,}990$ psi.

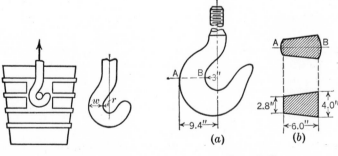

FIG. 19-16   FIG. 19-17

19-10. A typical 20-ton crane hook is shown in Fig. 19-17a. The cross-section at AB and an approximately equivalent trapezoidal cross-section are shown in (b).

Calculate the stress caused by a load of 20 tons.   Use the simplified cross-section, and assume the resultant of the load to act 3.3 in. from the 4.0-in. edge of the cross-section.

BEAMS WITH LOADS INCLINED TO THE PRINCIPAL AXES OF INERTIA

19-13. Maximum Stresses Resulting from Inclined Moment.   One of the limitations stated when considering the common flexure formula was that the loads must be in the plane of a principal axis of inertia of the beam cross-section.[6]   The effect of loads not in the plane of a principal axis of inertia will now be considered.

For simplicity consider first a beam with a rectangular cross-section and with loads in a plane passing through the centroid of the cross-section and making an angle α with the principal axis, as shown in Fig. 19-18a. The law of summation of effects shows that the stresses at any point can

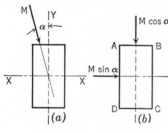

Fig. 19-18

be found by adding the stresses caused by each of the two components of the loads (or moments) parallel, respectively, to the two axes shown in Fig. 19-18b.   If this beam is a beam on two supports, the stress at A is found by adding two compressive stresses;   the stress at C is the sum of two tensile stresses.   The stress at B is the algebraic sum of compressive stress due to $M \cos \alpha$ and tensile stress due to $M \sin \alpha$, and the stress at D is the algebraic sum of compression due to $M \sin \alpha$ and tension due to $M \cos \alpha$.

A convenient expression for the maximum stress at a cross-section of this beam is derived as follows: Let M be the bending moment at the cross-section, and let the moment act in a plane making an angle α with the Y axis.   Let the section modulus with respect to the X axis be Z_x, and the section modulus with respect to the Y axis be Z_y.   Let n be the ratio of Z_x to Z_y, or $Z_x = nZ_y$.   The maximum bending stress (at C) due to the given bending moment M is

$$S = \frac{M \cos \alpha}{Z_x} + \frac{M \sin \alpha}{Z_y} = \frac{M}{Z_x} (\cos \alpha + n \sin \alpha) \qquad (19\text{-}1)$$

[6] The principal axes of inertia at any point of any given area are the two rectangular axes through that point for which the values of I are a maximum and minimum, respectively.   If the point is the centroid of the area, the axes are called the *principal centroidal axes*.   In this discussion, whenever "principal axes" are referred to, it will be understood that the centroidal axes are meant.   If an area has an axis of symmetry, that axis is one of the principal axes.   See Appendix B.

But M/Z_x is the maximum bending stress that would result from a bending moment M in the plane of the Y axis.   Hence the maximum stress due to an inclined bending moment is $(\cos \alpha + n \sin \alpha)$ times the maximum bending stress caused by the same bending moment if applied in the plane of the Y axis.   For small angles $\cos \alpha$ is very nearly unity ($\cos 8° = 0.99$), and consequently for small angles of inclination of load the percentage *increase* in stress due to the inclination of the bending moment is very closely $100n \sin \alpha$.

Equation 19-1 applies to solid and hollow rectangular sections, to I and H sections.   It also applies to all sections that contain two axes of symmetry and have such a shape that the point where the stress is maximum under the oblique moment is a point that is as remote as any other point on the cross-section from both the X axis and the Y axis.

It should also be noted that, for equation 19-1 (which is derived from the ordinary flexure formula) to apply, the plane of loading must be such that no torsional forces act on the beam.   This condition is met, for all beams that have two axes of symmetry, if the plane of loading passes through the centroid of the cross-section.

Example. A bending moment M acts at an inclination of 5° with the Y axis of the cross-section of a 24-in. 100-lb American standard I-beam (Fig. 19-19).   Compare the resulting maximum stress with that which would be produced by the same moment acting in the plane of the Y axis.

Solution: For this beam, $Z_x = 197.6$ and $Z_y = 13.4$, whence $n = 14.75$.   Since $\cos 5° = 0.996$, and $\sin 5° = 0.0872$, $n \sin \alpha = 14.75 \times 0.0872 = 1.29$.   Inclination of the plane of loading therefore increases the maximum stress by 129 per cent, or the maximum stress under the inclined moment is 2.29 times what it would be if the moment were in the plane of the Y axis.

Fig. 19-19

For most I-beams, the ratio n of the section moduli is very large, and this makes any slight obliquity of loading very severe in its effects.   The value of n is smaller for the wide-flange beams, so that obliquity of loading is less important, but even in them it has serious effects, as the table (p. 360) shows.

19-14. Position of Neutral Axis.   When a beam is stressed by a bending moment which is in one of the principal planes of the beam, the neutral axis of the cross-section is perpendicular to the plane of the bending moment.   When the moment acts in a plane inclined to the principal axes of the beam, however, *the neutral axis is not perpendicular to the plane of bending.*

Considering the beam of rectangular cross-section pictured in Fig. 19-20, and using the procedure discussed in Art. 19-13, it is found that the

Beam	$\dfrac{Z_x}{Z_y} = n$	Ratio of $\dfrac{\text{Maximum stress for inclined moment}}{\text{Maximum stress when } \alpha = 0}$ for the following values of α		
		1°	2°	5°
24-in., 100-lb I	$\dfrac{197.6}{13.4}$ 14.75	1.26	1.51	2.29
24-in. WF 100-lb	$\dfrac{248.9}{33.9}$ 7.35	1.13	1.26	1.64
12-in., 31.8-lb I	$\dfrac{36.0}{3.8}$ 9.48	1.16	1.33	1.82
12-in. WF 31-lb	$\dfrac{39.4}{6.1}$ 6.45	1.11	1.23	1.56

stresses at the four corners of the cross-section have the values shown. But if all stresses are within the proportional limit, the stress at any point of the cross-section is proportional to the distance of the point from the neutral axis. By proportion, therefore, the point of zero stress along

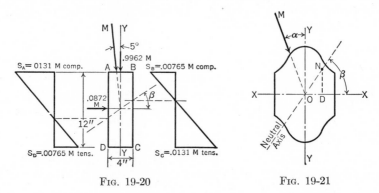

FIG. 19-20   FIG. 19-21

the line BC is located at 4.43 in. from B, and the corresponding point along AD at the same distance from D. The neutral axis therefore has the position shown. Let β be the angle which it makes with the X axis. Then $\tan \beta = 1.57/2 = 0.785$, and $\beta = 38°\ 08'$. A shift of 5° in the plane of loading has produced a shift of 38° in the direction of the neutral axis.

A general expression for the value of the angle β in terms of the moments of inertia I_x and I_y and the angle α will now be derived. The area shown in Fig. 19-21 represents the cross-section of a beam the principal axes of which are X–X and Y–Y. The vector marked M represents the resultant bending moment and lies in the plane of the loads. Let N be any point on the neutral axis. Since the bending stress at N is zero, the tensile stress at N due to the horizontal component of M equals the compressive stress at N due to the vertical component of M, or

$$\frac{M \sin \alpha \times OD}{I_y} = \frac{M \cos \alpha \times ND}{I_x}$$

$$\frac{ND}{OD} = \frac{I_x \sin \alpha}{I_y \cos \alpha} = \frac{I_x}{I_y} \tan \alpha$$

But $ND/OD = \tan \beta$. Therefore $\tan \beta = (I_x/I_y) \tan \alpha$.

If this expression is applied to the first of the beams included in the table of Art. 19-13, and α is taken as $1°$, $I_x/I_y = 2{,}372/48.4 = 49.0$, and $\tan 1° = 0.0175$. Whence $\tan \beta = 49.0 \times 0.0175 = 0.858$, and $\beta = 40° 38'$. An almost imperceptible change in the plane of loading has caused a large shift in the direction of the neutral axis.

The bending stress *at any given point* on the cross-section of a beam can be determined by the principles of Art. 19-13, without locating the position of the neutral axis. But if the cross-section of the beam has a shape such that, under an oblique loading, it is not obvious what point of the cross-section will be most distant from the neutral axis (Fig. 19-21), the neutral axis can be located by means of the equation just given, and then the point of maximum stress can be determined by inspection or measurement, after which the stress at that point can be found.

The following example applies the principles developed in this and the previous articles to a beam which possesses the additional complication that the directions of the principal axes are not initially known but have to be determined.

Example. Calculate the allowable bending moment for a $5 \times 3 \times \frac{1}{2}$ in. L (Fig. 19-22) if the allowable bending stress is 16,000 psi. The bending moment is due to vertical loads, and the angle is placed with the 5-in. leg vertical and above the 3-in. leg. Assume that the plane of bending moments is properly placed so as to avoid twisting (see *shear center*, Art. 19-17). Compare the allowable bending moment thus found with one-half of the allowable bending moment for two similar angles with the 5-in. legs fastened back to back to form a symmetrical section.

Solution: For an angle such as this, the moments of inertia given in structural handbooks are not the principal moments of inertia. The first step in determining the principal moments is to find the angle θ at which the principal axes $X'–X'$ and $Y'–Y'$ are inclined to the axes $X–X$ and $Y–Y$. (Since the bending moment acts in a plane parallel to the $Y–Y$ axis, the angle θ will equal the angle α which measures the obliquity of the loading.) After θ has been found, the values of the principal moments of inertia, $I_{x'}$ and $I_{y'}$, can be determined.

Appendix B derives the equations from which θ, $I_{x'}$, and $I_{y'}$ can be found, and an example in that Appendix shows that, for a $5 \times 3 \times \frac{1}{2}$ in. angle, $\theta = 19° 40'$, $I_{x'} = 10.45$ in.^{4}, and $I_{y'} = 1.58$ in.^{4}

Figure 19-23 shows the cross-section of the beam with the principal axes. The neutral axis will evidently lie in the second and fourth quadrants, making an angle with X'–X' given by the equation

$$\tan \beta = \frac{I_{x'}}{I_{y'}} \tan \alpha = \frac{10.45}{1.58} \tan 19° \, 40' = 2.36 \qquad \text{whence} \quad \beta = 67° \, 02'$$

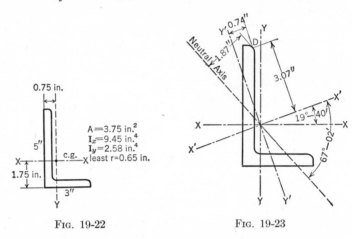

$$A = 3.75 \text{ in.}^2$$
$$I_x = 9.45 \text{ in.}^4$$
$$I_y = 2.58 \text{ in.}^4$$
least $r = 0.65$ in.

FIG. 19-22   FIG. 19-23

It can now be determined that D is the point most distant from the neutral axis, and it is at this point that the maximum stress will occur. The relation between stress at D and bending moment M is given by

$$S_D = \frac{M_{x'}c_{x'}}{I_{x'}} + \frac{M_{y'}c_{y'}}{I_{y'}} = \frac{M \cos 19° \, 40' \; c_{x'}}{I_{x'}} + \frac{M \sin 19° \, 40' \; c_{y'}}{I_{y'}}$$

Whence
$$16,000 = \frac{0.942M \times 3.07}{10.45} + \frac{0.336M \times 0.74}{1.58}$$

$$= 0.277M + 0.157M = 0.434M$$

Therefore
$$M = 16,000/0.434 = 36,900 \text{ lb-in.}$$

For two $5 \times 3 \times \frac{1}{2}$ in. angles fastened back to back forming a symmetrical section,

$$S = Mc_x/I_x \qquad \text{or} \qquad 16,000 = M \times 3.25/(2 \times 9.45)$$

whence $M = 93,000$ lb-in. for the two angles, or 46,500 lb-in. allowable for each of the angles.

PROBLEMS

19-11. The purlins of a roof consist of 8-in., 11.5-lb channels resting on roof trusses 16 ft center to center. The inclination of the roof is 1 to 3, as shown in Fig. 19-24. Each purlin supports 48 sq ft of roof, which weighs 25 lb per sq ft. Calculate the maximum stress in the channels, assuming that torsional stresses do not occur.   *Ans.* $S = 14,900$ psi.

19-12. A $4 \times 4 \times \frac{1}{2}$ in. angle is used as a cantilever beam.   Calculate the maximum stress resulting from a given bending moment M in a vertical plane (a) if the angle is turned as shown in Fig. 19-25a; (b) if the angle is turned as shown in Fig. 19-25b.

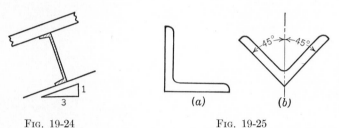

<table>
<tr><td>Fɪɢ. 19-24</td><td>(a)</td><td>(b)</td></tr>
<tr><td></td><td colspan="2">Fɪɢ. 19-25</td></tr>
</table>

19-15. Deflection of Beams Due to Loads Not in Plane of Principal Axis.   If a load is applied to a beam not in the plane of the principal axis of inertia but with its line of action passing through the centroid of the cross-section as shown in Fig. 19-26, the deflection at any point may be regarded as the vector sum of two displacements.   The beam will be deflected horizontally by the horizontal component of the load and

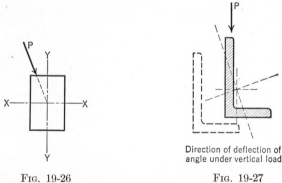

Direction of deflection of angle under vertical load

Fɪɢ. 19-26   Fɪɢ. 19-27

vertically by the vertical component of the load.   The horizontal deflection is a function of the horizontal component of the load and I_y, whereas the vertical deflection is a function of the vertical component of the load and I_x.

In the angle discussed in the foregoing example, the component of the bending moment in the direction of the $Y'-Y'$ axis causes a deflection in that direction, and the component of the moment in the direction of the $X'-X'$ axis causes a deflection in that direction.   An angle loaded in this manner therefore does not deflect straight downward, but deflects sidewise as well (Fig. 19-27).

PROBLEMS

19-13. A beam of rectangular cross-section h in. deep and b in. wide has a load inclined $\alpha°$ to the vertical. Calculate α in order that H and V components of the deflection shall be equal.

19-14. A 12-in., 31.8-lb American standard beam rests on two supports 20 ft. center to center and carries a vertical uniform load of 6,000 lb. The web of the beam is tilted 4.0° from the vertical. Calculate the horizontal and vertical components of the deflection of the midpoint of the beam.

19-15. A $4 \times 4 \times \frac{1}{2}$ in. angle is used as a cantilever beam 10 ft long. It carries a vertical concentrated load at the end of 240 lb. The legs of the angle are vertical and horizontal, respectively. Calculate the horizontal and vertical components of the deflection at the end caused by the concentrated load.

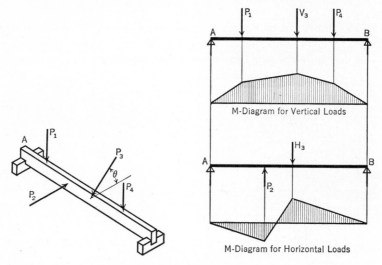

Fig. 19-28

19-16. Stresses Caused by Loads Not in a Single Plane.

The beam AB shown in Fig. 19-28 carries loads the lines of action of which do not lie in a single plane but all of which are perpendicular to the longitudinal axis of the beam. If the deflections are small, the stresses and deflections may be found as follows: Resolve each load into its two components parallel, respectively, to the two planes containing the principal axes of inertia.

Draw a bending-moment diagram for the components in the X plane and a separate bending-moment diagram for the components in the Y plane. Then for any point of any cross-section the bending stress may be calculated from

$$S = \pm M_V c_x / I_x \pm M_H c_y / I_y$$

If deflections in either the H or V direction are large, twisting of the beam results from the fact that the loads in the other direction no longer lie in a *plane*.

PROBLEMS

19-16. A 4×6 in. (actual size) wood beam 12 ft long, with the 6-in. face vertical, is supported at the end and carries a vertical load of 600 lb at the midpoint and two horizontal loads of 100 lb, each 32 in. from the midpoint. Calculate the maximum bending stress.

19-17. Solve Problem 19-16 if one of the horizontal loads is omitted.

19-18. In Fig. 19-28 the beam is a wooden beam 4×10 in. (actual size) and 10 ft long. $P_1 = 100$ lb, $P_2 = 100$ lb, $P_4 = 150$ lb, $V_3 = 120$ lb, $H_3 = 160$ lb. Distances from the left reaction to the respective loads are 1.8 ft, 3.6 ft, 5.3 ft, and 7.7 ft. Calculate the maximum bending stress.

BEAMS WITH CROSS-SECTIONS HAVING NO VERTICAL AXIS OF SYMMETRY; SHEAR CENTER

19-17. Shear Center. The common theory of flexure assumes that the bent beam is not subjected to any resultant torque which would tend to cause the successive cross-sections of the beam to rotate with respect to one another. This condition is ordinarily met by using beams that have a vertical plane of symmetry, so that each cross-section of the beam intersects this plane in an axis of symmetry. If the resultant of the loads applied at any cross-section coincides with this axis, no torsion is produced.

Beams having cross-sections without a vertical axis of symmetry, however, are not infrequently used. The ordinary channel section (Fig. 19-29 a and b) is an illustration. It might be supposed that such a section would not be twisted about its longitudinal axis if loads were applied to it in the vertical plane containing the centroids of the successive cross-sections. Experiment shows, however, that this is not true. Under such a load, the beam twists as shown.

This can be demonstrated by use of a small model. A strip of tin 3 in. wide and about 20 in. long is formed into a channel by means of two bends parallel to the long dimensions.[7] One end is rigidly fastened to a block of wood, and a small square tin plate is soldered to the other end (Fig. 19-30). The beam is supported as a cantilever by attaching the block of wood to a fixed support. A load is applied to the upper edge of the square of tin by a pencil or other object held in the hand. If a vertical load is first applied at the edge of the flange away from the web, the beam twists as would be expected. But when the load is

[7] Even a cardboard model will give fairly satisfactory results.

moved closer to the web until it is over the centroid of the cross-section, the twist does not disappear. *A vertical centroidal load causes torsion.* However, if the plane of the load is shifted *to the other side of the web,* a position can be found where no twisting of the beam is apparent. If

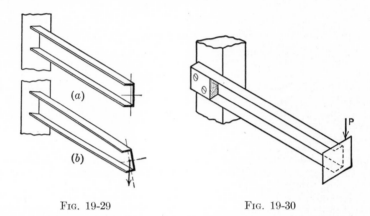

FIG. 19-29   FIG. 19-30

loads are applied vertically in this plane of bending, they do not cause any torsion of the beam, and the flexure formula may be used correctly. The intersection of the horizontal axis of symmetry of the cross-section with the line of action of a vertical load so applied as not to cause any twist of the beam is called the *shear center* of the cross-section.

For any beam the plane of loading should pass through the shear centers of the successive cross-sections, and it is important, therefore, to be able to locate the shear center. For a beam with a vertical axis of symmetry, the shear center is simply the centroid of the cross-section. For a channel section, and for certain other sections that do not possess a vertical axis of symmetry, the position of the shear center may be found, closely enough for practical purposes, by the reasoning that will be given in Art. 19-19.

19-18. Transverse Shearing Stresses in Beams. First, however, it is desirable to consider the existence of certain horizontal shearing stresses which may occur on transverse planes of a beam. Consider as an example a beam (Fig. 19-31) of *I* cross-section used as a cantilever and loaded at the end with a load *P* (not shown) applied directly over the top of the web. This beam is shown in Fig. 19-31a. As it bends, the top flanges lengthen. The forces which stretch these flanges must be shearing forces exerted by the web, which is considered as extending through the flanges, on the vertical surface of each flange where it joins the web.   If the material is weak in shear, failure in shear along these surfaces may result, and the flanges may separate from the web as shown in Fig. 19-31b.

Figure 19-32 shows a beam of channel cross-section bent by loads (not shown).   Consider a segment of the top flange in the form of a rectangular block between two transverse planes at A and B.   On the BC face

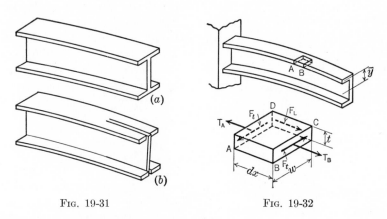

FIG. 19-31   FIG. 19-32

there is a resultant tensile force T_B, and on the AD face a force T_A. For the cantilever beam shown, T_A is greater than T_B, since the bending moment at A is greater than that at B.   There must be a force equal to $T_A - T_B$ acting on the DC face, as shown.   This is the resultant F_L of the shearing stresses.

$$F_L = T_A - T_B$$

Then, if S_s is assumed uniform over the thickness t,

$$S_s t dx = \frac{M_A \bar{y}}{I} tw - \frac{M_B \bar{y}}{I} tw$$

whence

$$S_s = \left(\frac{M_A - M_B}{dx}\right)\frac{w\bar{y}}{I} = \frac{Vw\bar{y}}{I}$$

Shearing stresses must also exist on the transverse faces AD and BC in the directions shown by the arrows.   These stresses are variable, being of the same intensity as S_s at the edge of the face adjoining the web and being zero at the outer edge of the flange.   It follows from the above equation that for a flange of uniform thickness, as in the diagram, this variation in shearing stress is uniform.

19-19. Location of Shear Center. The transverse force F_T is the average shearing stress times the area.

$$F_T = \frac{Vw\bar{y}}{2I} \, tw = \frac{Vw^2\bar{y}t}{2I}$$

The effect of these transverse shearing forces which act on the flanges will now be considered. In Fig. 19-33 is shown a segment of the free end of the cantilever beam shown in Fig. 19-32, cut off by a section through AD. This is shown as viewed from the cut end. The resultant forces acting on this cut end are shown by vectors and are as follows: (1) the resultant tensile and compressive forces T and C constituting the resisting moment; (2) the resultants of the transverse shearing

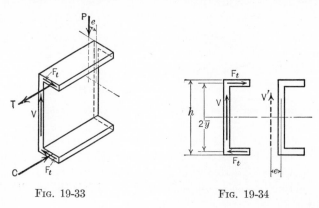

FIG. 19-33   FIG. 19-34

stresses on the cross-section of the flanges, designated F_t and acting in the directions indicated; (3) the resultant V of the vertical shearing stresses on the plane AD, which is, of course, upward on the segment shown. The actual vertical shearing unit stresses on this plane have been shown to vary from zero at the top and bottom to a maximum at the neutral axis, and consequently the vertical force on the flanges is a very small part of the total. The resultant on the entire section in any ordinary channel acts not far from the center of the web and in this discussion is assumed to act at the center of the web.

It can now be seen why the force P, if it is not to twist the beam, must act *not* through the centroid of the cross-section, but through a point on the opposite side of the web. The resultant of the force V and the couple $2\bar{y}F_t$ (Fig. 19-34) is a force V' (which equals V) and which acts to the left of the line of action of V a distance e such that $V'e = 2\bar{y}F_t$. Therefore, unless P is applied e in. to the left of the line of action of V, it will rotate the segment (clockwise as seen in Fig. 19-34).

Since $V' = V$,

$$e = \frac{2\bar{y}F_t}{V} = \frac{2 \times Vw^2\bar{y}t \times \bar{y}}{2I \times V} = \frac{w^2\bar{y}^2t}{I}$$

$$= \frac{\text{Area of flange} \times w\bar{y}^2}{I}$$

Since $wt\bar{y}^2$ is approximately the I of one flange, a close approximation to the above value for e is $\dfrac{I \text{ of flange} \times w}{I}$.

But the I of one flange is approximately $\bar{y}^2 \times$ area of one flange, and the I of the rectangular web equals $Ak^2 =$ area of web $\times h^2/12$. Also

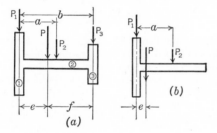

FIG. 19-35

$\bar{y}$ is generally only slightly less than $h/2$. If the above values are substituted for the I of one flange, the I of the web and $h/2$ for y, there results the equation

$$e = \frac{w}{2 + \dfrac{\text{Area of web}}{3 \times \text{Area of one flange}}}$$

If the thickness of the web equals the thickness of the flange, this becomes

$$e = \frac{w}{2 + (h/3w)}$$

which shows that for this type of section e is less than $\frac{1}{2}w$ but approaches $\frac{1}{2}w$ as the width of the flange increases relative to the depth of the section. If $h = 3w$, $e = \frac{1}{3}w$, which is a reasonable value for common structural channels.

Two other types of cross-section that have no vertical axis of symmetry and that are in common use are shown in Fig. 19-35. The section shown in Fig. 19-35a may be regarded as equivalent to three beams each of rectangular cross-section.   In order that bending shall occur without twisting, each of these three beams must have the same deflection, which is also the deflection of the beam as a whole.   For this to be the case

$$\frac{P_1}{I_1} = \frac{P_2}{I_2} = \frac{P_3}{I_3} = \frac{P}{I} = \frac{P}{I_1 + I_2 + I_3}$$

in which P_1, P_2, and P_3 are components of the applied load P.   These three beams can receive the required loads only if P is applied where the resultant of P_1, P_2, and P_3 falls.   This is the case if $Pe = P_2a + P_3b$.

Hence $e = \dfrac{aP_2 + bP_3}{P} = \dfrac{aI_2 + bI_3}{I}$.

By similar reasoning for the section shown in Fig. 19-35b, $e = aI_2/I$.

PROBLEMS

19-19. A 10-in. 33.6-lb ship channel has flanges which are 4.1 in. wide and 0.575 in. thick (average).   The web is 0.575 in. thick.   Calculate the distance from the back of the channel to the plane of loads if torsion is to be avoided.

19-20. A beam has a cross-section like that shown in Fig. 19-35a.   The metal is all 1 in. thick.   The over-all width is 10 in., and the heights of the flanges are 8 in. and 5 in., respectively.   Calculate the position of the plane of loading if torsion is to be avoided.   *Ans.   e = 1.8 in.*

20

Eccentrically Loaded Connections

20-1. Introduction. When members of a frame are joined to one another by rivets, the most satisfactory distribution of loads on the various rivets results when the line of action of the force on each of the members passes through the centroid of the cross-sections of the group of rivets which connect that member to the others as shown in Fig. 20-1a. Similarly, in a welded joint the line of action of the load should pass through the centroid of the welds as shown in Fig. 20-1b. In a member with a cross-section having a centroid unequally distant from the edges of the member this leads to the use of unequal lengths of fillets on the two edges, as noted in Art. 4-8.

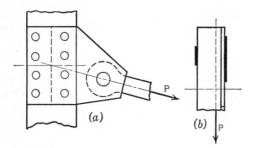

FIG. 20-1

When the foregoing conditions are met, it can generally be assumed that the same amount of load is carried by each rivet or by each inch of fillet. But there are situations in which it is not possible to have the rivets or fillets so placed that their centroid lies on the action line of the load. The stresses that exist in cases of this sort will now be discussed.

20-2. Eccentrically Loaded Riveted Connection. In Fig. 20-2 the load P is equivalent to an equal and parallel force P passing through the centroid of the rivet areas, and a couple Pe. The centroidal force P may be assumed to load each of the rivets equally, so that the force which each exerts on the bracket is P/n and is in a direction opposite

371

to P. The couple Pe tends to rotate the bracket clockwise (and indeed does rotate it slightly, since the materials involved are not absolutely rigid). The point about which this rotation occurs is *the centroid of the rivet areas*. This will now be shown.

In Fig. 20-3 let O be the center about which the slight rotation of a plate occurs in consequence of a moment M applied to the plate. It is here assumed that the position of O with respect to the centroid of the rivet cross-sections is unknown and is to be determined. Assume any pair of rectangular axes through O as shown. Let c be the distance from

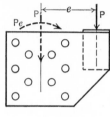

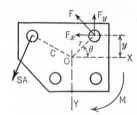

Fig. 20-2   Fig. 20-3

O to the most distant rivet, and r the distance from O to any other rivet. If S is the shearing unit stress in the most distant rivet, the shearing unit stress in a rivet at a distance r is $(r/c)S$, since the shearing deformation in each rivet is proportional to the distance of that rivet from the center of rotation. The force exerted by a rivet at a distance r from O is $F = (r/c)SA$, in which A is the cross-sectional area of the rivet. Let θ be the angle between the X axis and the radius from O to the rivet. Then the component of F parallel to the X axis is

$$F_x = (r/c)SA \sin\theta$$

But for any rivet $r \sin \theta$ is y, the distance from the X axis to that rivet. Hence $F_x = (S/c)Ay$. For all the rivets $\Sigma F_x = 0$, or

$$(S/c)\Sigma Ay = 0$$

Since S/c does not equal zero, $\Sigma Ay = 0$. But if $\Sigma Ay = 0$, the X axis passes through the centroid of the cross-sectional areas of all the rivets.

Similar reasoning shows that the Y axis also passes through the centroid of the cross-sectional areas of all rivets. Consequently the point about which the plate rotates coincides with the centroid of the cross-sectional areas of all the rivets.

It follows that the force F developed by each rivet in resisting the moment M is proportional to the distance of that rivet from the centroid of the rivet cross-sections. In a joint such as is shown in Fig. 20-4 the stress on the most distant rivet may be regarded as having two components. One component is due to the moment Pe and acts tangentially (in a direction perpendicular to the radius). Let this component of stress be S_T. The other component of stress is the "direct" stress $S_P = P/nA$.

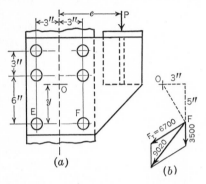

FIG. 20-4

To determine the stress S_T due to the moment Pe the equation $\Sigma M_0 = 0$ is written. The tangential force on any rivet will be $S_T Ar/c$, and the moment of this force is $S_T Ar^2/c$. The sum of the moments of all rivets is $(S_T A/c)\Sigma r^2$. Hence $(S_T A/c)\Sigma r^2 - Pe = 0$, whence

$$S_T = Pec/A\Sigma r^2 \qquad (20\text{-}1)$$

It is generally convenient to compute Σr^2 by noting that $\Sigma r^2 = \Sigma x^2 + \Sigma y^2$. It is not necessary to compute r. The value of S_T must be such that the resultant of S_T and S_P does not exceed the specified allowable stress.

Example. The plate shown in Fig. 20-4a is the near plate of two similar plates riveted to the flanges of a column. The two plates support a load P of 42,000 lb (each plate supporting 21,000 lb). The rivets are $\frac{7}{8}$ in., and allowable shearing stress is 15,000 psi. Assume that thickness of column flanges and plate is such that bearing will not govern. Calculate the maximum allowable value of the eccentricity e.

Solution: The centroid of the rivets lies on the vertical axis of symmetry, and the distance above EF is found by $y = \Sigma Ay/\Sigma A$.

$$y = \frac{2A \times 6 + 2A \times 9}{6A} = \frac{12 + 18}{6} = 5 \text{ in.}$$

The most distant rivets are E and F, for which $c = \sqrt{3^2 + 5^2} = 5.83$ in. The allowable load on a rivet $= 0.601 \times 15,000 = 9,020$ lb. The direct load on each rivet equals $21,000/6 = 3,500$ lb. To determine the force available in rivet F for resisting moment the diagram shown in (b) is drawn. Lay off 3,500 lb vertically through F, and from the point of this vector draw a line perpendicular to OF. Swing an arc with length of 9,020 lb with F as its center until it intersects the line just drawn. The available tangential force scales 6,700 lb. Calculate $\Sigma r^2 = \Sigma x^2 + \Sigma y^2 = 6 \times 3^2 + 2 \times 5^2 + 2 \times 1^2 + 2 \times 4^2 = 54 + 50 + 2 + 32 = 138.$

$$M = \frac{S_T A}{c} \Sigma r^2 = \frac{6,700}{5.83} \times 138 = 158,000 \text{ lb-in.}$$

$$21,000e = 158,000$$

$$e = 7.55 \text{ in.}$$

PROBLEMS

20-1. The reaction of the beam shown in Fig. 20-5 is 10,000 lb. The rivets are $\frac{3}{4}$ in. Calculate the maximum shearing stress. Assume that bearing stress does not govern. *Ans.* $S_s = 14,300$ psi.

20-2. The rivets connecting the plate shown in Fig. 20-6 are $\frac{7}{8}$-in. rivets, and the allowable shearing stress is 15,000 psi. Calculate the maximum allowable value of d. Plate thickness is such that bearing stress does not govern.

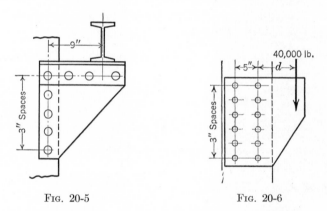

Fig. 20-5   Fig. 20-6

20-3. In Fig. 20-4 let the rivets be $\frac{3}{4}$ in., let $P = 30,000$ lb (15,000 lb on one plate), and let $e = 8$ in. Determine the maximum shearing stress on a rivet.

20-4. In Fig. 20-6 let the rivets be $\frac{3}{4}$ in., and let the allowable shearing stress be 15,000 psi. Change 40,000 to 24,000 and determine the allowable value of d.

20-5. In Fig. 20-5 let the rivets be $\frac{7}{8}$ in., and let the allowable shearing stress be 13,500 psi. Determine the allowable beam reaction on the bracket.

20-3. Eccentrically Loaded Welded Connections.

The process of reasoning that has just been applied to riveted connections establishes the fact that the torque on an eccentrically loaded welded connection tends to rotate the connection about *the centroid of the group of weld areas*. The force exerted, as a result of the torque on any short length of fillet, is therefore proportional to the distance of that short length of fillet from the centroid of the weld areas. Also the sum of the moments of these forces must equal the torque. These facts will be used to develop an expression connecting the torque Pe with the maximum force (in pounds per linear inch of fillet) exerted on the weld.

A steel plate attached to a structural member by three fillet welds, L_1, L_2, L_3, is shown in Fig. 20-7. Point O is the centroid of the welds. Let it first be assumed that forces exert a couple of M lb-in. on the plate. The welds hold the plate in equilibrium, and the force exerted on the plate by the weld at any point such as N is perpendicular to ON. Let K lb

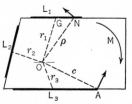

FIG. 20-7

per in. be the maximum intensity of load on the welds. This will occur at A, the point most distant from O, and will act in a direction perpendicular to the radius OA.

At any point N the load per inch will be $(\rho/c)K$. The force exerted on the plate by a length of weld dL at N will be $(\rho/c)K\,dL$. The moment of this force with respect to O is $(\rho^2/c)K\,dL = (K/c)\rho^2\,dL$. The moment exerted by the entire fillet L_1 may be represented by the integral $\dfrac{K}{c}\displaystyle\int_0^{L_1}\rho^2\,dL$. The integral is analogous to $\displaystyle\int \rho^2\,dA$, the polar moment of inertia of an area. Therefore $\displaystyle\int \rho^2\,dL$ will be called the polar moment of inertia of the line L_1 with respect to O.

Let G be the midpoint of L_1, and let r_1 be the distance from O to G. By the method used in mechanics for deriving the moment of inertia of a slender rod it can be shown that for the line L_1

$$\int \rho^2\,dL = \frac{1}{12}L_1{}^3 + L_1 r_1{}^2$$

Hence the moment exerted by the weld L_1 equals

$$\frac{K}{c}\left(\frac{1}{12}L_1{}^3 + L_1 r_1{}^2\right) = \frac{KL_1}{c}\left(\frac{1}{12}L_1{}^2 + r_1{}^2\right)$$

The total external moment is balanced by the sum of the moments of all welds. Hence

$$M = \frac{K}{c}\Sigma\left[L\left(\frac{L^2}{12} + r^2\right)\right] \qquad (20\text{-}2)$$

Now consider the case in which the resultant of the loads is a downward load P the line of action of which is e in. from O. This loading is equivalent to a load P through O and a couple Pe. The load P through the centroid will cause a load per inch on all welds which equals $P/\Sigma L$. The tangential load per inch K must be reduced so that the resultant of $P/\Sigma L$ and K does not exceed the *specified* allowable load per inch. When K has been determined the allowable M can be computed by formula 20-2.

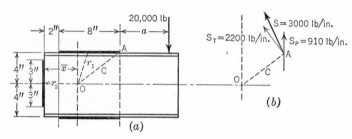

Fig. 20-8

Example. A steel member to carry a vertical eccentric load of 20,000 lb is welded to a column with three lines of $\frac{5}{16}$ fillet welds as shown in Fig. 20-8. Specifications for steel structures permit a load in any direction of 3,000 lb per in. of fillet, for $\frac{5}{16}$-in. fillet. Determine the maximum allowable distance a.

Solution: The number of pounds per inch of fillet required for direct stress = 20,000/22 = 910 lb per in. The position of the centroid is given by

$$\bar{x} = \frac{16 \times 6 + 6 \times 0}{22} = 4.36 \text{ in.}$$

and the distance to the most remote point is $c = \sqrt{5.64^2 + 4^2} = \sqrt{31.8 + 16} = \sqrt{47.8} = 6.91$ in.

$$r_1{}^2 = 4^2 + 1.64^2 = 16 + 2.7 = 18.7; \ r_1 = 4.33 \text{ in.}$$

also $r_2 = 4.36$ in.

The number of pounds per inch at the most remote point of the fillet available for resisting the moment of the load is determined by the vector diagram shown in (b) and is $S_T = 2,200$ lb per in. The allowable moment is

$$M = \frac{2,200}{6.91}\left[2 \times 8\left(18.7 + \frac{64}{12}\right) + 6\left(4.36^2 + \frac{36}{12}\right)\right]$$

$$= 318(384 + 132) = 164,000 \text{ lb-in.}$$

Hence

$$e = 164,000/20,000 = 8.20 \text{ in.} \quad \text{and} \quad a = 8.20 - 5.64 = 2.56 \text{ in.}$$

PROBLEMS

20-6. The welded joint shown in Fig. 20-9 resists a load P of 30,000 lb applied as shown. Is the resulting maximum load per inch of fillet within the specifications for $\frac{5}{16}$-in. fillet?   *Ans.* Load per inch is 3,040 lb.

20-7. A welded connection is shown in Fig. 20-10. Determine the distance d for which the allowable value of P will be greatest. If the fillets are $\frac{5}{16}$ in., what is the allowable P when d has the value found?

20-8. If, in Fig. 20-10, d is 5 in., and the fillets are $\frac{1}{4}$ in., what is the allowable value of P?

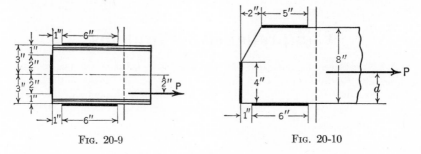

FIG. 20-9   FIG. 20-10

20-9. In Fig. 20-9 the welds are $\frac{3}{8}$-in. fillets (3,600 lb per in.). Calculate the allowable load P.

20-10. In Fig. 20-10, $P = 30,000$ lb and $d = 4.5$ in. Calculate the maximum stress per inch in the weld, and indicate where it occurs.

21

Comprehensive Problems

21-1. A cableway having a span of 1,200 ft and designed to handle 150-ton loads was used for handling material and equipment during the construction of the Hoover dam. To adjust the six $3\frac{1}{2}$-in. wire ropes to the same tension (and sag) there were six toggles operated by hydraulic jacks. (*See Engineering News-Record*, Dec. 21, 1933, p. 760.)

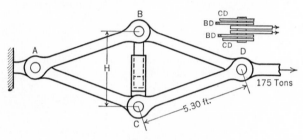

Fig. 21-1

You are asked to determine certain dimensions for a somewhat similar toggle shown in Fig. 21-1. The pull on the toggle is 175 tons. The dimension H may vary from 3 ft minimum, to 4 ft maximum. All eyebars are 5.30 ft long, center to center of pins. The jack will be operated by oil under a pressure of 2,800 psi. This pressure acts on the end area of the ram. The ram and cylinder will be ground to a close running fit, and suitable packing to insure oil tightness is to be provided but is not shown.

Determine the following:

(*a*) Number of inches of motion of *D*.

(*b*) Required diameter of ram. Make the diameter the next larger one-tenth inch.

(*c*) The shell thickness of the cylinder. It may be necessary to consider this a "thick cylinder" (see Fig. 4-11).

(*d*) Thickness of eyebars. The width of these will be 6 in.

(*e*) Diameter of pins at *A* and *D*.

(*f*) Diameter of pins at *B* and *C*.

For the cylinder use an allowable stress of 10,000 psi, tension; for other parts use 0.8 of the A.I.S.C. stresses.

21-2. An elevated steel tank (Fig. 21-2) is to be built to hold a heavy chemical used in industrial processes in a manufacturing plant. The liquid weighs 108 lb per cu ft. It has been decided to make the diameter of the tank 18 ft and the height 22 ft. The tank will rest on a 6-in. concrete slab supported by beams as shown in (*b*).

Beams B and D will be riveted to four steel columns, which will rest on concrete footings. The top of each footing will be 20 ft below the top of the slab. Each column footing will bear on excellent gravel 5 ft below the top of the footing. In a structure of this type substantial bracing is very important. There will be cross bracing on each side as shown.

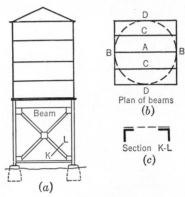

Plan of beams
(b)

Section K-L
(c)

(a)

FIG. 21-2

(a) Calculate the tons of liquid in tank when full. (b) Calculate the thickness of each ring of shell plate (four rings). Minimum thickness to be $\frac{5}{16}$ even if required calculated thickness is less. Thickness to be next even $\frac{1}{16}$ greater than calculated thickness. (c) Select lightest wide-flange beams for A, B, C, D. Apportion total weight of tank and slab to beams A, C, D. In doing this, great accuracy is not possible and is not important. Assume that the two beams B carry total weight of tank and slab less load carried by beams D. (d) Select lightest wide-flange columns that comply with specifications. (e) Calculate size of steel bearing plates on bottom of columns. (f) Calculate net area required for the diagonal bracing. Assume only the tension diagonal to act. The bracing is to resist either a wind load of 40 lb per sq ft on projected area of tank or an assumed horizontal force of 10 per cent of total weight on columns, whichever is larger. Each brace to consist of two equal angles. Select suitable angles assuming two $\frac{3}{4}$-in. rivet holes out of each angle. Minimum thickness $\frac{5}{16}$ in. (g) Calculate required dimensions of square base of concrete column footings

Allowable Stresses. For shell of tank 15,000 psi tension but assume vertical welded joints are 90 per cent efficient. Structural framing, A.R.E.A. specifications (Table IX). Bearing of column footings on gravel 5 tons per sq ft.

Additional Assumptions. Roof of tank weighs 20 lb per sq ft of horizontal projection. Floor of tank to be $\frac{5}{16}$-in. plates. Weight of concrete 150 lb per cu ft.

21-3. The diagrams of Fig. 21-3 show approximate dimensions of an automobile jack which is manufactured from steel plates and rolled rods. The threaded rod has a square end to which a socket bar can be fitted. The threaded rod is turned by this bar. At C and C' there are nuts through which the threaded bar passes. As the rod is turned, the nuts C and C' either are brought nearer together (raising the load) or are separated (lowering the load). Additional devices for increasing the stability are used but are not shown in the diagram. They do not affect the stresses.

The low position is shown approximately by the dotted diagram of the right-hand members.

When the jack is in such a position that pins B, D, D', and B' are all in the same horizontal plane, and is carrying a load of 1,200 lb, calculate the following unit stresses:

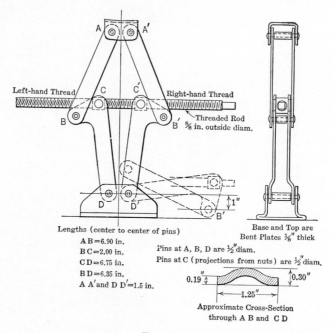

Lengths (center to center of pins)
A B = 6.90 in.
B C = 2.00 in.
C D = 6.75 in.
B D = 6.35 in.
A A' and D D' = 1.5 in.

Pins at A, B, D are ½" diam.
Pins at C (projections from nuts) are ½" diam.

Base and Top are
Bent Plates ⅛" thick

0.19"   0.30"
1.25"

Approximate Cross-Section
through A B and C D

Fig. 21-3

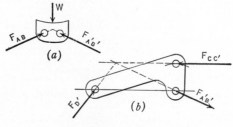

(a)

F_{AB} $F_{A'B'}$ W

$F_{CC'}$

$F_{D'}$ $F_{A'B'}$

(b)

Fig. 21-4

(a) Tensile stress in screw.
(b) Shearing stress in pins of nuts at C and C'.
(c) Shearing stress in pins at A and B.
(d) Shearing stress in pins at D and D'.
(e) Bearing stress between pins and plates at A, B, C, and D.
(f) Combined bending and direct stress in member BCD at a section 5 in. from D (where it begins to widen). At this section it is not "dished."

(g) Average compressive stress in *AB*. *AB* is a column. The plate has been dished as shown to increase its radius of gyration. Compare the average compressive stress with the allowable *P/A* given by the Rankine formula of Art. 13-16 for a flat (not dished) member of this width and thickness.

In finding the forces acting on the members, draw free-body diagrams, as shown in Fig. 21-4. Members *AB* and *A′B′* are two force members (the force exerted by each of them coincides in direction with the axis of the member). Member *BCD* is a "three-force" member acted on by the three forces shown. These meet in a point. The directions of the forces at *B* and at *C* are known. A force polygon can be drawn for each of the free bodies.

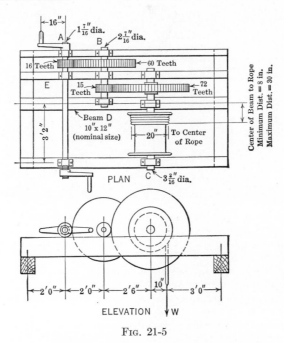

Fɪɢ. 21-5

21-4. A simple hoist is to be built for temporary use. Parts are available as shown in Fig. 21-5.

(a) What load *W* can two men hold if each exerts a force of 150 lb on a crank? Neglect any frictional force.

(b) Calculate the torsional stresses in the shafts *A*, *B*, and *C* when this load is on the hoist.

(c) Each crank is keyed to shaft *A* with one key $2\frac{1}{2}$ in. long, $\frac{3}{8}$ in. square, sunk $\frac{3}{16}$ in. into shaft. Calculate the shearing and bearing stresses in the key.

(d) Calculate maximum bending and longitudinal shearing stress in beam *D* when *W* has the value found in (a). Assume weights as follows: drum and rope, 700 lb; each bearing, 20 lb; gear wheel on shaft *C*, 300 lb. Note that vertical forces exist between the gear wheel on shaft *C* and the pinion on shaft *B*. Assume that the effects of these forces are equally divided between beams *D* and *E* and result in a downward force at shaft *C* and an upward force at shaft *B*. The position of weight W along the drum should be taken as that which causes greatest load on beam D. In calculating the part of W carried by beam D, ignore the supporting effect of beam E on shaft C. One-inch-diameter holes are bored vertically through beam D for attaching bearings. To be safe, assume that such a hole may occur where bending moment is maximum.

21-5. In a certain shop it is necessary to support loads of 3,500 and 14,000 lb, respectively. The arrangement shown in Fig. 21-6 is suggested. The beam A and bracket are welded together, and the beam is bolted to a column at each end.

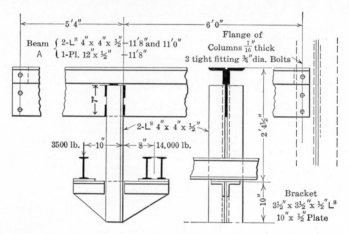

Fɪɢ. 21-6

Is this construction satisfactory as far as stresses are concerned? The following stresses should be considered:

(a) Tensile and compressive stresses in beam due to bending. (Is it necessary to reduce the allowable stress because of unsupported top flange of beam?)

(b) Shearing and bearing stresses in bolts connecting beam to columns.

(c) Stresses in vertical bracket angles.

(d) Shear and bending stresses in bottom cross plate of bracket. (The other ends of the I-beams which load the bracket are rigidly fastened so that the I-beams cannot move longitudinally.)

(e) Maximum load per inch in $\frac{5}{16}$-in. fillet weld connecting the vertical angles to the $\frac{1}{2}$-in. plate of the beam A. Each angle is attached with 12.5 in. of fillet in five 2.5-in. lengths, as shown.

21-6. A wooden frame building is to have columns spaced 12 ft on centers in one direction and 16 ft on centers in the other, as shown in Fig. 21-7. The second floor is to be designed to carry a live load of 100 lb per sq ft. The flooring is to be carried on joists, and the joists on girders, as shown. Joists are to be of eastern hemlock, prime structural grade, 16 in. on centers. Girders are to be of Douglas fir, select structural grade. In design of the floor system, weight of joists and girders is to be given whatever consideration it merits. Load is to be transmitted from the girders to the columns through cast-iron column caps, which will be designed for the job. Load transmitted from column B to column A is 90,000 lb.

(a) Select joists of proper size, using stresses as given in Table XI. Assume weight of flooring at 5 lb per sq ft.

(b) Select girders of proper size to support the joists. Load on the girders may be treated as if uniformly distributed.

(c) Determine the necessary length m of the brackets on the column caps so that side grain compression on the girders will not be excessive.

(d) Design column A. It is to be of square cross-section, of Douglas fir, select structural grade. Column A is 14 ft long.

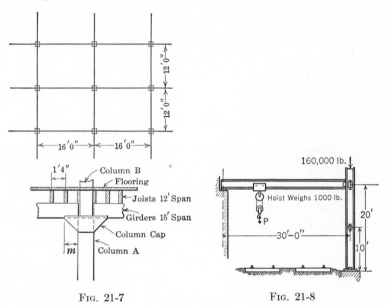

FIG. 21-7   FIG. 21-8

(e) Calculate the change in elevation of the floor at the middle of the panel which occurs when the full live load is put on the floor. Assume that the deflection of the flooring between the joists is negligible and that no change occurs in the elevation of the lower end of columns A.

21-7. For loading materials at a factory, the arrangement illustrated in Fig. 21-8 is used. A hoist, carried on the lower flange of a 24-in. WF 100-lb beam is used to handle loads that come into a factory on railroad tracks beneath the hoist. Appropriate stops prevent the hoist load from coming within 2 ft of either end of the beam, but it may have any intermediate position. The right-hand end of the beam is riveted to the flange of a 20-in. 65.4-lb I-beam used as a column and braced at midlength in the weak direction. In addition the column carries a nominally axial load of 160,000 lb.

(a) Determine the allowable hoist load P to accord with the A.R.E.A. specifications (Table IX).

(b) What is the least number of $\frac{3}{4}$-in. rivets that may be used to connect the clip angles to the flange of the column?

21-8. The beam AC shown in Fig. 21-9 is built into a rigid body at end A, the shaft *ED* is fixed against rotation at *E*, and a metal arm is shrunk on the shaft at *D*. The end of the arm and the end of the beam are both just in contact at *C* when there is no load on the beam. A load *P* of 100 lb is applied to the beam as shown.

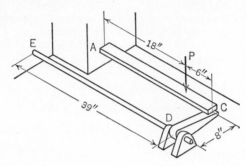

FIG. 21-9

Beam *AC* is of aluminum alloy, 2 in. wide and $\frac{1}{2}$ in. thick ($E = 11,000,000$ psi). The shaft *ED* is steel, $\frac{1}{2}$ in. in diameter. Calculate the maximum bending stress and the maximum shearing stress in the beam and the maximum stress in the shaft caused by the load *P*.

APPENDIX A

Centroids of Areas

Locating the Centroid of an Area. The distance from a chosen axis to the centroid of a given area is expressed by

$$\bar{y} = \frac{\int y\, dA}{\int dA} \qquad \text{or} \qquad \bar{y} = \frac{\Sigma Ay}{\Sigma A} = \frac{A_1 y_1 + A_2 y_2 + A_3 y_3 + \cdots}{A_1 + A_2 + A_3 + \cdots}$$

The first of these formulas is used to determine the location of the centroid of an area the boundary of which is a curve that can be expressed by a mathematical equation. The quantities occurring in this

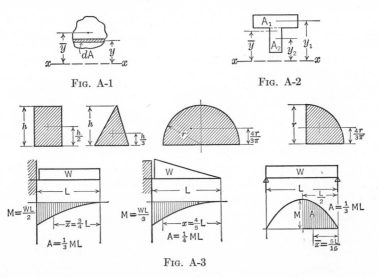

Fig. A-1   Fig. A-2

Fig. A-3

formula are illustrated in Fig. A-1. Textbooks on mechanics should be consulted for examples of the use of that formula.

The second formula is the one commonly used by engineers and applies to areas that can be divided into elementary shapes (rectangles, triangles, and semicircles) such as the area shown in Fig. A-2.

385

The positions of the centroids of some common elementary areas are shown in Fig. A-3. The lower ones are moment diagrams for beams with the given loadings and are used in area-moment calculations.

Calculating the Distance to the Centroid of an Area. The example below illustrates the calculation of the distance from a chosen axis to the centroid of a composite area.

Example. Determine the position of the centroid of the shaded area shown in Fig. A-4.

Solution: The centroid lies on the vertical axis of symmetry. To determine its position on this axis its distance from the lower boundary will be calculated. The area will be divided into the lower 2 × 4 in. rectangle, a 2 × 6 in. rectangle, and the triangle above. The following arrangement of calculations is convenient.

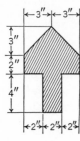

A	y	Ay
2 × 4 = 8	2	16
2 × 6 = 12	5	60
3 × 3 = 9	7	63
$\Sigma A = 29$		$\Sigma Ay = 139$

$$\bar{y} = \frac{\Sigma Ay}{A} = \frac{139}{29} = 4.79 \text{ in.}$$

Fig. A-4

Centroids of Cross-Sections of Thin-Walled Members. Beams and columns made of sheet metal are coming into wide use. The centroid of the cross-section of

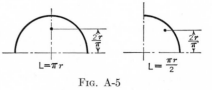

Fig. A-5

such a member may be found with close approximation by treating the cross-section as a bent line.

The centroid of a straight line is at its midpoint. The location of the centroid of a semicircular arc and of a 90° arc is shown in Fig. A-5. Treated as a bent line, the cross-section of a thin-walled beam can generally be divided into straight lines and circular arcs.

Example. A cross-section of a sheet-metal beam is shown in Fig. A-6. Calculate the distance from the x axis to the centroid, assuming it to be the same as for the line.

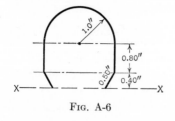

Fig. A-6

L	y	Ly
2 × 0.5　= 1.0	0.2	0.2
2 × 0.80 = 1.6	0.8	1.28
$\pi \times 1$　= 3.14	1.836	5.77
$\Sigma L = 5.74$		$\Sigma Ly = 7.25$

$$\bar{y} = \frac{\Sigma Ly}{\Sigma L} = \frac{7.25}{5.74} = 1.262 \text{ in.}$$

APPENDIX B

The Moment of Inertia of a Plane Area

Moment of Inertia by Integration. Let the area marked A in Fig. A-7 represent any plane area, and let the axis $X–X$ be any axis in the plane of the area. If the area is divided into small elementary areas (one of which is shown) and each elementary area is multiplied by the square of its distance from the given axis, then the sum of all these products is a quantity called the moment of inertia of the area with respect to the given axis. The units are inches raised to the fourth power, or in⁴., if all dimensions are in inches. The summing up of all the products may be performed by integration, and this sum may be respresented as an integral. Thus,

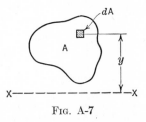

Fig. A-7

$$I_x = \int y^2 \, dA$$

The proper limits must be given to the integral so that the operation indicated sums up $y^2 \, dA$ for all the elementary areas which compose the given area. Moment of inertia is always a plus quantity, since y^2 is plus even though y is negative. An expression or formula for the moment of inertia of any of the common geometric areas with respect to some specified axis may be derived by integration. Expressions for the moment of inertia of the most commonly used areas are given in tabular form in Table XV, Appendix C.

An example illustrating the derivation of such an expression is given below.

Example. Calculate I for a triangle with respect to an axis through the vertex parallel to the base.

Solution: Figure A-8 represents any triangle, and the shaded strip represents any strip across this parallel to the axis. The length of this strip is $b\, y/h$, and consequently its area is $(b/h)y \, dy$.

$$I = \int y^2 \, dA = \frac{b}{h} \int_0^h y^3 \, dy = \frac{b}{h} \frac{y^4}{4}\Big]_0^h = \frac{bh^3}{4}$$

It should be noted that the moment of inertia of an area with respect to an axis does not equal the product of the area by the square of the distance from the axis to the centroid of the area.

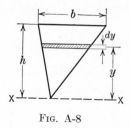

Fig. A-8

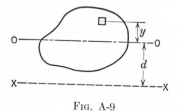

Fig. A-9

Parallel-Axis Theorem. A relation exists between I_0, the value of the moment of inertia of a plane area with respect to an axis through the centroid of the area, and I_x, the moment of inertia of the same area with respect to a parallel axis not through the centroid. This is expressed by

$$I_x = I_0 + Ad^2$$

in which d is the distance between the axes.

Proof: The area in Fig. A-9 represents any plane area. The axis O–O is any axis through the centroid in the plane of the area, and the axis X–X is a parallel axis. The area dA is any elementary area, its distance from axis O–O being y, which is $+$ as shown, but is $-$ for any dA below axis O–O.

$$I_x = \int (d \pm y)^2 \, dA = \int (y^2 \pm 2yd + d^2) \, dA$$

$$= \int y^2 \, dA \pm 2d \int y \, dA + d^2 \int dA$$

But $\int y \, dA$ is the moment of the area with respect to axis O–O. Since this is the centroidal axis, this moment is zero and

$$I_x = \int y^2 \, dA + d^2 \int dA$$

Hence

$$I_x = I_0 + Ad^2$$

This may be written $I_0 = I_x - Ad^2$, which shows that I with respect to a centroidal axis is less than I for any parallel axis.

Example.   Calculate values of the moment of inertia with respect to a centroidal axis parallel to the base for a triangle, using value for I in the previous example.

Solution:

$$I_0 = I_x - Ad^z = \frac{bh^3}{4} - \frac{bh}{2} \times \left(\frac{2h}{3}\right)^2 = \frac{bh^3}{4} - \frac{2bh^3}{9} = \frac{bh^3}{36}$$

***I* of Composite Areas.**   Many plane areas used in structural engineering can be divided into elementary shapes, such as rectangles, triangles, and semicircles, for each of which an expression for I_0 is known or can be looked up.   In such cases no integration is necessary to calculate the moment of inertia of the given area with respect to any axis.

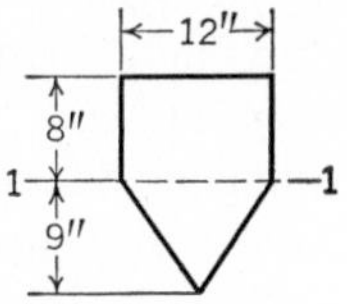

Example.   Using $I_0 = bd^3/12$ for a rectangle and $I_0 = bd^3/36$ for a triangle, calculate the moment of inertia of the area shown in Fig. A-10 with respect to its horizontal centroidal axis.

Fig. A-10

Solution: The area will be divided into a rectangle and a triangle by the line shown.   The distance from this line (axis 1–1) to the centroidal axis *O–O* of the whole area is

$$\bar{y} = \frac{+8 \times 12 \times 4 - 6 \times 9 \times 3}{8 \times 12 + 6 \times 9} = \frac{384 - 162}{96 + 54} = +\frac{222}{150} = +1.48 \text{ in.}$$

The plus sign indicates that the centroid is above the axis, 1–1.

For the rectangle, $\qquad\qquad I = \dfrac{1}{12} bd^3 = \dfrac{12 \times 8 \times 8 \times 8}{12} =\quad 512 \text{ in.}^4$

to "transfer" to axis *O–O*, add $\qquad\qquad\qquad Ad^2 = 96 \times 2.52^2 =\quad 609$

For the triangle, $\qquad\qquad\quad I = \dfrac{1}{36} bd^3 = \dfrac{12 \times 9 \times 9 \times 9}{36} =\quad 243$

to "transfer" to axis *O–O*, add $\qquad\qquad\qquad Ad^2 = 54 \times 4.48^2 =\quad 1{,}086$

Therefore I_0 for the whole area $\qquad\qquad\qquad\qquad\qquad\qquad\quad = 2{,}450 \text{ in.}^4$

Radius of Gyration.   The radius of gyration of an area with respect to a given axis is a distance found by the equation

$$r = \sqrt{I/A}$$

in which r is the radius of gyration, and I is the moment of inertia of the area with respect to the given axis.   It will be noted from the equation that, if I is given in in.^{4} and A is in in.^{2}, then r is in inches.

Cross-Sections of Thin-Walled Members.   Beams and columns made of sheet metal are now used in construction where light weight is important, and the use of such members is increasing.   The sheet metal is formed into tubes or other prismatic shapes by pressing the metal sheets.

Approximate values for the moment of inertia of cross-sections of thin-walled members are obtained by the same methods as are used for areas.

In Table XVI, Appendix C, values are given for moments of inertia and radii of gyration of straight lines and circular arcs. Using these values it is possible to calculate the moment of inertia and radius of gyration of most cross-sections of sheet-metal beams.

POLAR MOMENT OF INERTIA OF A PLANE AREA

If the moment of inertia is calculated with respect to an axis which is *perpendicular* to the plane of the area, the result is called the *polar* moment of inertia of the area with respect to the axis. In Fig. A-11 the axis Z–Z represents an axis perpendicular to the plane of the given

area. Then, $I_z = \int r^2 \, dA$.

Since for any elementary area $r^2 = x^2 + y^2$

$$\int r^2 \, dA = \int (x^2 + y^2) \, dA = \int x^2 \, dA + \int y^2 \, dA = I_x + I_y$$

Hence the polar moment of inertia of a given area with respect to a given axis equals the sum of the two rectangular moments of inertia

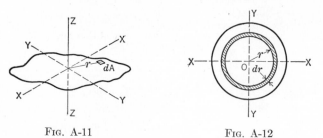

FIG. A-11   FIG. A-12

with respect to any two axes perpendicular to each other in the plane of the area, and intersecting at the foot of the polar axis.

The polar moment of inertia of a circle, with respect to an axis through the center, is used in the solution of problems involving stresses in circular shafting and an expression for this will now be derived.

In Fig. A-12 the axis with reference to which the polar moment is wanted is perpendicular to the plane of the paper and passes through O, the center of the circle. The elementary area dA is taken in the form of a ring, the radius of which is r and the radial width of which is dr. The area $dA = 2\pi r \, dr$, and $r^2 \, dA = 2\pi r^3 \, dr$. Summing up this quantity for all the rings which compose the circle,

$$I_z = 2\pi \int_0^R r^3 \, dr = \left. \frac{2\pi r^4}{4} \right]_0^R = \frac{\pi R^4}{2}$$

It follows that the rectangular moment of inertia I_x or I_y is one-half this, or $I_x = \pi R^4/4$. For a "hollow circle" the moment of inertia with respect to an axis through the center equals the moment of inertia of a circle with the outer radius minus the moment of inertia of a circle with the inner radius.

PRINCIPAL MOMENTS OF INERTIA

Product of Inertia of a Plane Area. The quantity $\int xy \, dA$ for a given area (Fig. A-13) with respect to two rectangular axes is called the product of inertia with respect to the given pair of axes. If either axis is an axis of symmetry, then $\int xy \, dA$ is zero. Unlike moment of inertia, the product of inertia with respect to a pair of axes may be negative. The symbol P_{xy} is commonly used for product of inertia.

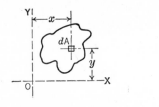

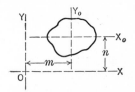

FIG. A-13   FIG. A-14

In Fig. A-14, X_0 and Y_0 are a pair of rectangular axes through the centroid of the area shown. X and Y are, respectively, parallel to and distant n and m from X_0 and Y_0. Let $\bar{P}_{xy}$ be the product of inertia with respect to the centroidal pair of axes.

Then $P_{xy} = \bar{P}_{xy} + mnA$ or $\bar{P}_{xy} = P_{xy} - mnA$, in which m and n may be positive or negative. This relation can be established in the same way as the similar theorem for moments of inertia.

Example. Determine the product of inertia of a rectangle (Fig. A-15) with respect to axes coinciding with two intersecting sides.

Solution:

$$P_{xy} = \bar{P}_{xy} + mnA = 0 + \frac{b}{2} \times \frac{h}{2} \times bh = +\frac{b^2 h^2}{4}$$

FIG. A-15

If the axes coincide with the top edge and left-hand side or with the bottom edge and the right-hand side of the rectangle, P_{xy} is negative.

Example. Determine the product of inertia for a right triangle with respect to the pair of centroidal axes parallel, respectively, to the base and altitude.

Solution: The value of P_{xy} will first be found with respect to a pair of axes one of which coincides with a side of the triangle and the other of which passes through the apex and is parallel to the base. For the area dA shown (Fig. A-16) the area is $(b/h)y\,dy$.

$$P_{xy} = \int_0^h y \times \frac{b}{2h} y \times \frac{b}{h} y\,dy = \int_0^h \frac{b^2}{2h^2} y^3\,dy = \frac{b^2}{h^2} \times \frac{h^4}{8} = \frac{b^2 h^2}{8}$$

With respect to a pair of parallel centroidal axes,

$$\bar{P}_{xy} = P_{xy} - mnA = \frac{b^2 h^2}{8} - \frac{bh}{2} \times \frac{b}{3} \times \frac{2}{3} h = \frac{b^2 h^2}{72}$$

If an area can be divided into simple shapes, such as triangles or rectangles, the product of inertia of the entire area with respect to a given pair of axes is the algebraic sum of the products of inertia with respect to the same pair of axes, of the several component simple shapes.

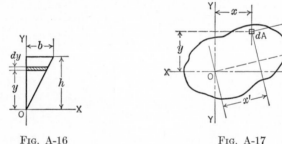

FIG. A-16   FIG. A-17

Principal Moments of Inertia: Principal Axes. The principal axes of inertia at any point of any given area are the two rectangular axes through that point with respect to which the values of I are a maximum and minimum, respectively. If the point is the centroid of the area, the axes are called the *principal centroidal axes*. When principal axes of inertia are mentioned without reference to any point, the axes referred to are centroidal axes. If an area has an axis of symmetry, that axis is one of the principal axes. The two values of I with respect to the two principal axes are called the *principal moments of inertia*.

The inclination of the principal axes to any other rectangular axes is found by substituting values in an expression which is derived as shown below.

Figure A-17 represents any plane figure. OX and OX' represent two axes, the included angle being θ. A value of $I_{x'}$ is desired. It is evident that $y' = y \cos \theta - x \sin \theta$, and $x' = x \cos \theta + y \sin \theta$.   Hence,

$$I_{x'} = \int y'^2 \, dA = \int (y \cos \theta - x \sin \theta)^2 \, dA$$

Expanding this, there results:

$$I_{x'} = I_x \cos^2 \theta + I_y \sin^2 \theta - 2P_{xy} \sin \theta \cos \theta$$

Similarly,

$$I_{y'} = \int x'^2 \, dA = \int (x \cos \theta + y \sin \theta)^2 \, dA$$

Whence

$$I_{y'} = I_x \sin^2 \theta + I_y \cos^2 \theta + 2P_{xy} \sin \theta \cos \theta$$

By the usual methods it may be found that the value of θ for which I_x is maximum or minimum is given by $\tan 2\theta = 2P_{xy}/(I_y - I_x)$.

The two values of θ resulting from this are 90° apart and give the directions of the axes through O for which I is respectively maximum and minimum.   By substituting the values of θ found from this formula in the equations for $I_{x'}$ and $I_{y'}$ above, the values of the principal moments of inertia are found.

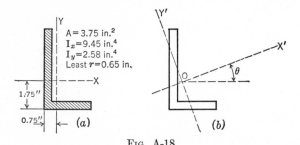

FIG. A-18

Example.   The properties of a $5 \times 3 \times \frac{1}{2}$ in. angle are shown in Fig. A-18a. Determine the inclination of the principal axes of inertia, and calculate the principal moments of inertia for this area.

Solution: The value of P_{xy} is first calculated.   The area is divided into two rectangles by extending the upper edge of the horizontal flange.   For each of these areas $P_{xy} = \bar{P}_{xy} + mnA$ in which $\bar{P}_{xy} = 0$.   For entire area

$$P_{xy} = 0 + (4.5 \times 0.5) \times (-0.5) \times 1 + 0 + (3.0 \times 0.5) \times (-1.5) \times 0.75$$
$$= -1.125 - 1.687 = -2.812 \text{ in.}^4$$

The angle of inclination of the principal axes is found from

$$\tan 2\theta = \frac{2P_{xy}}{I_y - I_x} = \frac{-5.625}{2.58 - 9.45} = 0.819$$

Hence $2\theta = 39° \, 19'$ and $\theta = 19° \, 40'$, as shown in Fig. A-18b.

The principal moments of inertia are found as follows:

$$I_{x'} = I_x \cos^2 \theta + I_y \sin^2 \theta - 2P_{xy} \sin \theta \cos \theta$$
$$= 9.45 \times 0.9417^2 + 2.58 \times 0.3364^2 + 2 \times 2.812 \times 0.3364 \times 0.9417$$
$$= 8.38 + 0.29 + 1.78 = 10.45 \text{ in.}^4$$

$$I_{y'} = I_x \sin^2 \theta + I_y \cos^2 \theta + 2P_{xy} \sin \theta \cos \theta$$
$$= 9.45 \times 0.3364^2 + 2.58 \times 0.9417^2 - 2 \times 2.812 \times .3364 \times 0.9417$$
$$= 1.07 + 2.29 - 1.78 = 1.58 \text{ in.}^4$$

The above values of the principal moments of inertia can also be found by using the value of the minimum radius of gyration r and the cross-sectional area A as given in the steel handbooks. Since

$$I_{y'} = Ar^2 = 3.75 \times 0.65^2 = 1.58 \text{ in.}^4 \qquad \text{and} \qquad I_x + I_y = I_{x'} + I_{y'}$$

then

$$9.45 + 2.58 = I_{x'} + 1.58 \qquad \text{whence} \qquad I_{x'} = 10.45 \text{ in.}^4$$

APPENDIX C

Tables

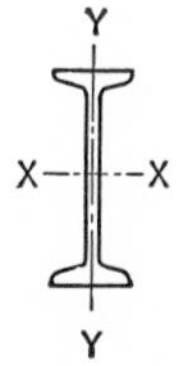

TABLE II

Elements of American Standard Beams

Nominal Size, in.	Weight per Foot, lb.	Area, in.²	Depth, in.	Flange Width, in.	Web Thickness in.	Axis X-X			Axis Y-Y		
						I, in.⁴	I/c, in.³	r, in.	I, in.⁴	I/c, in.³	r, in.
24 × 7⅞	120.0	35.13	24.00	8.048	.798	3010.8	250.9	9.26	84.9	21.1	1.56
	105.9	30.98	24.00	7.875	.625	2811.5	234.3	9.53	78.9	20.0	1.60
24 × 7	100.0	29.25	24.00	7.247	.747	2371.8	197.6	9.05	48.4	13.4	1.29
	90.0	26.30	24.00	7.124	.624	2230.1	185.8	9.21	45.5	12.8	1.32
	79.9	23.33	24.00	7.000	.500	2087.2	173.9	9.46	42.9	12.2	1.36
20 × 7	95.0	27.74	20.00	7.200	.800	1599.7	160.0	7.59	50.5	14.0	1.35
	85.0	24.80	20.00	7.053	.653	1501.7	150.2	7.78	47.0	13.3	1.38
20 × 6¼	75.0	21.90	20.00	6.391	.641	1263.5	126.3	7.60	30.1	9.4	1.17
	65.4	19.08	20.00	6.250	.500	1169.5	116.9	7.83	27.9	8.9	1.21
18 × 6	70.0	20.46	18.00	6.251	.711	917.5	101.9	6.70	24.5	7.8	1.09
	54.7	15.94	18.00	6.000	.460	795.5	88.4	7.07	21.2	7.1	1.15
15 × 5½	50.0	14.59	15.00	5.640	.550	481.1	64.2	5.74	16.0	5.7	1.05
	42.9	12.49	15.00	5.500	.410	441.8	58.9	5.95	14.6	5.3	1.08
12 × 5¼	50.0	14.57	12.00	5.477	.687	301.6	50.3	4.55	16.0	5.8	1.05
	40.8	11.84	12.00	5.250	.460	268.9	44.8	4.77	13.8	5.3	1.08
12 × 5	35.0	10.20	12.00	5.078	.428	227.0	37.8	4.72	10.0	3.9	0.99
	31.8	9.26	12.00	5.000	.350	215.8	36.0	4.83	9.5	3.8	1.01
10 × 4⅝	35.0	10.22	10.00	4.944	.594	145.8	29.2	3.78	8.5	3.4	0.91
	25.4	7.38	10.00	4.660	.310	122.1	24.4	4.07	6.9	3.0	0.97
8 × 4	23.0	6.71	8.00	4.171	.441	64.2	16.0	3.09	4.4	2.1	0.81
	18.4	5.34	8.00	4.000	.270	56.9	14.2	3.26	3.8	1.9	0.84
7 × 3⅝	20.0	5.83	7.00	3.860	.450	41.9	12.0	2.68	3.1	1.6	0.74
	15.3	4.43	7.00	3.660	.250	36.2	10.4	2.86	2.7	1.5	0.78
6 × 3⅜	17.25	5.02	6.00	3.565	.465	26.0	8.7	2.28	2.3	1.3	0.68
	12.5	3.61	6.00	3.330	.230	21.8	7.3	2.46	1.8	1.1	0.72
5 × 3	14.75	4.29	5.00	3.284	.494	15.0	6.0	1.87	1.7	1.0	0.63
	10.0	2.87	5.00	3.000	.210	12.1	4.8	2.05	1.2	0.82	0.65
4 × 2⅝	9.5	2.76	4.00	2.796	.326	6.7	3.3	1.56	0.91	0.65	0.58
	7.7	2.21	4.00	2.660	.190	6.0	3.0	1.64	0.77	0.58	0.59
3 × 2⅜	7.5	2.17	3.00	2.509	.349	2.9	1.9	1.15	0.59	0.47	0.52
	5.7	1.64	3.00	2.330	.170	2.5	1.7	1.23	0.46	0.40	0.53

TABLE III

WIDE-FLANGE BEAMS **WF**

Elements of Sections

Nominal Size, in.	Weight per Foot, lb.	Area, in.²	Depth, in.	Flange Width, in.	Web Thickness, in.	Axis X-X			Axis Y-Y		
						I, in.⁴	I/c, in.³	r, in.	I, in.⁴	I/c, in.³	r, in.
36 × 16½	300	88.17	36.72	16.655	.945	20,290.2	1105.1	15.17	1225.2	147.1	3.73
22 beams omitted (depths of 36″, 33″, and 30″)											
27 × 14	177	52.10	27.31	14.090	.725	6728.6	492.8	11.36	518.9	73.7	3.16
	160	47.04	27.08	14.023	.658	6018.6	444.5	11.31	458.0	65.3	3.12
	145	42.68	26.88	13.965	.600	5414.3	402.9	11.26	406.9	58.3	3.09
27 × 10	114	33.53	27.28	10.070	.570	4080.5	299.2	11.03	149.6	29.7	2.11
	102	30.01	27.07	10.018	.518	3604.1	266.3	10.96	129.5	25.9	2.08
	94	27.65	26.91	9.990	.490	3266.7	242.8	10.87	115.1	23.0	2.04
24 × 14	160	47.04	24.72	14.091	.656	5110.3	413.5	10.42	492.6	69.9	3.23
	145	42.62	24.49	14.043	.608	4561.0	372.5	10.34	434.3	61.8	3.19
	130	38.21	24.25	14.000	.565	4009.5	330.7	10.24	375.2	53.6	3.13
24 × 12	120	35.29	24.31	12.088	.556	3635.3	299.1	10.15	254.0	42.0	2.68
	110	32.36	24.16	12.042	.510	3315.0	274.4	10.12	229.1	38.0	2.66
	100	29.43	24.00	12.000	.468	2987.3	248.9	10.08	203.5	33.9	2.63
24 × 9	94	27.63	24.29	9.061	.516	2683.0	220.9	9.85	102.2	22.6	1.92
	84	24.71	24.09	9.015	.470	2364.3	196.3	9.78	88.3	19.6	1.89
	76	22.37	23.91	8.985	.440	2096.4	175.4	9.68	76.5	17.0	1.85
21 × 13	142	41.76	21.46	13.132	.659	3403.1	317.2	9.03	385.9	58.8	3.04
	127	37.34	21.24	13.061	.588	3017.2	284.1	8.99	338.6	51.8	3.01
	112	32.93	21.00	13.000	.527	2620.6	249.6	8.92	289.7	44.6	2.96
21 × 9	96	28.21	21.14	9.038	.575	2088.9	197.6	8.60	109.3	24.2	1.97
	82	24.10	20.86	8.962	.499	1752.4	168.0	8.53	89.6	20.0	1.93
21 × 8¼	73	21.46	21.24	8.295	.455	1600.3	150.7	8.64	66.2	16.0	1.76
	68	20.02	21.13	8.270	.430	1478.3	139.9	8.59	60.4	14.6	1.74
	62	18.23	20.99	8.240	.400	1326.8	126.4	8.53	53.1	12.9	1.71
18 × 11¾	114	33.51	18.48	11.833	.595	2033.8	220.1	7.79	255.6	43.2	2.76
	105	30.86	18.32	11.792	.554	1852.5	202.2	7.75	231.0	39.2	2.73
	96	28.22	18.16	11.750	.512	1674.7	184.4	7.70	206.8	35.2	2.71
18 × 8¾	85	24.97	18.32	8.838	.526	1429.9	156.1	7.57	99.4	22.5	2.00
	77	22.63	18.16	8.787	.475	1286.8	141.7	7.54	88.6	20.2	1.98
	70	20.56	18.00	8.750	.438	1153.9	128.2	7.49	78.5	17.9	1.95
	64	18.80	17.87	8.715	.403	1045.8	117.0	7.46	70.3	16.1	1.93
18 × 7½	60	17.64	18.25	7.558	.416	984.0	107.8	7.47	47.1	12.5	1.63
	55	16.19	18.12	7.532	.390	889.9	98.2	7.41	42.0	11.1	1.61
	50	14.71	18.00	7.500	.358	800.6	89.0	7.38	37.2	9.9	1.59
16 × 11½	96	28.22	16.32	11.533	.535	1355.1	166.1	6.93	207.2	35.9	2.71
	88	25.87	16.16	11.502	.504	1222.6	151.3	6.87	185.2	32.2	2.67
16 × 8½	78	22.92	16.32	8.586	.529	1042.6	127.8	6.74	87.5	20.4	1.95
	71	20.86	16.16	8.543	.486	936.9	115.9	6.70	77.9	18.2	1.93
	64	18.80	16.00	8.500	.443	833.8	104.2	6.66	68.4	16.1	1.91
	58	17.04	15.86	8.464	.407	746.4	94.1	6.62	60.5	14.3	1.88
16 × 7	50	14.70	16.25	7.073	.380	655.4	80.7	6.68	34.8	9.8	1.54
	45	13.24	16.12	7.039	.346	583.3	72.4	6.64	30.5	8.7	1.52
	40	11.77	16.00	7.000	.307	515.5	64.4	6.62	26.5	7.6	1.50
	36	10.59	15.85	6.992	.299	446.3	56.3	6.49	22.1	6.3	1.45

Nominal Size, in.	Weight per Foot, lb.	Area, in.²	Depth, in.	Flange Width, in.	Web Thickness, in.	Axis X-X			Axis Y-Y		
						I, in.⁴	I/c, in.³	r, in.	I, in.⁴	I/c, in.³	r, in.
14 × 16	426	125.25	18.69	16.695	1.875	6610.3	707.4	7.26	2359.5	282.7	4.34
	398	116.98	18.31	16.590	1.770	6013.7	656.9	7.17	2169.7	261.6	4.31
	370	108.78	17.94	16.475	1.655	5454.2	608.1	7.08	1986.0	241.1	4.27
	342	100.59	17.56	16.365	1.545	4911.5	559.4	6.99	1806.9	220.8	4.24
	314	92.30	17.19	16.235	1.415	4399.4	511.9	6.90	1631.4	201.0	4.20
	287	84.37	16.81	16.130	1.310	3912.1	465.5	6.81	1466.5	181.8	4.17
	264	77.63	16.50	16.025	1.205	3526.0	427.4	6.74	1331.2	166.1	4.14
	246	72.33	16.25	15.945	1.125	3228.9	397.4	6.68	1226.6	153.9	4.12
	237	69.69	16.12	15.910	1.090	3080.9	382.2	6.65	1174.8	147.7	4.11
	228	67.06	16.00	15.865	1.045	2942.4	367.8	6.62	1124.8	141.8	4.10
	219	64.36	15.87	15.825	1.005	2798.2	352.6	6.59	1073.2	135.6	4.08
	211	62.07	15.75	15.800	0.980	2671.4	339.2	6.56	1028.6	130.2	4.07
	202	59.39	15.63	15.750	0.930	2538.8	324.9	6.54	979.7	124.4	4.06
	193	56.73	15.50	15.710	0.890	2402.4	310.0	6.51	930.1	118.4	4.05
	184	54.07	15.38	15.660	0.840	2274.8	295.8	6.49	882.7	112.7	4.04
	176	51.73	15.25	15.640	0.820	2149.6	281.9	6.45	837.9	107.1	4.02
	167	49.09	15.12	15.600	0.780	2020.8	267.3	6.42	790.2	101.3	4.01
	158	46.47	15.00	15.550	0.730	1900.6	253.4	6.40	745.0	95.8	4.00
	150	44.08	14.88	15.515	0.695	1786.9	240.2	6.37	702.5	90.6	3.99
	142	41.85	14.75	15.500	0.680	1672.2	226.7	6.32	660.1	85.2	3.97
14 × 14½	136	39.98	14.75	14.740	0.660	1593.0	216.0	6.31	567.7	77.0	3.77
	127	37.33	14.62	14.690	0.610	1476.7	202.0	6.29	527.6	71.8	3.76
	119	34.99	14.50	14.650	0.570	1373.1	189.4	6.26	491.8	67.1	3.75
	111	32.65	14.37	14.620	0.540	1266.5	176.3	6.23	454.9	62.2	3.73
	103	30.26	14.25	14.575	0.495	1165.8	163.6	6.21	419.7	57.6	3.72
	95	27.94	14.12	14.545	0.465	1063.5	150.6	6.17	383.7	52.8	3.71
	87	25.56	14.00	14.500	0.420	966.9	138.1	6.15	349.7	48.2	3.70
14 × 12	84	24.71	14.18	12.023	0.451	928.4	130.9	6.13	225.5	37.5	3.02
	78	22.94	14.06	12.000	0.428	851.2	121.1	6.09	206.9	34.5	3.00
14 × 10	74	21.76	14.19	10.072	0.450	796.8	112.3	6.05	133.5	26.5	2.48
	68	20.00	14.06	10.040	0.418	724.1	103.0	6.02	121.2	24.1	2.46
	61	17.94	13.91	10.000	0.378	641.5	92.2	5.98	107.3	21.5	2.45
14 × 8	53	15.59	13.94	8.062	0.370	542.1	77.8	5.90	57.5	14.3	1.92
	48	14.11	13.81	8.031	0.339	484.9	70.2	5.86	51.3	12.8	1.91
	43	12.65	13.68	8.000	0.308	429.0	62.7	5.82	45.1	11.3	1.89
14 × 6¾	38	11.17	14.12	6.776	0.313	385.3	54.6	5.87	24.6	7.3	1.49
	34	10.00	14.00	6.750	0.287	339.2	48.5	5.83	21.3	6.3	1.46
	30	8.81	13.86	6.733	0.270	289.6	41.8	5.73	17.5	5.2	1.41
12 × 12	190	55.86	14.38	12.670	1.060	1892.5	263.2	5.82	589.7	93.1	3.25
	161	47.38	13.88	12.515	0.905	1541.8	222.2	5.70	486.2	77.7	3.20
	133	39.11	13.38	12.365	0.755	1221.2	182.5	5.59	389.9	63.1	3.16
	120	35.31	13.12	12.320	0.710	1071.7	163.4	5.51	345.1	56.0	3.13
	106	31.19	12.88	12.230	0.620	930.7	144.5	5.46	300.9	49.2	3.11
	99	29.09	12.75	12.190	0.580	858.5	134.7	5.43	278.2	45.7	3.09
	92	27.06	12.62	12.155	0.545	788.9	125.0	5.40	256.4	42.2	3.08
	85	24.98	12.50	12.105	0.495	723.3	115.7	5.38	235.5	38.9	3.07
	79	23.22	12.38	12.080	0.470	663.0	107.1	5.34	216.4	35.8	3.05
	72	21.16	12.25	12.040	0.430	597.4	97.5	5.31	195.3	32.4	3.04
	65	19.11	12.12	12.000	0.390	533.4	88.0	5.28	174.6	29.1	3.02
				25 beams omitted (depths of 12″, 10″, and 8″)							
8 × 8	48	14.11	8.50	8.117	0.405	183.7	43.2	3.61	60.9	15.0	2.08
	40	11.76	8.25	8.077	0.365	146.3	35.5	3.53	49.0	12.1	2.04
	35	10.30	8.12	8.027	0.315	126.5	31.1	3.50	42.5	10.6	2.03
	31	9.12	8.00	8.000	0.288	109.7	27.4	3.47	37.0	9.2	2.01
8 × 6½	28	8.23	8.06	6.540	0.285	97.8	24.3	3.45	21.6	6.6	1.62
	24	7.06	7.93	6.500	0.245	82.5	20.8	3.42	18.2	5.6	1.61
8 × 5¼	20	5.88	8.14	5.268	0.248	69.2	17.0	3.43	8.5	3.2	1.20
	17	5.00	8.00	5.250	0.230	56.4	14.1	3.36	6.7	2.6	1.16

TABLE IV

Elements of American Standard Channels

Nominal Size, in.	Weight per Foot, lb.	Area, in.^{2}	Depth, in.	Flange Width, in.	Web Thickness, in.	Axis X-X			Axis Y-Y			
						I, in.^{4}	I/c, in.^{3}	r, in.	I, in.^{4}	I/c, in.^{3}	r, in.	x, in.
15 × 3⅜	50.0	14.64	15.00	3.716	.716	401.4	53.6	5.24	11.2	3.8	.87	.80
	40.0	11.70	15.00	3.520	.520	346.3	46.2	5.44	9.3	3.4	.89	.78
	33.9	9.90	15.00	3.400	.400	312.6	41.7	5.62	8.2	3.2	.91	.79
12 × 3	30.0	8.79	12.00	3.170	.510	161.2	26.9	4.28	5.2	2.1	.77	.68
	25.0	7.32	12.00	3.047	.387	143.5	23.9	4.43	4.5	1.9	.79	.68
	20.7	6.03	12.00	2.940	.280	128.1	21.4	4.61	3.9	1.7	.81	.70
10 × 2⅝	30.0	8.80	10.00	3.033	.673	103.0	20.6	3.42	4.0	1.7	.67	.65
	25.0	7.33	10.00	2.886	.526	90.7	18.1	3.52	3.4	1.5	.68	.62
	20.0	5.86	10.00	2.739	.379	78.5	15.7	3.66	2.8	1.3	.70	.61
	15.3	4.47	10.00	2.600	.240	66.9	13.4	3.87	2.3	1.2	.72	.64
9 × 2½	20.0	5.86	9.00	2.648	.448	60.6	13.5	3.22	2.4	1.2	.65	.59
	15.0	4.39	9.00	2.485	.285	50.7	11.3	3.40	1.9	1.0	.67	.59
	13.4	3.89	9.00	2.430	.230	47.3	10.5	3.49	1.8	0.97	.67	.61
8 × 2¼	18.75	5.49	8.00	2.527	.487	43.7	10.9	2.82	2.0	1.0	.60	.57
	13.75	4.02	8.00	2.343	.303	35.8	9.0	2.99	1.5	0.86	.62	.56
	11.5	3.36	8.00	2.260	.220	32.3	8.1	3.10	1.3	0.79	.63	.58
7 × 2⅜	14.75	4.32	7.00	2.299	.419	27.1	7.7	2.51	1.4	0.79	.57	.53
	12.25	3.58	7.00	2.194	.314	24.1	6.9	2.59	1.2	0.71	.58	.53
	9.8	2.85	7.00	2.090	.210	21.1	6.0	2.72	0.98	0.63	.59	.55
6 × 2	13.0	3.81	6.00	2.157	.437	17.3	5.8	2.13	1.1	0.65	.53	.52
	10.5	3.07	6.00	2.034	.314	15.1	5.0	2.22	0.87	0.57	.53	.50
	8.2	2.39	6.00	1.920	.200	13.0	4.3	2.34	0.70	0.50	.54	.52
5 × 1¾	9.0	2.63	5.00	1.885	.325	8.8	3.5	1.83	0.64	0.45	.49	.48
	6.7	1.95	5.00	1.750	.190	7.4	3.0	1.95	0.48	0.38	.50	.49
4 × 1⅝	7.25	2.12	4.00	1.720	.320	4.5	2.3	1.47	0.44	0.35	.46	.46
	5.4	1.56	4.00	1.580	.180	3.8	1.9	1.56	0.32	0.29	.45	.46
3 × 1½	6.0	1.75	3.00	1.596	.356	2.1	1.4	1.08	0.31	0.27	.42	.46
	5.0	1.46	3.00	1.498	.258	1.8	1.2	1.12	0.25	0.24	.41	.44
	4.1	1.19	3.00	1.410	.170	1.6	1.1	1.17	0.20	0.21	.41	.44

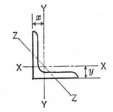

TABLE V

ELEMENTS OF EQUAL ANGLES

Size, in.	Thickness, in.	Weight per Foot, lb.	Area, in.²	Axis X-X and Axis Y-Y				Axis Z-Z
				I, in.⁴	I/c, in.³	r, in.	x or y, in.	r, in.
8 × 8	1⅛	56.9	16.73	98.0	17.5	2.42	2.41	1.56
	1	51.0	15.00	89.0	15.8	2.44	2.37	1.56
	⅞	45.0	13.23	79.6	14.0	2.45	2.32	1.57
	¾	38.9	11.44	69.7	12.2	2.47	2.28	1.57
	⅝	32.7	9.61	59.4	10.3	2.49	2.23	1.58
	⁹⁄₁₆	29.6	8.68	54.1	9.3	2.50	2.21	1.58
	½	26.4	7.75	48.6	8.4	2.50	2.19	1.59
6 × 6	1	37.4	11.00	35.5	8.6	1.80	1.86	1.17
	⅞	33.1	9.73	31.9	7.6	1.81	1.82	1.17
	¾	28.7	8.44	28.2	6.7	1.83	1.78	1.17
	⅝	24.2	7.11	24.2	5.7	1.84	1.73	1.18
	⁹⁄₁₆	21.9	6.43	22.1	5.1	1.85	1.71	1.18
	½	19.6	5.75	19.9	4.6	1.86	1.68	1.18
	⁷⁄₁₆	17.2	5.06	17.7	4.1	1.87	1.66	1.19
	⅜	14.9	4.36	15.4	3.5	1.88	1.64	1.19
	⁵⁄₁₆	12.5	3.66	13.0	3.0	1.89	1.61	1.19
5 × 5	⅞	27.2	7.98	17.8	5.2	1.49	1.57	0.97
	¾	23.6	6.94	15.7	4.5	1.51	1.52	0.97
	⅝	20.0	5.86	13.6	3.9	1.52	1.48	0.98
	½	16.2	4.75	11.3	3.2	1.54	1.43	0.98
	⁷⁄₁₆	14.3	4.18	10.0	2.8	1.55	1.41	0.98
	⅜	12.3	3.61	8.7	2.4	1.56	1.39	0.99
	⁵⁄₁₆	10.3	3.03	7.4	2.0	1.57	1.37	0.99
4 × 4	¾	18.5	5.44	7.7	2.8	1.19	1.27	0.78
	⅝	15.7	4.61	6.7	2.4	1.20	1.23	0.78
	½	12.8	3.75	5.6	2.0	1.22	1.18	0.78
	⁷⁄₁₆	11.3	3.31	5.0	1.8	1.23	1.16	0.78
	⅜	9.8	2.86	4.4	1.5	1.23	1.14	0.79
	⁵⁄₁₆	8.2	2.40	3.7	1.3	1.24	1.12	0.79
	¼	6.6	1.94	3.0	1.1	1.25	1.09	0.80
3½ × 3½	½	11.1	3.25	3.6	1.5	1.06	1.06	0.68
	⁷⁄₁₆	9.8	2.87	3.3	1.3	1.07	1.04	0.68
	⅜	8.5	2.48	2.9	1.2	1.07	1.01	0.69
	⁵⁄₁₆	7.2	2.09	2.5	0.98	1.08	0.99	0.69
	¼	5.8	1.69	2.0	0.79	1.09	0.97	0.69
3 × 3	½	9.4	2.75	2.2	1.1	0.90	0.93	0.58
	⁷⁄₁₆	8.3	2.43	2.0	0.95	0.91	0.91	0.58
	⅜	7.2	2.11	1.8	0.83	0.91	0.89	0.58
	⁵⁄₁₆	6.1	1.78	1.5	0.71	0.92	0.87	0.59
	¼	4.9	1.44	1.2	0.58	0.93	0.84	0.59
	³⁄₁₆	3.71	1.09	0.96	0.44	0.94	0.82	0.59
2½ × 2½	½	7.7	2.25	1.2	0.72	0.74	0.81	0.49
	⅜	5.9	1.73	0.98	0.57	0.75	0.76	0.49
	⁵⁄₁₆	5.0	1.47	0.85	0.48	0.76	0.74	0.49
	¼	4.1	1.19	0.70	0.39	0.77	0.72	0.49
	³⁄₁₆	3.07	0.90	0.55	0.30	0.78	0.69	0.49

Smaller angles are rolled but not listed here.

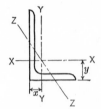

TABLE VI

Elements of Unequal Angles

Size, in.	Thickness, in.	Weight per Foot, lb.	Area, in.²	Axis X-X				Axis Y-Y				Axis Z-Z
				I, in.⁴	I/c, in.³	r, in.	y, in.	I, in.⁴	I/c, in.³	r, in.	x, in.	r, in.
9 × 4	1	40.8	12.00	97.0	17.6	2.84	3.50	12.0	4.0	1.00	1.00	0.83
	⅞	36.1	10.61	86.8	15.7	2.86	3.45	10.8	3.6	1.01	0.95	0.84
	¾	31.3	9.19	76.1	13.6	2.88	3.41	9.6	3.1	1.02	0.91	0.84
	⅝	26.3	7.73	64.9	11.5	2.90	3.36	8.3	2.6	1.04	0.86	0.85
	⁹⁄₁₆	23.8	7.00	59.1	10.4	2.91	3.33	7.6	2.4	1.04	0.83	0.85
	½	21.3	6.25	53.2	9.3	2.92	3.31	6.9	2.2	1.05	0.81	0.85
8 × 6	1	44.2	13.00	80.8	15.1	2.49	2.65	38.8	8.9	1.73	1.65	1.28
	⅞	39.1	11.48	72.3	13.4	2.51	2.61	34.9	7.9	1.74	1.61	1.28
	¾	33.8	9.94	63.4	11.7	2.53	2.56	30.7	6.9	1.76	1.56	1.29
	⅝	28.5	8.36	54.1	9.9	2.54	2.52	26.3	5.9	1.77	1.52	1.29
	⁹⁄₁₆	25.7	7.56	49.3	9.0	2.55	2.50	24.0	5.3	1.78	1.50	1.30
	½	23.0	6.75	44.3	8.0	2.56	2.47	21.7	4.8	1.79	1.47	1.30
	⁷⁄₁₆	20.2	5.93	39.2	7.1	2.57	2.45	19.3	4.2	1.80	1.45	1.31
6 × 4	⅞	27.2	7.98	27.7	7.2	1.86	2.12	9.8	3.4	1.11	1.12	0.86
	¾	23.6	6.94	24.5	6.3	1.88	2.08	8.7	3.0	1.12	1.08	0.86
	⅝	20.0	5.86	21.1	5.3	1.90	2.03	7.5	2.5	1.13	1.03	0.86
	⁹⁄₁₆	18.1	5.31	19.3	4.8	1.90	2.01	6.9	2.3	1.14	1.01	0.87
	½	16.2	4.75	17.4	4.3	1.91	1.99	6.3	2.1	1.15	0.99	0.87
	⁷⁄₁₆	14.3	4.18	15.5	3.8	1.92	1.96	5.6	1.9	1.16	0.96	0.87
	⅜	12.3	3.61	13.5	3.3	1.93	1.94	4.9	1.6	1.17	0.94	0.88
	⁵⁄₁₆	10.3	3.03	11.4	2.8	1.94	1.92	4.2	1.4	1.17	0.92	0.88
5 × 3½	¾	19.8	5.81	13.9	4.3	1.55	1.75	5.6	2.2	0.98	1.00	0.75
	⅝	16.8	4.92	12.0	3.7	1.56	1.70	4.8	1.9	0.99	0.95	0.75
	½	13.6	4.00	10.0	3.0	1.58	1.66	4.1	1.6	1.01	0.91	0.75
	⁷⁄₁₆	12.0	3.53	8.9	2.6	1.59	1.63	3.6	1.4	1.01	0.88	0.76
	⅜	10.4	3.05	7.8	2.3	1.60	1.61	3.2	1.2	1.02	0.86	0.76
	⁵⁄₁₆	8.7	2.56	6.6	1.9	1.61	1.59	2.7	1.0	1.03	0.84	0.76
	¼	7.0	2.06	5.4	1.6	1.61	1.56	2.2	0.83	1.04	0.81	0.76
4 × 3	½	11.1	3.25	5.1	1.9	1.25	1.33	2.4	1.1	0.86	0.83	0.64
	⁷⁄₁₆	9.8	2.87	4.5	1.7	1.25	1.30	2.2	1.0	0.87	0.80	0.64
	⅜	8.5	2.48	4.0	1.5	1.26	1.28	1.9	0.87	0.88	0.78	0.64
	⁵⁄₁₆	7.2	2.09	3.4	1.2	1.27	1.26	1.7	0.73	0.89	0.76	0.65
	¼	5.8	1.69	2.8	1.0	1.28	1.24	1.4	0.60	0.90	0.74	0.65
3 × 2½	½	8.5	2.50	2.1	1.0	0.91	1.00	1.3	0.74	0.72	0.75	0.52
	⁷⁄₁₆	7.6	2.21	1.9	0.93	0.92	0.98	1.2	0.66	0.73	0.73	0.52
	⅜	6.6	1.92	1.7	0.81	0.93	0.96	1.0	0.58	0.74	0.71	0.52
	⁵⁄₁₆	5.6	1.62	1.4	0.69	0.94	0.93	0.90	0.49	0.74	0.68	0.53
	¼	4.5	1.31	1.2	0.56	0.95	0.91	0.74	0.40	0.75	0.66	0.53

Many other sizes of unequal angles are rolled.

TABLE VII

U. S. Standard Screw Threads

Diameter and area at root of thread

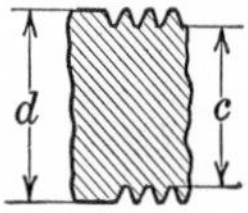

Diameter		Area		Diameter		Area	
Total d, In.	Net c, In.	Total Dia., d, Sq. In.	Net Dia., c, Sq. In.	Total d, In.	Net c, In.	Total Dia., d, Sq. In.	Net Dia., c, Sq. In.
¼	.185	.049	.027	2½	2.176	4.909	3.716
⅜	.294	.110	.068	2¾	2.426	5.940	4.619
½	.400	.196	.126	3	2.629	7.069	5.428
⅝	.507	.307	.202	3¼	2.879	8.296	6.509
¾	.620	.442	.302	3½	3.100	9.621	7.549
⅞	.731	.601	.419	3¾	3.317	11.045	8.641
1	.837	.785	.551	4	3.567	12.566	9.993
1⅛	.939	.994	.693	4¼	3.798	14.186	11.330
1¼	1.065	1.227	.890	4½	4.028	15.904	12.741
1⅜	1.158	1.485	1.054	4¾	4.256	17.721	14.221
1½	1.284	1.767	1.294	5	4.480	19.635	15.766
1⅝	1.389	2.074	1.515	5¼	4.730	21.648	17.574
1¾	1.491	2.405	1.744	5½	4.953	23.758	19.268
1⅞	1.616	2.761	2.049	5¾	5.203	25.967	21.262
2	1.712	3.142	2.300	6	5.423	28.274	23.095
2¼	1.962	3.976	3.021				

Thickness of standard nut equals nominal diameter of bolt.

TABLE VIII

Standard Welded Steel Pipe

(National Tube Company Standard)

Size, In.	Diameters, Inches		Thick-ness, Inches	Cross-section		Size, In.	Diameters, Inches		Thick-ness, Inches	Cross-section	
	External	Internal		Area of Metal, Sq. In.	Moment of Inertia, In.⁴*		External	Internal		Area of Metal, Sq. In.	Moment of Inertia, In.⁴*
⅛	.405	.269	.068	.072	.0011	5	5.563	5.047	.258	4.300	15.2
¼	.540	.364	.088	.125	.0033	6	6.625	6.065	.280	5.581	28.1
⅜	.675	.493	.091	.167	.0073	8	8.625	8.071	.277	7.265	63.3
½	.840	.622	.109	.250	.0171	8	8.625	7.981	.322	8.399	72.5
¾	1.050	.824	.113	.333	.0370	10	10.750	10.192	.279	9.178	125.8
1	1.315	1.049	.133	.494	.0873	10	10.750	10.136	.307	10.072	137.5
1¼	1.660	1.380	.140	.669	.195	10	10.750	10.020	.365	11.908	160.7
1½	1.900	1.610	.145	.799	.310	12	12.750	12.090	.330	12.876	248.5
2	2.375	2.067	.154	1.075	.666	12	12.750	12.000	.375	14.567	279.3
2½	2.875	2.469	.203	1.704	1.53	14 O.D.	14.000	13.250	.375	16.052	372.8
3	3.500	3.068	.216	2.228	3.02	15 O.D.	15.000	14.250	.375	17.230	461.0
3½	4.000	3.548	.226	2.680	4.79	16 O.D.	16.000	15.250	.375	18.408	562.1
4	4.500	4.026	.237	3.174	7.23						

*Rectangular moment of inertia with respect to a diameter.

APPENDIX C

TABLE IX

ALLOWABLE STRESSES — STRUCTURAL STEEL, CAST IRON AND MASONRY
(All stresses are given in pounds per square inch)

STRUCTURAL STEEL FOR BRIDGES AND BUILDINGS

A.I.S.C. (Steel Building Frames)   A.R.E.A. (Bridges)

Tension and Short Compression Members

	A.I.S.C.	A.R.E.A.
Tension (net section)	20,000	18,000
Compression (on short lengths)	20,000	18,000

Axially Loaded Columns

$$\frac{P}{A} = 17,000 - 0.485 \frac{L^2}{r^2}$$

for $\dfrac{L}{r}$ not over 120.

Riveted Ends

$$\frac{P}{A} = 15,000 - \frac{1}{4}\left(\frac{L}{r}\right)^2$$

Pinned Ends

$$\frac{P}{A} = 15,000 - \frac{1}{3}\left(\frac{L}{r}\right)^2$$

Beams

Tension (bending)   20,000   18,000

Compression $18,000 - 5\left(\dfrac{L}{b}\right)^2$

$\dfrac{ld}{bt}$ less than 600 . . . .   20,000 $\dfrac{L}{b}$ not more than 40

$\dfrac{ld}{bt}$ more than 600 . . . . $\dfrac{12,000,000}{ld/bt}$

Shearing on web   13,000   11,000

Rivets, Pins, Bolts

Bending on pins   30,000   27,000

Shearing

On rivets, pins, and
  turned bolts in
  reamed holes   15,000

On power-driven
  rivets and pins 13,500

On unfinished bolts   10,000

On turned bolts and
  hand-driven rivets . . 11,000

Bearing

Rivets, turned bolts in reamed or
  drilled holes

Power-driven rivets . . . 27,000

  in double shear   40,000

  in single shear   32,000   Turned bolts

Unfinished bolts

  and hand-driven

  in double shear   25,000   rivets   20,000

  in single shear   20,000

Pins   32,000   Pins   24,000

TABLE IX (*Continued*)

CAST IRON

(A.R.E.A. Buildings)

Axial compression (short lengths) 12,000

Bending, tension 3,000

    compression 12,000

Shearing 3,000

Columns .... $\dfrac{P}{A} = 12,000 - 60\,\dfrac{L}{r}$

MASONRY

Bearing, on granite.................................... 800

    on concrete.. 600

    on sandstone and limestone.......................... 400

    on hard brick, cement mortar........................ 250

The American Institute of Steel Construction specifications are widely used in building codes. American Railway Engineering Association specifications for steel railway bridges are more conservative because of more severe conditions of use. Both specifications are based on use of steel designated as A7 by the American Society for Testing Materials. For this steel the specifications require:

> Tensile strength   60,000 to 72,000 psi.
> Yield point, minimum 0.5 tensile strength
>   but not less than 33,000 psi.

Because specifications contain restrictions and explanations that cannot be given in a brief table, original specifications should be used in actual design.

TABLE X

Commercial Measurement of Lumber. Lumber is sold by *board foot* measure. A board foot is one-twelfth of a cubic foot; that is, a timber 12 × 12 in. × 12 ft long contains 144 board feet. A board foot is usually assumed to weigh 3 lb to 4 lb.

Lumber dealers sell many standard sizes which are usually called by the nominal dimensions of the cross-section, as, for instance, a "two by four" or a "ten by twelve."

The nominal cross-sectional dimensions are commonly in multiples of 1 in. up to 4 in., above which they are in multiples of 2 in. The actual dimensions of lumber are less than the nominal dimensions because of shrinkage and the removal of wood by the saw and planer. For dressed lumber, dimensions of 4 in. or less may be $\frac{3}{8}$ in. scant. Larger dimensions may be $\frac{1}{2}$ in. less than nominal sizes.* The dimensions of rough (unplaned) lumber approach more nearly the nominal sizes, but are still somewhat scant. In calculations involving the strength of lumber the actual dressed sizes should be used. The number of board feet is based on nominal sizes, however.

* National Lumber Manufacturers Association standards. Practice varies somewhat in different localities.

APPENDIX C

TABLE XI

ALLOWABLE STRESSES FOR LUMBER

Allowable stresses for lumber conforming to the standards of grading of the National Lumber Manufacturers Association and used in accordance with the highest standards of design and workmanship.
(Based on recommendations of the National Lumber Manufacturers Association, 1952.)

Species	Allowable Stresses, psi				Modulus of Elasticity, psi
	Compression Parallel to Grain*	Compression Perpendicular to Grain	Bending	Horizontal Shearing	
Cypress, Tidewater red	1,125	360	1,300	120	1,200,000
Douglas fir (coast region)					
Select structural	1,450	415	1,900	120	1,600,000
Structural	1,325	415	1,700	120	1,600,000
Hemlock, Eastern, prime structural	775	360	1,200	60	1,100,000
Oak, commercial red and white	1,375	600	1,950	145	1,500,000
Pine, longleaf southern					
Prime structural	1,400	455	2,000	120	1,600,000
Structural	1,300	455	1,800	120	1,600,000
Spruce, Eastern, structural	975	300	1,300	95	1,200,000

If structure is not continuously dry, multiply stress given in any column of the table by the factor given below in the same column.

Occasionally wet but quickly dry	0.90	0.65	0.85	1.00	1.00
Generally damp or wet	0.80	0.65	0.70	1.00	1.00

* If the unsupported length of a compression member exceeds 11 times the least width, the allowable stress must be determined by a column formula (Chap. 13).

For all woods listed in this table there are grades for which the allowable stresses are higher than those given above and other grades for which the allowable stresses are lower than those given. Designers of timber structures should consult *National Design Specifications for Stress Grade Lumber and Its Fastenings* recommended by the National Lumber Manufacturers Association.

TABLE XII

PHYSICAL PROPERTIES OF MATERIALS

Material	Weight, lb per cu ft	Coefficient of Thermal Expansion per Deg F	Ultimate Strength		Elongation in 2 in., %	Modulus of Elasticity, psi
			Tensile, psi	Compressive, psi		
Ferrous Metals:						
Steel 0.15% C or less	⎫	0.0000061 −	45,000		30	⎫ 30,000,000
0.20–0.30% C		0.0000073	60,000		25	(Often
0.40–0.60% C	⎬490	average	75,000		20	29,000,000
0.70–0.85% C		0.0000065	110,000		10	or less)
1.00% C and over	⎭		105,000		small	⎭
Cast Iron						
Gray	⎫450	⎫0.0000062	15,000 − 25,000	80,000 − 150,000	small	12,000,000
Malleable			35,000 − 58,000	80,000 − 150,000	15–4.5	25,000,000
Wrought Iron	480	0.0000067	45,000 − 50,000		40–20	27,000,000
Non-Ferrous Metals:						
Aluminum	⎫	⎫	12,000 −			⎫
Annealed Sheets	⎬165	⎬0.0000123	15,000		30–20	⎬10,000,000
Wire (Hard drawn)	⎭	⎭	25,000 − 55,000		8–2	⎭
Copper						
Annealed	⎫550	⎫0.0000093	35,000		50	15,000,000
Wire (Hard drawn)	⎭	⎭	50,000		9	17,000,000
Brass (30% Zn)						
Cast	⎫530	⎫0.0000105	40,000	60,000	35	⎫14,000,000
Rolled	⎭	⎭	60,000		5	⎭
Bronze (10% Sn)	510	0.0000099	33,000	56,000	10	10,000,000
Duralumin						
Quenched and aged	⎫		55,000 − 65,000		20	⎫
Quenched, aged and rolled	⎬174		75,000 − 80,000		.	⎬10,300,000
Non-metallic Materials:						
Stone or						
Gravel Concrete						
8½ gal. water per sack of cement	⎫	⎫		2,000*		⎫2,000,000 −
7½ do.	⎬150	⎬0.000006		2,800		4,000,000
6½ do.				3,600		increasing
6 do.	⎭	⎭		4,000		with strength
Cinder concrete	110					
Lumber						
Southern pine (dense)	50	⎫		4,300		1,600,000
Douglas fir (coast)	40			3,900		1,600,000
Hemlock (western)	40			2,900		1,400,000
Spruce (red, white and Sitka)	33	⎬0.000003		2,600		1,200,000
Cypress	48			3,900		1,200,000
White Oak	60	⎭		3,500		1,500,000

Values in the table are typical. For an individual specimen, the values (particularly those for strength, elongation and modulus of elasticity) may differ considerably from those given. Strengths and moduli of elasticity of lumber are for forces applied parallel to the grain.

* "Joint Code" values for 28-day concrete.

APPENDIX C

TABLE XIII

Deflections and Slopes of Cantilever Beams

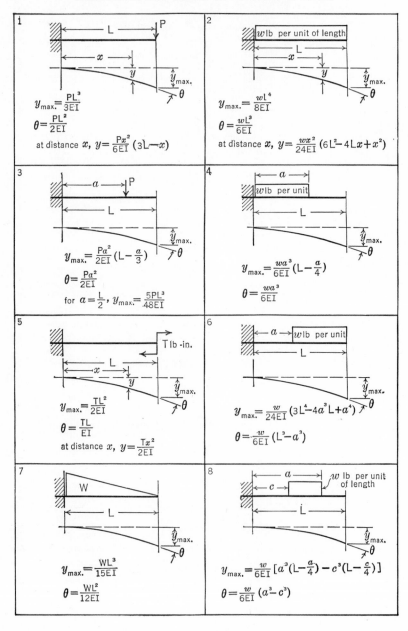

1

$$y_{max.} = \frac{PL^3}{3EI}$$

$$\theta = \frac{PL^2}{2EI}$$

at distance x, $y = \frac{Px^2}{6EI}(3L-x)$

2

w lb per unit of length

$$y_{max.} = \frac{wL^4}{8EI}$$

$$\theta = \frac{wL^3}{6EI}$$

at distance x, $y = \frac{wx^2}{24EI}(6L^2 - 4Lx + x^2)$

3

$$y_{max.} = \frac{Pa^2}{2EI}\left(L - \frac{a}{3}\right)$$

$$\theta = \frac{Pa^2}{2EI}$$

for $a = \frac{L}{2}$, $y_{max.} = \frac{5PL^3}{48EI}$

4

w lb per unit

$$y_{max.} = \frac{wa^3}{6EI}\left(L - \frac{a}{4}\right)$$

$$\theta = \frac{wa^3}{6EI}$$

5

T lb -in.

$$y_{max.} = \frac{TL^2}{2EI}$$

$$\theta = \frac{TL}{EI}$$

at distance x, $y = \frac{Tx^2}{2EI}$

6

a — w lb per unit

$$y_{max.} = \frac{w}{24EI}(3L^4 - 4a^3L + a^4)$$

$$\theta = \frac{w}{6EI}(L^3 - a^3)$$

7

W

$$y_{max.} = \frac{WL^3}{15EI}$$

$$\theta = \frac{WL^2}{12EI}$$

8

w lb per unit of length

$$y_{max.} = \frac{w}{6EI}\left[a^3\left(L - \frac{a}{4}\right) - c^3\left(L - \frac{c}{4}\right)\right]$$

$$\theta = \frac{w}{6EI}(a^3 - c^3)$$

TABLE XIV

Deflections and Slopes of Beams on Two Supports

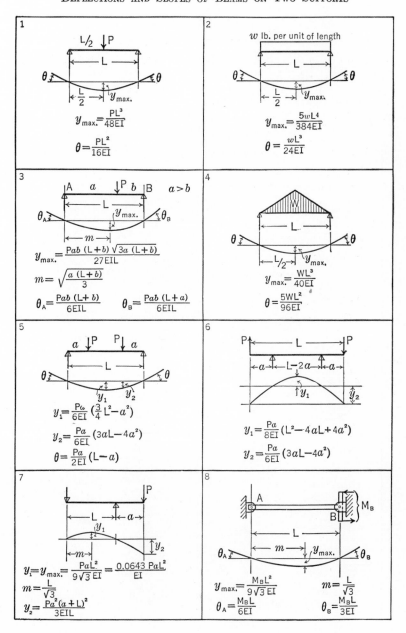

1

$$y_{max.} = \frac{PL^3}{48EI}$$

$$\theta = \frac{PL^2}{16EI}$$

2

w lb. per unit of length

$$y_{max.} = \frac{5wL^4}{384EI}$$

$$\theta = \frac{wL^3}{24EI}$$

3

$a > b$

$$y_{max.} = \frac{Pab\,(L+b)\,\sqrt{3a\,(L+b)}}{27EIL}$$

$$m = \sqrt{\frac{a\,(L+b)}{3}}$$

$$\theta_A = \frac{Pab\,(L+b)}{6EIL} \qquad \theta_B = \frac{Pab\,(L+a)}{6EIL}$$

4

$$y_{max.} = \frac{WL^3}{40EI}$$

$$\theta = \frac{5WL^2}{96EI}$$

5

$$y_1 = \frac{Pa}{6EI}\left(\frac{3}{4}L^2 - a^2\right)$$

$$y_2 = \frac{Pa}{6EI}\,(3aL - 4a^2)$$

$$\theta = \frac{Pa}{2EI}\,(L-a)$$

6

$$y_1 = \frac{Pa}{8EI}\,(L^2 - 4aL + 4a^2)$$

$$y_2 = \frac{Pa}{6EI}\,(3aL - 4a^2)$$

7

$$y_1 = y_{max.} = \frac{PaL^2}{9\sqrt{3}\,EI} = \frac{0.0643\,PaL^2}{EI}$$

$$m = \frac{L}{\sqrt{3}}$$

$$y_2 = \frac{Pa^2(a+L)^2}{3EIL}$$

8

$$y_{max.} = \frac{M_B L^2}{9\sqrt{3}\,EI} \qquad m = \frac{L}{\sqrt{3}}$$

$$\theta_A = \frac{M_B L}{6EI} \qquad \theta_B = \frac{M_B L}{3EI}$$

APPENDIX C

TABLE XV

MOMENT OF INERTIA OF AREAS

See Appendix B.

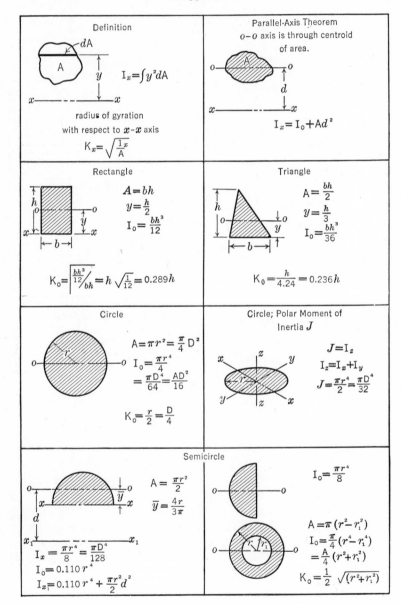

Definition

$$I_x = \int y^2 dA$$

radius of gyration
with respect to x-x axis

$$K_x = \sqrt{\frac{I_x}{A}}$$

Parallel-Axis Theorem

o–o axis is through centroid of area.

$$I_x = I_0 + Ad^2$$

Rectangle

$$A = bh$$
$$y = \frac{h}{2}$$
$$I_0 = \frac{bh^3}{12}$$

$$K_0 = \sqrt{\frac{bh^3}{12}\Big/ bh} = h\sqrt{\frac{1}{12}} = 0.289h$$

Triangle

$$A = \frac{bh}{2}$$
$$y = \frac{h}{3}$$
$$I_0 = \frac{bh^3}{36}$$

$$K_0 = \frac{h}{4.24} = 0.236h$$

Circle

$$A = \pi r^2 = \frac{\pi}{4}D^2$$
$$I_0 = \frac{\pi r^4}{4}$$
$$= \frac{\pi D^4}{64} = \frac{AD^2}{16}$$

$$K_0 = \frac{r}{2} = \frac{D}{4}$$

Circle; Polar Moment of Inertia J

$$J = I_z$$
$$I_z = I_x + I_y$$
$$J = \frac{\pi r^4}{2} = \frac{\pi D^4}{32}$$

Semicircle

$$A = \frac{\pi r^2}{2}$$
$$\bar{y} = \frac{4r}{3\pi}$$

$$I_x = \frac{\pi r^4}{8} = \frac{\pi D^4}{128}$$
$$I_0 = 0.110 r^4$$
$$I_{x_1} = 0.110 r^4 + \frac{\pi r^2}{2}d^2$$

$$I_0 = \frac{\pi r^4}{8}$$

$$A = \pi (r^2 - r_1^2)$$
$$I_0 = \frac{\pi}{4}(r^4 - r_1^4)$$
$$= \frac{A}{4}(r^2 + r_1^2)$$
$$K_0 = \frac{1}{2}\sqrt{(r^2 + r_1^2)}$$

TABLE XVI

MOMENTS OF INERTIA OF THIN AREAS

Values are approximate but nearly exact if thickness is small in comparison to other dimensions.

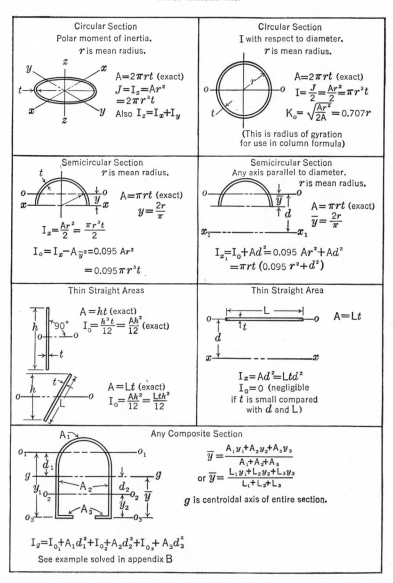

Circular Section
Polar moment of inertia.
r is mean radius.

$A = 2\pi rt$ (exact)
$J = I_z = Ar^2$
$= 2\pi r^3 t$
Also $I_z = I_x + I_y$

Circular Section
I with respect to diameter.
r is mean radius.

$A = 2\pi rt$ (exact)
$I = \dfrac{J}{2} = \dfrac{Ar^2}{2} = \pi r^3 t$
$K_o = \sqrt{\dfrac{Ar^2}{2A}} = 0.707r$

(This is radius of gyration for use in column formula)

Semicircular Section
r is mean radius.

$A = \pi rt$ (exact)
$y = \dfrac{2r}{\pi}$

$I_x = \dfrac{Ar^2}{2} = \dfrac{\pi r^3 t}{2}$

$I_o = I_x - A\overline{y}^2 = 0.095\,Ar^2$
$= 0.095\,\pi r^3 t$

Semicircular Section
Any axis parallel to diameter.
r is mean radius.

$A = \pi rt$ (exact)
$\overline{y} = \dfrac{2r}{\pi}$

$I_{x_1} = I_o + Ad^2 = 0.095\,Ar^2 + Ad^2$
$= \pi rt\,(0.095\,r^2 + d^2)$

Thin Straight Areas

$A = ht$ (exact)
$I_o = \dfrac{h^3 t}{12} = \dfrac{Ah^2}{12}$ (exact)

$A = Lt$ (exact)
$I_o = \dfrac{Ah^2}{12} = \dfrac{Lth^2}{12}$

Thin Straight Area

$A = Lt$

$I_x = Ad^2 = Ltd^2$
$I_o = 0$ (negligible if t is small compared with d and L)

Any Composite Section

$\overline{y} = \dfrac{A_1 y_1 + A_2 y_2 + A_3 y_3}{A_1 + A_2 + A_3}$

or $\overline{y} = \dfrac{L_1 y_1 + L_2 y_2 + L_3 y_3}{L_1 + L_2 + L_3}$

g is centroidal axis of entire section.

$I_g = I_{o_1} + A_1 d_1^2 + I_{o_2} + A_2 d_2^2 + I_{o_3} + A_3 d_3^2$

See example solved in appendix B

Index

(The numbers refer to pages.)

INDEX

$$\tan 2\theta_s = \frac{S_x - S_y}{2S_s}$$

$$\sin 2\theta_s = \frac{\frac{1}{2}(S_x - S_y)}{\sqrt{\left(\frac{S_x - S_y}{2}\right)^2 + S_s^2}}$$

$$\cos 2\theta_s = \frac{S_s}{\sqrt{\left(\frac{S_x - S_y}{2}\right)^2 + S_s^2}}$$

From Page 271

$$S_s' = \frac{(S_x - S_y)}{2}\sin 2\theta_s + S_s \cos 2\theta_s$$

$$S_s' = \frac{(S_x - S_y)}{2} \cdot \frac{\frac{(S_x - S_y)}{2}}{\sqrt{\left(\frac{S_x - S_y}{2}\right)^2 + S_s^2}} + S_s \cdot \frac{S_s}{\sqrt{\left(\frac{S_x - S_y}{2}\right)^2 + S_s^2}}$$

$$S_s' = \frac{\left[\left(\frac{S_x - S_y}{2}\right)^2 + S_s^2\right]}{\left[\left(\frac{S_x - S_y}{2}\right)^2 + S_s^2\right]^{\frac{1}{2}}} = \sqrt{\left(\frac{S_x - S_y}{2}\right)^2 + S_s^2}$$

(15-8) on Page 272